TABLE OF ATOMIC MASS
(Based on Carbon-12, the Most Common Isotope of Carbon)

Element	Symbol	Atomic number	Atomic mass	Element	Symbol	Atomic number	Atomic mass
Actinium	Ac	89	(227)	Mendelevium	Md	101	(256)
Aluminum	Al	13	26.9815	Mercury	Hg	80	200.59
Americium	Am	95	(243)	Molybdenum	Mo	42	95.94
Antimony	Sb	51	121.75	Neodymium	Nd	60	144.24
Argon	Ar	18	39.948	Neon	Ne	10	20.179
Arsenic	As	33	74.9216	Neptunium	Np	93	237.0482
Astatine	At	85	(210)	Nickel	Ni	28	58.71
Barium	Ba	56	137.34	Niobium	Nb	41	92.9064
Berkelium	Bk	97	(249)	Nitrogen	N	7	14.0067
Beryllium	Be	4	9.01218	Nobelium	No	102	(254)
Bismuth	Bi	83	208.9806	Osmium	Os	76	190.2
Boron	B	5	10.81	Oxygen	O	8	15.9994
Bromine	Br	35	79.904	Palladium	Pd	46	106.4
Cadmium	Cd	48	112.40	Phosphorus	P	15	30.9738
Calcium	Ca	20	40.08	Platinum	Pt	78	195.09
Californium	Cf	98	(251)	Plutonium	Pu	94	(242)
Carbon	C	6	12.011	Polonium	Po	84	(210)
Cerium	Ce	58	140.12	Potassium	K	19	39,102
Cesium	Cs	55	132.9055	Praseodymium	Pr	59	140.9077
Chlorine	Cl	17	35.453	Promethium	Pm	61	(145)
Chromium	Cr	24	51.996	Protactinium	Pa	91	231.0359
Cobalt	Co	27	58.9332	Radium	Ra	88	226.0254
Copper	Cu	29	63.546	Radon	Rn	86	(222)
Curium	Cm	96	(247)	Rhenium	Re	75	186.2
Dysprosium	Dy	66	162.50	Rhodium	Rh	45	102.9055
Einsteinium	Es	99	(254)	Rubidium	Rb	37	85.4678
Erbium	Er	68	167.26	Ruthenium	Ru	44	101.07
Europium	Eu	63	151.96	Samarium	Sm	62	150.4
Fermium	Fm	100	(253)	Scandium	Sc	21	44.9559
Fluorine	F	9	18.9984	Selenium	Se	34	78.96
Francium	Fr	87	(223)	Silicon	Si	14	28.086
Gadolinium	Gd	64	157.25	Silver	Ag	47	107.868
Gallium	Ga	31	69.72	Sodium	Na	11	22.9898
Germanium	Ge	32	72.59	Strontium	Sr	38	87.62
Gold	Au	79	196.9665	Sulfur	S	16	32.06
Hafnium	Hf	72	178.49	Tantalum	Ta	73	180.9479
Hahnium	Ha	105	(260)	Technetium	Tc	43	98.9062
Helium	He	2	4.00260	Tellurium	Te	52	127.60
Holmium	Ho	67	164.9303	Terbium	Tb	65	158.9254
Hydrogen	H	1	1.0080	Thallium	Tl	81	204.37
Indium	In	49	114.82	Thorium	Th	90	232.0381
Iodine	I	53	126.9045	Thulium	Tm	69	168.9342
Iridium	Ir	77	192.22	Tin	Sn	50	118.69
Iron	Fe	26	55.847	Titanium	Ti	22	47.90
Krypton	Kr	36	83.80	Tungsten	W	74	183.85
Kurchatovium	Ku	104	(257)	Uranium	U	92	238.029
Lanthanum	La	57	138.9055	Vanadium	V	23	50.9414
Lawrencium	Lr	103	(257)	Xenon	Xe	54	131.30
Lead	Pb	82	207.2	Ytterbium	Yb	70	173.04
Lithium	Li	3	6.941	Yttrium	Y	39	88.9059
Lutetium	Lu	71	174.97	Zinc	Zn	30	65.37
Magnesium	Mg	12	24.305	Zirconium	Zr	40	91.22
Manganese	Mn	25	54.9380				

Basic Modern Chemistry

Third Edition
SI Metric

Basic Modern Chemistry

Third Edition
SI Metric

Samuel Madras
York University

Jean-Paul Gravel
Deux-Montagnes Regional High School

John Stratton
Lester B. Pearson Collegiate Institute

Gordon Hall
David Thompson High School

McGraw-Hill Ryerson Limited

Toronto   Montreal   New York   St. Louis   San Francisco   Auckland   Beirut   Bogotá
Düsseldorf   Johannesburg   Lisbon   London   Lucerne   Madrid   Mexico   New Delhi
Panama   Paris   San Juan   São Paulo   Singapore   Sydney   Tokyo

BASIC MODERN CHEMISTRY
THIRD EDITION

ISBN-0-07-082726-5

    3 4 5 6 7 8 9 10   BP   7 6 5

Printed and bound in Canada

Cartoons: Roy Condy

Canadian Cataloguing in Publication Data

Main entry under title:

Basic modern chemistry

Second ed. 1969, by J.-P. Gravel, G. G. Hall and S. Madras.

Includes index.
ISBN 0-07-082726-5

1. Chemistry.   I. Madras, Samuel, date.   II. Gravel,
Jean-Paul, date.   Basic modern chemistry.

QD33.B38 1978   540   C78-001397-2

Cover photo from *Exploring Minerals and Crystals* by
Robert I. Gait, McGraw-Hill Ryerson Ltd., 1972.

The optical spectra chart in Chapter 5 is from *Chemistry* by
Sienko and Plane. Copyright © 1976 by McGraw-Hill Inc.
Used with permission of McGraw-Hill Book Company.

The photo on page 143 is from the Soil Conservation Service,
USDA.

Metric Commission Canada has granted use of the
National Symbol for Metric Conversion.

PREFACE

During the period since the publication of the previous edition great changes have occurred in the public view of science and chemistry. The realization that survival depends upon an altered attitude to the entire conduct of life, both social and personal, with less emphasis upon profligate consumption and more on the protection of the environment is perhaps the greatest cultural change on a global scale of our time.

Environmental issues have a core that needs to be understood scientifically. Whether we think of the future of the biosphere, the adequacy of food supply, the finiteness of resources, the pollution of air and water by industrial wastes, the need for recycling and conservation, the uncertain prospects for fossil fuels and some other forms of energy, science remains one of the most crucial bridges between problem and solution.

The environment is chemical and behaves according to chemical principles. An understanding of the one requires an understanding of the other. Yet for too long, such interconnection was neglected. For the sustained and concerted effort that is required, the relevance of chemical facts and principles to environmental concerns should be indicated and explored. Since air, water, food and energy are components of the biosphere as well as necessities of life as we know it, where these topics are discussed for their chemistry, their functions in the environment as well as their interrelations among themselves are indicated.

The text has been reviewed by the Canadian Government Specifications Board for correct usage of SI units and symbols according to the appropriate National Standards of Canada.

The authors are grateful to the many teachers who have responded to the questionnaire sent out by McGraw-Hill Ryerson and who have offered many valuable suggestions for this edition. In particular, the authors would like to thank Prof. J. R. Friesen of the University of Waterloo, editor of *Chem 12-13*, for his useful comments at the early stages of preparation. Also, thanks go to Roy Condy, the cartoonist, Rosina Daillie and Joanne Culley of McGraw-Hill Ryerson, and to Margaret Gillespie for her many useful suggestions and comments.

S. M.
J. P. G.
J. S.
G. H.

Contents

1
THE ATOM

Portrait of Robert Boyle: 1627-1691
British physicist and chemist

The Bettmann Archive

CHAPTER 1

CHEMISTRY, SCIENCE AND THE ENVIRONMENT

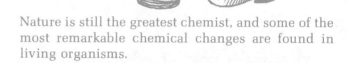

1:1   Definition of Chemistry

Chemistry deals with matter and its changes. Chemists are particularly interested in these changes where one or more substances are transformed into others quite different from the original. They try to understand the chemical changes in a very profound sense. They picture the submicroscopic particles involved such as atoms, molecules, and electrons. They try to determine how these interact and what energies are released or required. This is all done to have greater control over chemical change whether it occurs in an industrial process, a research experiment, or in a living organism. There is always the hope of finding new and better materials for the service of people everywhere.

1:2   The Work of Chemists

Chemists are interested in the properties and composition of all forms of matter that surround them. Air, water, food, cloth, steel, cement, glass, and gasoline, as well as any other material one could name, are all examples of matter.

Nature is still the greatest chemist, and some of the most remarkable chemical changes are found in living organisms.

The chemist's work is to be seen all around us — on the farm, in the home, and in industry. Chemical products and methods are used by the farmer to produce better crops and livestock and by the food-processing industries to prepare foods and protect them from spoilage. Vitamins produced in laboratories are added to foods for enrichment. Our homes are decorated with paints and enamels, textiles, plastics, and glass. The convenience of the automobile is possible largely because of the chemical reactions that help produce gasoline and oils, steel, rubber, and even the pavement of our streets and highways.

Most of these products are made in factories, where chemical changes and reactions are supervised by industrial chemists. Raw materials from mines, forests, oil wells, and oceans are turned into products for our use by means of chemical processes. For example, the pulp and paper industry uses chemical reactions to convert the wood of the tree into paper and cellulose products.

1:3   Chemistry, Life and the Biosphere

We should not forget, however, that Nature is still the greatest chemist, and some of the most remarkable chemical changes are found in living organisms. Hundreds of chemical reactions go on harmoniously to provide the normal functioning of the individual animal or plant.

Air and water are heated by solar energy, giving rise to winds and currents to produce climate. Together with the nutrients in the soil these factors set the stage for life on land and in the sea. The combination of air, water, land, and life on the surface of the Earth is called the *biosphere*.

The lives of people and society also depend on the biosphere. By using the resources of the Earth, industry, agriculture, transportation, and medicine have been developed and they are now part of the human environment.

Chemistry is one of the sciences needed to understand the biosphere and the environment. It can help us to judge how people can live harmoniously with Nature rather than harm it through careless and excessive abuse.

1:4   Human Curiosity

People have always been curious about Nature, and many theories, and even legends and myths, have resulted from this curiosity. The ancient Greeks had some interesting ideas about matter, but these were based on speculation and were not checked by experiment. Most believed that there were only four elements: air, earth, fire, and water. However, some believed that matter was made of small, invisible particles which they called atoms. "There is nothing but atoms and void," said Democritus.

Today we believe once again that matter consists of elements or combinations of elements, and that the elements are composed of atoms. Our belief, however, is based upon experimental proof, direct or indirect, whereas the beliefs of the ancient Greeks were based upon speculation.

During the Middle Ages, the alchemists searched for the "Philosopher's Stone," a subtle substance which would change base metals, like lead, into precious metals such as silver and gold. They failed in their quest but did succeed in discovering many other substances. They also developed methods and processes that were later to prove useful in chemistry. It is interesting to compare their attitudes with those of modern scientists. The alchemists often hid their knowledge in

The Board of Education for the Borough of North York
Guido's Studio, Downsview, Ontario

Study through observation

Louis Pasteur, French biochemist, and great benefactor of humanity, who proved that germs caused many diseases

secrecy; the modern chemist, on the other hand, is anxious to publish what he finds and explain what he knows.

Chemistry is one of the physical sciences. It is intimately related to physics and mathematics. The modern ideas of the structure of atoms can be expressed by using the concepts of physics and the language of mathematics.

Biology and medicine are closely allied to chemistry. Many major advances in these fields have been and are being made through the application of chemical knowledge. Animals and plants are composed of different kinds of matter that are constantly undergoing many, perhaps hundreds, of different chemical changes.

1:5 The Scientific Method

The Renaissance saw a revival of learning, but even more important than the revival was a renewed emphasis on investigation and experiment as methods of learning. Francis Bacon proposed that, in order to learn, one should consult Nature rather than the ancient authorities. He emphasized that it was necessary to collect facts before proposing theories or explanations. This method of learning became known as the *scientific method*.

One of the pioneers of chemistry was Robert Boyle. He devoted himself to experimental work and did much to further the development of the scientific method. He discarded the view that air, earth, fire, and water were elements and suggested instead that only those substances that could not be decomposed into simpler substances by chemical methods should be called elements.

The first step in applying the scientific method is to recognize the problem at hand. For example, an automobile tire is observed to be harder on a hot day than on a cold day, even though the amount of air in it has not been changed. Upon checking, it is found that the air pressure in the tire is higher on the hot day. Is there a relationship between the temperature and the pressure of the air in the tire? To answer this question, one should gather as much information as possible by experiment. If an apparatus were set up in which the pressure of air is measured at different temperatures, a relationship between temperature and pressure might then be found.

If, in repeating an experiment, a definite regularity is found in the results, it may be stated in the form of a scientific law. A *scientific law* is a statement of a regularity of behaviour in Nature that has been tested and proved.

A *theory* is an attempt to explain the observed facts. Preferably, a theory should be the simplest explanation of the facts for which it is proposed; it should also explain as many facts as possible.

Often a theory may have to be changed to explain newly discovered facts. In this way theories of science gradually change from time to time. The basic observed facts remain the same, while our ideas change with increasing knowledge.

Derby Art Gallery

The discovery of phosphorus and its power to glow

QUESTIONS

1. Chemistry is the study of the transformation of one or more substances into completely new substances. Why would a chemist want to know exactly how a transformation takes place?

2. What problems are chemists faced with if they wish to explain the transformations that involve individual molecules?

3. Give at least three examples not mentioned in this chapter that show how chemicals are used to control events in your life.

4. The biosphere is that part of the environment in which life can exist. Think of at least three natural chemical reactions that take place in the biosphere.

5. Chemistry is that area of science between physics and biology. How can the ideas of physics be applied to biology through chemistry?

6. Contrast the contributions to learning made by Francis Bacon and Robert Boyle.

7. A homeowner kept monthly records showing the amount of money spent on natural gas to keep his home at a uniform temperature all year round. The results are shown in the following table:

Month	Natural Gas
January	$30
February	$45
March	$35
April	$32
May	$25
June	$8
July	$0
August	$2
September	$7
October	$12
November	$18
December	$28

(i) Show how the homeowner could use the scientific method to try to explain the trend shown by these observations.

(ii) What additional information would be helpful in arriving at an explanation?

(iii) What theory or theories can you put forward to explain these observations?

(iv) Is it possible to propose a scientific law based only on this information?

CHAPTER 2

MATTER AND ENERGY

Of what is the Earth composed? What makes up soil, air, water, plants, animals, and everything else?

The physical world may be described in terms of matter and energy. Matter only exists and undergoes changes, while energy can also cause or be the result of such changes.

2:1 Properties of Matter

Matter is best described and recognized by its *properties*. These are identifying features such as density, colour, state, boiling point, melting point, and similar characteristics.

Properties of substances may be chemical and physical. A *chemical property* of a substance is its behaviour during chemical change. For example, carbon burns in oxygen to yield the gas carbon dioxide. Sodium reacts vigorously with water to form sodium hydroxide and hydrogen. Platinum does not react with water. Each example is only one of many chemical properties of the substance named.

A *physical property* of a substance is a characteristic that can be determined without causing a change in the composition of the substance. The melting point and crystalline form are physical properties of a solid. The boiling point and freezing point are physical properties of a liquid.

2:2 The Measurement of Properties

To describe properties quantitatively, they must be measured, and such measurement requires standard units with which the properties can be compared. All measurements are, in reality, only comparisons. The length of a pencil can be measured only by reference to a scale on which units of length are printed. A brief discussion on measurements is given in Appendix 1.

In science, the most widely used units are those of the SI* metric system. Length is measured in metres and centimetres, mass in kilograms and grams, volume in litres and cubic metres. The metric system consistently uses multiples and submultiples of ten; for example,

*SI stands for Le Système International d'Unités

1 metre = 10 decimetres
      = 100 centimetres
      = 1000 millimetres.

Metric system prefixes are presented in Table 2.1 and in Appendix 3.

TABLE 2.1

Common Prefixes Used in the Metric System

micro	$= \dfrac{1}{1\ 000\ 000}$	deca	= 10
milli	$= \dfrac{1}{1000}$	hecto	= 100
centi	$= \dfrac{1}{100}$	kilo	= 1000
deci	$= \dfrac{1}{10}$	mega	= 1 000 000

In the chemical laboratory, the quantities used are expressed most conveniently in terms of centimetres and grams as the units of length and mass. In other studies, the metre and the kilogram may prove more convenient.

Mass

The term *mass* is used to express the amount of matter in a body and is related to its inertia.

A convenient unit of mass for chemical work is the gram (g), an arbitrarily chosen amount of matter. The mass of very large amounts of matter is often expressed in kilograms. One kilogram (1 kg) is equal to 1000 g. The mass of a very small quantity of matter may be expressed in milligrams. One milligram (1 mg) is equal to 0.001 g; 1 g of matter contains 1000 mg.

A dime has a mass of about 2.5 g; a spoonful of water has a mass of about 5 g.

In symbols

1 kg = 1000 g
1 g = 1000 mg

Courtesy National Research Council, Ottawa

An ultraprecise balance for accurately intercomparing mass

Weight

The *weight* of a given amount of matter, as measured on or near the Earth, is the force exerted on the mass by the gravitational attraction of the Earth. Since weight is a force exerted on a mass, weight and mass are not identical.

A given object would have a much smaller weight on the moon than on the Earth because the gravitational attraction of the moon is much less than that of the Earth. The mass of an object is the same on the Earth as on the moon because the amount of matter is constant. In interstellar space an object may have no weight at all but its mass is the same as on Earth.

Length and Volume

The unit of length in the metric system is the metre (m). Since the metre is a rather large unit, the centimetre (cm) is commonly used. The centimetre

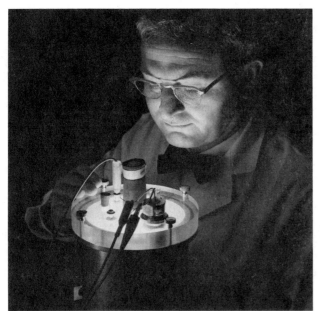

A scientist adjusts krypton-86 lamp. The wave length of the orange-red light emitted by the lamp has recently been adopted as the International Standard of Length.

is equal to 0.01 m. The millimetre (mm) is equal to 0.001 m. There are 10 mm in a centimetre, 100 cm in a metre and 1000 mm in a metre.

The volume of a substance is the amount of space it occupies. The volume of a regular object or vessel may be calculated from its dimensions.

The chemist often uses the litre (L) as the unit of volume for liquid measurement. The litre was designed as the volume of 1 kg of water. One litre is equal to 1000 cm³, and 1 cm³ is equal to one millilitre (mL). The millilitre is exactly 0.001 L.

Their representation in symbols is:

$$1 \text{ km} = 1000 \text{ m}$$
$$1 \text{ m} = 100 \text{ cm}$$
$$1 \text{ m} = 1000 \text{ mm}$$
$$1 \text{ L} = 1000 \text{ cm}^3$$
$$1 \text{ mL} = 1 \text{ cm}^3$$
$$1 \text{ m}^3 = 1000 \text{ L}$$

Density

Density is the mass per unit volume, and refers to the compactness of a sample of matter.

The density of a substance is found by dividing its mass by its volume. The formula for this operation is:

$$\text{Density} = \frac{\text{mass}}{\text{volume}}$$

$$\text{or } D = \frac{m}{V}$$

TABLE 2.2

Densities of a Few Common Substances in kg/m³

Aluminum	2 700	Platinum	21 730
Calcium	1 550	Potassium	870
Copper	8 300	Silver	10 420
Cork	240	Sodium	970
Diamond	3 500	Sulfur	2 000
Gold	19 300	Tin	7 240
Ice	900	Tungsten	18 600
Iron	7 850	Uranium	18 700
Lead	11 340	Wood (oak)	750
Magnesium	1 740	Zinc	7 040

2:3 Physical and Chemical Changes

One of the striking properties of matter is its ability to undergo changes. In some changes the material alters its size, shape, or state, but not its composition. This occurs when a sheet of paper is cut, a rock is chipped, or a metal is drawn out as a wire. Such changes are *physical changes*.

In other cases the composition of the matter is altered, as when paper burns or metal corrodes. The products of these changes have different chemical compositions and properties from those of the original materials. Such changes are *chemical changes.*

In this century, it has been discovered that matter can undergo a third kind of change. This type is more profound than either a physical or chemical change, since it involves the nuclei of the atoms in the matter. Examples of such changes would be the explosion of a nuclear bomb or the processes by which the sun emits its light and heat. Such changes are *nuclear changes.*

Reproduced with permission of Richard E. Orville — State University of N.Y. at Albany

Benjamin Franklin was an American scientist and statesman whose experiments led to an understanding of the nature of the electrical charge. This is an old drawing of his most famous experiment.

2:4   Forms of Energy and Chemical Changes

Energy is the ability to do work. From physics we learn that every moving body has *kinetic energy.* *Potential energy* is the energy a body has because of its position, its condition, or its chemical nature. For example, the water behind a dam has potential energy. When the water falls, this energy is changed to kinetic energy.

All changes are either caused by energy or else they liberate energy. Physical changes usually involve the smallest amounts of energy, while nuclear changes involve by far the greatest. Chemical changes sometimes produce very large amounts of energy. Such chemical energy may appear as *heat energy* in the burning of fuels, as *electrical energy* in the dry cell of a flashlight, as *mechanical energy* in an explosion, or as *light energy* in a photoflash bulb. Chemical substances which are able to release energy when they react contain stored-up or *chemical energy.* Sometimes energy is absorbed by substances to bring about chemical change as, for instance, when heat and light are required for the transformation of carbon dioxide and water into sugars and starches found in plants.

2:5   The Great Importance of Energy

Energy is needed for everything. In order to walk, run and grow we get energy from food. Water evaporates from oceans and lakes to form clouds and rain, returning the needed moisture to the soil. All these processes are made possible by solar energy.

Fuels are substances that release energy by chemical reaction. The energy from gasoline powers the car. The energy from heating oil provides homes and buildings with warmth. Electricity makes lighting a familiar convenience. Furthermore, oil, gas and coal are valuable raw materials that can be converted into useful products. Every day, large amounts of energy are brought into a city for the many activities that make up its busy life.

The fuels we use for energy are the decomposed remains of plants and animals that lived millions of years ago. These "fossil fuels" are convenient for use in industry, transportation and homes, but unfortunately, their supply is limited and running out. Also, the use of these fuels has caused some environmental problems. Carbon monoxide from cars is a serious pollutant of city air. Oil spills do great damage to the oceans and beaches. The mining of coal may lead to the spoilage of land that is stripped away.

We are also concerned that the heat produced by the large amount of energy being used may begin to cause climatic changes for the planet and all forms of life.

For the above reasons, much thought is being given to the problem of what our future energy sources are likely to be. While this problem is difficult to solve, one thing appears certain. The energy that will be used in the future will be quite different from what is used today, just as today's energy supply is different from what it was in the past. Since energy is fundamental to everything, any change in the type of energy used is bound to bring with it a drastic change in the way people live.

2:6 Heat and Temperature

Heat or thermal energy is related to molecular motion and is one of the most important physical concepts. Wherever there is molecular motion there is heat and vice versa.

The temperature of a body indicates whether or not the body is hotter or colder than something else. The temperature also shows whether heat will flow from the material to its surroundings or in the reverse direction.

Temperature is related to heat. If two objects at different temperatures are placed in contact, heat flows from the hotter to the cooler one until their temperatures are the same.

The most common temperature scale used internationally by scientists is the *Celsius*, formerly called the centigrade scale as suggested by Celsius in 1742. On this scale there are 100 degrees Celsius or gradations of temperature between two fixed points. These are 0°C, at which water freezes, and 100°C, at which water boils at standard atmospheric pressure (Table 2.3).

A most important scale is the Kelvin scale in which zero kelvins of temperature represents the absence of heat, or at least minimum energy. The Kelvin scale is often called the Absolute scale because its zero is believed to be the lowest possible limit of temperature in the universe (Fig. 2.1).

A kelvin* is equal to a (Celsius) degree temperature, and 0 K corresponds to −273°C (more accurately, −273.16°C). The temperature 0°C is the same as 273 K. To convert any Celsius reading to the corresponding kelvin reading, 273 is added to the Celsius reading, while 273 is subtracted from a kelvin reading to obtain a Celsius reading:

$$K = °C + 273$$
$$°C = K - 273$$

TABLE 2.3

Comparisons of the "Fixed" Points

	°C	K
Boiling point of water	100	373
Freezing point of water	0	273
Differences	100	100

*Temperature on the Kelvin scale is read without the degree symbol or word. For example, 100 K is read as one hundred kelvins.

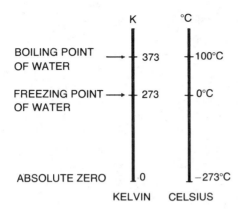

Fig. 2.1:
Kelvin and Celsius scales

The Joule
The unit of heat used by chemists is the *joule* (J). One gram of water absorbs 4.19 J when its temperature is raised one degree Celsius. The *kilojoule* (kJ) is used to identify large amounts of heat. One kilojoule is equal to 1000 J.*

2:7   The Conservation Laws

Matter is continuously changing. However, it has been found that in all physical and chemical changes there is no change in the mass of the materials being transformed. The French chemist, Lavoisier, tried to learn about chemical changes by weighing the quantities of the substances used in chemical reactions. He observed that even though substances are transformed into completely different ones in a chemical change, there was no apparent destruction or creation of matter. The mass seemed to remain exactly the same. To all appearances, when a candle burns it is destroyed; but appearances are often misleading. When the reactants and products of a chemical reaction are weighed accurately, even if a substance is changed to a gas, there is no apparent change of mass. Lavoisier expressed his finding as the *Law of Conservation of Mass: In a chemical change the sums of the masses of the original reactants and of the final products are seemingly the same.* Apparently mass is neither created nor destroyed in a chemical change.

Energy can similarly be changed from one form to another, and it was also thought that it was not created or destroyed during transformations. This is the essence of the *Law of Conservation of Energy.* However, in 1905 Einstein showed that matter can manifest itself in two distinct forms; it may appear either as a material substance occupying space and having mass, or it may appear as energy. The relationship between mass and energy is given by the formula:

$$E = mc^2$$

where E is the energy, m is the mass, and c is the speed of light. In nuclear changes a small amount of mass does disappear; but the mass is converted into energy, and the amount of energy released is equivalent to the mass destroyed. The above laws are combined in the general statement that the mass-energy of a system cannot change.

2:8   The States of Matter and Changes of State

Matter may exist in three states: solid, liquid, or gas. A solid has definite volume and shape; a liquid has definite volume but no definite shape, because it takes on the shape of its container; and a gas has neither definite shape nor definite volume, because it expands indefinitely, if free to do so, until it fills its container.

*Formerly the unit of heat used by chemists was the *calorie*, defined as the amount of heat that can raise the temperature of 1 g of water one Celsius degree. The *kilocalorie* was equal to 1000 cal.

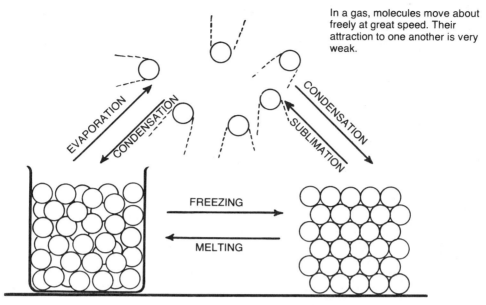

In a gas, molecules move about freely at great speed. Their attraction to one another is very weak.

In a liquid, molecules are attracted strongly to one another. They are densely packed but can still move about.

In a solid, the particles are attracted even more strongly still. They vibrate about their fixed positions.

Fig. 2.2:
Changes of state

The state in which a substance happens to exist depends on the temperature and the pressure. If the temperature and/or the pressure are changed, a substance may pass from one state to another. Such physical changes are called *changes of state*. These usually occur sharply when certain temperatures and pressures are reached. When they take place, heat is either absorbed or emitted.

Vaporization takes place when a liquid absorbs heat and turns into a gaseous form. When a gaseous substance changes to a liquid through loss of heat, the process is termed *condensation. Fusion* occurs when a solid absorbs heat and turns into a liquid. When a liquid loses heat and is transformed into a solid, *freezing* or solidification takes place. Several substances, such as "dry ice," may change directly from the solid state to that of a gas without liquefaction. This process is called *sublimation*. The reverse process, that is, the condensation of a gas to a solid is also possible. An example of such sublimation is the formation of frost. The various changes of state that matter can undergo are represented in Fig. 2.2.

QUESTIONS

1. (i) Give three examples of chemical properties for any two substances with which you are familiar.

    (ii) Give three examples of physical properties for each of the same substances you mentioned in 1 (i) above.

2. Decide whether the properties of the substances given below are physical or chemical properties:
    (i) hydrogen is a colourless gas;
    (ii) oxygen supports combustion;
    (iii) diamond is the hardest natural substance known;
    (iv) methyl alcohol boils at 78°C;
    (v) potassium is a soft metal;
    (vi) phosphorus ignites when exposed to air.

3. (i) What are the advantages of the metric system over any other system of measurement?

    (ii) Name the metric unit used to measure: length, volume, mass, time and temperature.

4. Define the terms:
    (i) kilogram;
    (ii) microsecond;
    (iii) megatonne;
    (iv) millimetre;
    (v) decilitre.

5. (i) Explain why, although the mass of an object is constant, its weight may not be.

    (ii) The gravitational pull of the moon is approximately $1/6$ that of the Earth's. How would the mass and weight for an object on earth compare with its mass and weight on the moon?

6. What advantage is there in basing the unit of length on the wave length of light coming from a particular element?

7. (i) Change 1.2 L to millilitres.

    (ii) What is the mass in milligrams and in kilograms of 1.2 L of water at 4°C?

    (iii) Convert 1080 mm to (a) centimetres; (b) decimetres; (c) metres.

8. Complete the following conversions in your notebook:
    (i)   3.7 m = _____?_____ cm
    (ii)   0.6 kg = _____?_____ g
    (iii) 4000 mL = _____?_____ L
    (iv)   12.7 km = _____?_____ m
    (v)   13 cm = _____?_____ mm

9. (i) Find the density of a material if 30.0 mL of it has a mass of 75.0 g.

    (ii) Find the volume occupied by 10.0 g of kerosene whose density is 0.88 g/mL.

10. Distinguish between the terms *physical* change, *chemical* change, and *nuclear* change.

11. Classify the following as physical or chemical changes:
    (i)   the rusting of an iron nail;
    (ii)   the toasting of bread;
    (iii)   the evaporation of water from a lake;
    (iv)   the formation of clouds;
    (v)   the tarnishing of silver;
    (vi)   the flashing of a bulb in a camera;
    (vii)   the liquefaction of air;
    (viii) the burning of a candle;
    (ix)   the melting of ice;
    (x)   the blowing of a horn.

12. (i)   What is energy?
    (ii)   What is the difference between potential and kinetic energy?
    (iii) List three different forms of energy and tell how one form might be changed into
           the others.
    (iv)   While there are many obvious advantages, there are some disadvantages associated
           with the use of energy by people. Describe some of the problems involved.

13. Which one of the following choices represents the type(s) of energy possessed by a light
    bulb falling down a well?
    (i)   kinetic energy only
    (ii)   potential energy only
    (iii) potential energy and kinetic energy
    (iv)   electrical energy

14. Do the following calculations:
    (i) $5 \times 10^5 \times 10^6$
    (ii) $\dfrac{1.5 \times 10^4}{3 \times 10^{-2}}$
    (iii) $3 \times 10^8 \times 4 \times 10^{-3}$
    (iv) $\dfrac{3 \times 10^{-2}}{1.5 \times 10^4}$

15. Do the following calculations:
    (i) $1.2 \times 10^5 \times 5.0 \times 10^2$
    (ii) $\dfrac{6.2 \times 10^3}{2.0 \times 10^{-2}}$
    (iii) $\dfrac{6.6 \times 10^6}{1.1 \times 10^{-2}}$
    (iv) $\dfrac{2 \times 10^{-3} \times 3.2 \times 10^4}{8 \times 10^2}$

16. Change the following to K: (i) $-273°C$; (ii) $-40°C$; (iii) $0°C$; (iv) $50°C$; (v) $273°C$.

17. Change the following to °C: (i) 500 K; (ii) 100 K; (iii) 272 K; (iv) 50 K; (v) 300 K.

18. (i) What is a joule?
    (ii) What is a kilojoule?

19. (i) Until the early 1900s, the Law of Conservation of Mass and the Law of Conservation of Energy were considered to be two separate laws. They have now been combined into the Law of Conservation of Mass-Energy. Why was this necessary?

    (ii) If 11.2 g of hydrogen combine chemically with 88.8 g oxygen to produce water, how many grams of water should be produced according to the Law of Conservation of Mass-Energy?

20. Discuss the meaning of the statement that the mass-energy sum of a system does not change.

21. Give the distinguishing characteristics of the three states of matter.

22. What factors determine the state of a particular substance?

23. Indicate the change of state involved when: (i) dew forms on blades of grass; (ii) water is boiling; (iii) moth balls (naphthalene) placed in woolen garments "disappear"; (iv) a tumbler full of ice is placed on a table; (v) the temperature drops below 0°C near a small pond.

3

THE COMPOSITION OF MATTER

3:1 Elements

All the materials in the universe are composed of relatively few simple substances called the elements. An *element* is a substance that cannot be decomposed by chemical means into simpler substances.

Over one hundred elements are known today. Elements are not found in equal abundance in nature. Indeed some have been synthesized only recently in nuclear reactors, and they exist in very small amounts. Fig. 3.1 presents an estimate of the relative abundance of some elements found in the Earth's crust. However, the importance of an element does not necessarily depend on its abundance. Carbon comprises less than 0.1 percent of the total; yet without this element no life could have developed on the Earth. Oxygen is an element that is both abundant and vitally important in many ways.

Elements are classified as metals or nonmetals for convenience. Metals are recognized by their lustre and high conductivity of heat and electricity. Some metals can be drawn into a wire; they are said to be ductile. Other metals can be hammered into various shapes; they are malleable. Some common metals are iron, copper, mercury, tin, lead, zinc, silver, and gold.

Important clues to the composition of matter were found when chemists began to measure four quantities accurately—mass, volume, temperature and pressure.

Examples of non-metals are carbon, sulfur, phosphorus, chlorine, and iodine. Their properties vary greatly. Carbon and silicon are solids and have a high melting point. Hydrogen and helium are gases which can be liquefied only at extremely low temperatures. As a general rule, non-metals are poor conductors of heat and electricity. They are neither ductile nor malleable.

3:2 Compounds

Elements combine with one another to form substances called *compounds*. These substances are homogeneous. Their properties and composition are the same throughout their entire mass. We are unable to distinguish particles of the constituent elements once they have combined to form a compound. Moreover, the properties of the compound are not like those of the free elements before combination. Water is a compound made of hydrogen and oxygen. Both of these elements in the free state are gases. Hydrogen is highly inflammable, whereas oxygen is not. However, oxygen supports combustion and life. The properties of water are entirely different from these.

Sodium, a soft metallic element, corrodes very rapidly in air and reacts with water vigorously. Chlorine, a non-metal, is a greenish-yellow poisonous gas. A piece of sodium thrown into an atmosphere of chlorine burns violently as these elements combine to form a compound, sodium chloride, which proves to be common table salt. Sodium chloride is a compound made of the elements sodium and chlorine, and yet its properties are different from those of the free elements.

3:3   Molecules and Ions: The Physical Units of Matter

Let us perform the following experiment mentally. If we pour half the water from one vessel to another, each half will retain the composition and properties of the whole. If we were to continue subdividing the water in the same way, presumably a point would be reached at which there would be a particle of water so small that it would be impossible to subdivide it further by physical methods. The smallest particle of water able to exist physically and still retain its composition is called a *molecule*.

Molecules are extremely small and generally

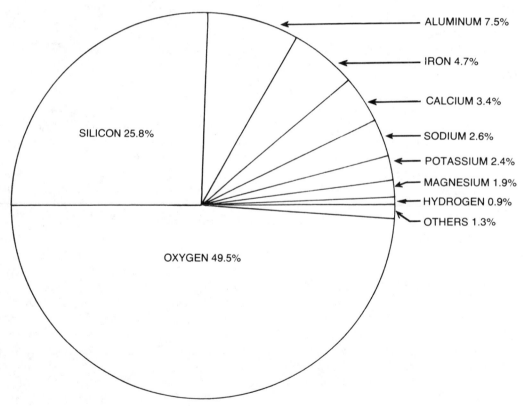

Fig. 3.1:
Approximate relative abundance of elements in the Earth's crust

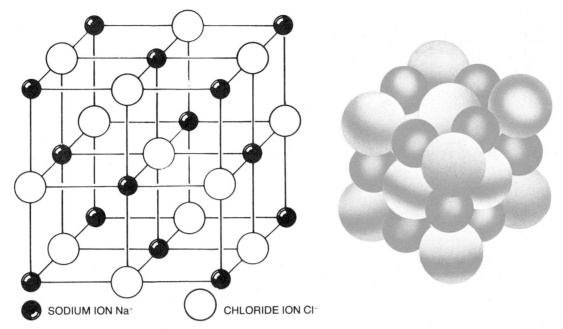

SODIUM ION Na⁺   CHLORIDE ION Cl⁻

Fig. 3.2:
The sodium chloride crystal

cannot be seen with the most powerful microscopes. Evidence for the existence of molecules had to be obtained indirectly, but more and more details about the structures of molecules are being amassed as chemistry progresses.

When salt is broken down into its finest particles, it is found that the smallest particles of which this compound is composed are electrically charged. These particles are called *ions*. In a salt crystal, there are sodium ions with a positive charge and chloride ions with a negative charge. The ions are arranged in the crystal so that each sodium ion is next to a chloride ion and vice versa (Fig. 3.2).

3:4   Atoms and their Symbols: The Chemical Units of Matter

Atoms are the smallest particles of matter able to undergo chemical change; consequently they are the basic chemical units of matter.

For the sake of convenience, brevity, and precision, the elements are represented by symbols which stand for the elements, the atoms of the elements and their atomic mass.*

A *symbol* consists of a capital letter only, or a capital letter and a small letter. H is the symbol for hydrogen, O for oxygen, and S for sulfur. If there

*In this book, the term **atomic mass** is used in preference to the older term **atomic weight.**

are several elements whose names begin with the same letter, two-letter symbols are used. Thus, since C stands for carbon, symbols of two letters are used for calcium (Ca), cadmium (Cd), cerium (Ce), cesium (Cs), cobalt (Co), and chromium (Cr). The second letter is always a small letter.

Some symbols are derived from the Latin names of the elements. The symbol for iron, Fe, is derived from ferrum; that of copper, Cu, from cuprum; of mercury, Hg, from hydrargyrum (Table 3.1). The symbols of all the elements will be found for ready reference in the table on the inside front cover of this book.

TABLE 3.1

**Symbols of Elements
Derived From Latin**

Element	Symbol	Source Name
Antimony	Sb	Stibium
Copper	Cu	Cuprum
Gold	Au	Aurum
Iron	Fe	Ferrum
Lead	Pb	Plumbum
Mercury	Hg	Hydrargyrum
Potassium	K	Kalium
Silver	Ag	Argentum
Sodium	Na	Natrium
Tin	Sn	Stannum
Tungsten	W	Wolfram

3:5   Formulas

A symbol stands for an atom of an element; a *formula* stands for a molecule of a substance. The formula of a molecule shows the symbols of its constituent elements together with their numbers placed below and to the right of each symbol. If only one atom of an element is to be found in the molecule, the number 1 is understood and is omitted. Thus, H_2O represents the molecule of water composed of two atoms of the element

hydrogen and one atom of the element oxygen. O_2 is the formula for the molecule of oxygen which contains two atoms. Occasionally, formulas will be met which contain parentheses, e.g., $Cu(NO_3)_2$. In such cases, the number below and to the right of the parenthesis multiplies through the atoms enclosed in it. Such parentheses in formulas will be explained later.

As we have learned, crystals of salts are made up of ions and not of molecules. The formula NaCl for common salt indicates that there are equal numbers of sodium ions, Na^+, and chloride ions, Cl^-, in its crystal structure. Similarly $CaCl_2$, the formula for calcium chloride salt, indicates that there are twice as many chloride ions, Cl^-, as calcium ions, Ca^{2+}, in its crystals.

Some common formulas are:

Water	H_2O
Hydrogen Chloride	HCl
Ammonia	NH_3
Methanol	CH_3OH

3:6   Mixtures and Solutions

A *mixture* is formed by simply blending a number of ingredients. For example, when sugar is dissolved in water, the resulting mixture is homogeneous even under a microscope. Such homogeneous mixtures are called *solutions*.

Some mixtures differ from solutions in that there are always at least two distinctly recognizable parts or phases, whereas a solution consists of only one phase. Such mixtures are heterogeneous and can be called *mechanical mixtures*. A piece of granite is an example of a mechanical mixture. A close look reveals the presence of different crystalline materials: quartz, feldspar, and mica.

A mixture may be, therefore, either homogeneous or heterogeneous, but it is always made up of two or more substances. Furthermore these substances may be mixed in any proportion if the mixture is heterogeneous. In the case of certain solutions, there is a limit to the solubility of one substance in another. Thus at 20°C no more than 36 g of sodium chloride will dissolve in 100 g of water. However, more dilute sodium chloride solutions of any desired composition may be prepared. The composition of a mixture is, therefore, variable. In this respect, it differs from a pure substance. Each of the components in a mixture keeps its original properties. The properties of a mixture are an "average" of those of the substances of which it is composed.

Some common mixtures are air, soil, paper, paint, and coal.

3:7   Chemical Equations

A *chemical equation* is an exact expression representing a chemical change. The reactants and the products are each represented by their chemical formulas. The reactants are written on the left-hand side, and the products on the right-hand side. An arrow separates the reactants from the products. For example:

$$2\,H_2 + O_2 \rightarrow 2\,H_2O$$

This equation tells us that two molecules of hydrogen combine with one molecule of oxygen to give two molecules of water.

It also tells us that each molecule of hydrogen contains two atoms, that each molecule of oxygen contains two atoms, and that each molecule of water contains two atoms of hydrogen and one atom of oxygen.

The numbers in front of the formulas are called *coefficients*. They show the number of molecules that react with each other and should not be confused with subscripts, which show the number of atoms of a particular kind in the molecule.

The expressions (g), (l), and (s) placed sometimes after the formulas of the reactants and products indicate the state, gaseous, liquid, or solid respectively, of the substances involved. Another expression frequently used is (aq) for aqueous, showing that the substance is in the form of a water solution.

It is by means of coefficients that we "balance" the equation. The full meaning of chemical equations unfolds with your growing acquaintance with chemical reactions.

3:8   The Composition of Water

The composition of water may be determined either by decomposing water into its elements (analysis) or by forming water from its elements (synthesis).

Analysis of Water: Composition by Volume
Water may be decomposed into hydrogen and oxygen by passing a direct current of electricity through water containing a small amount of sulfuric acid (Fig. 3.3). The acid is added to make water a better conductor of electricity, and does not take part in the reaction. The result of this process

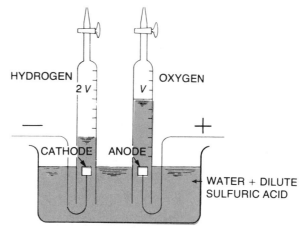

Fig. 3.3:
The electrolysis of water

called electrolysis is shown in the following equation:

$$water \rightarrow hydrogen + oxygen$$
$$2\ H_2O \rightarrow 2\ H_2 + O_2$$

The experiment is carried out in an apparatus consisting of two tubes fitted with platinum electrodes at one end and stopcocks at the other end. These permit the withdrawal of the gases for testing. The tubes are marked with a scale to permit measurement of the volumes of gases liberated.

Five important points are illustrated by this simple experiment:

1. An electric current can cause a chemical reaction; in this case the decomposition of water.
2. The products of decomposition of water are oxygen and hydrogen.
3. The gas that collects at the positive electrode (anode) is recognized as oxygen by the fact that it causes a flame to burn more brightly or a glowing splint to burst into flame.
4. The gas that collects at the negative electrode (cathode) is recognized as hydrogen by the fact that it catches fire when ignited and as it burns it produces water. This can be observed by inverting a cold, clear beaker over the hydrogen flame. A mist forms on the inside of the beaker.
5. The volume of the hydrogen evolved is twice as great as that of oxygen.

Synthesis of Water: Composition by Volume
Hydrogen gas and oxygen gas can be made to combine in a eudiometer, a heavy-walled glass tube fitted with two electrodes sealed through the glass near the closed end of the tube (Fig. 3.4).

Measured volumes of hydrogen and oxygen are

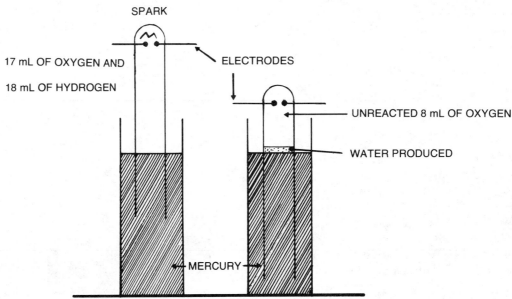

Fig. 3.4:
Synthesis of water (by volume)

mixed in the eudiometer. Then an electric spark is passed across the electrodes and the two gases combine forming water. The volumes of gases that combine can be compared.

In a typical experiment, the values of the volumes of gases measured were as follows:

1. Volume of hydrogen introduced   18 mL

2. Volume of oxygen introduced   17 mL

3. Volume of residual gas left in the tube   8 mL

The 8 mL of gas left in the eudiometer proved to be oxygen by the glowing splint test. Therefore, 17 mL − 8 mL = 9 mL of oxygen combined with 18 mL of hydrogen. The ratio of the volume of hydrogen to the volume of oxygen that combined is 18:9 or 2:1. Regardless of the original volumes mixed, the result is always the same: two volumes of hydrogen combine with one volume of oxygen to form water.

Synthesis of Water: Composition by Mass
When hydrogen is passed over hot copper (II) oxide, the hydrogen combines with the oxygen of the copper (II) oxide to form water, leaving behind the metallic copper. The copper (II) oxide is said to be reduced, while the hydrogen is oxidized in this reaction:

$$CuO + H_2 \rightarrow Cu + H_2O$$

The reaction between hydrogen and the oxygen of copper (II) oxide to form water provides an accurate method for finding the compositon of water by mass. The apparatus used in the reaction is shown in Fig. 3.5.

Hydrogen, generated by the reaction of an acid and a metal is passed through the drying tube (A), containing anhydrous calcium chloride, to remove any moisture in the stream of hydrogen. Such moisture can cause an error since it is not the product of the reaction being studied. The glass

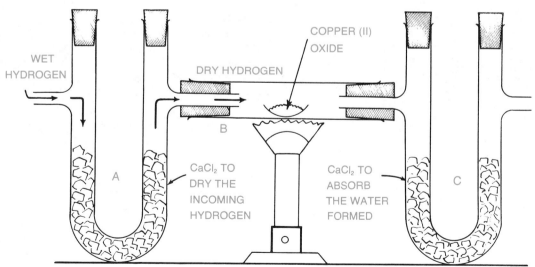

Fig. 3.5:
Synthesis of water (by mass)

tube (B) contains copper (II) oxide, and the drying tube (C) contains anhydrous calcium chloride to absorb the water formed by the hydrogen and the oxygen of the copper (II) oxide. Both tubes B and C are weighed before and after the reaction. The loss of mass by the copper (II) oxide indicates how much oxygen was removed by the hydrogen to form water, which may be weighed since it is collected in the drying tube C. Thus, it becomes evident how much oxygen is present in a weighed amount of water, and the composition of water can be calculated.

Example

In an experiment on the determination of the composition of water, the following data were obtained:

Mass of the Tube (B) containing Copper (II) Oxide

> Before: 60.46 g (1)
> After: 60.30 g (2)

Mass of the Drying Tube (C)

> Before: 75.40 g (3)
> After: 75.58 g (4)

From these data, let us calculate: (i) the mass of oxygen used up, (ii) the mass of water formed, (iii) the mass of hydrogen used, (iv) the percentage by mass of oxygen and hydrogen in water, and (v) the ratio of the mass of oxygen to hydrogen.

Calculation:

(i) Mass of the oxygen (equals loss of mass of the copper (II) oxide, tube B)

$$(1) - (2) = 0.16 \text{ g} \quad (5)$$

(ii) Mass of the water formed (equals gain in mass of the drying tube C):

$$(4) - (3) = 0.18 \text{ g} \quad (6)$$

(iii) Mass of hydrogen in the water (equals mass of the water formed minus mass of oxygen in the water):

$$(6) - (5) = 0.02 \text{ g}$$

(iv) Percentage of oxygen: $\dfrac{0.16}{0.18} \times 100 = 88.8$

Percentage of hydrogen: $\dfrac{0.02}{0.18} \times 100 = 11.1$

(v) Ratio of the mass of oxygen to hydrogen = 8:1

3:9 Classification of Substances: a Summary

When a sample of matter has the same composition throughout it is said to be *homogeneous;* but when the sample has unlike parts it is said to be *heterogeneous.* The recognizable parts in a sample of matter are often referred to as *phases.* Thus, a homogeneous sample of matter has one phase while a heterogeneous sample contains two or more phases.

Homogeneous substances can be further classified into two groups: *pure substances* of constant composition, and *solutions* which are homogeneous mixtures varying in composition. Some pure substances, called *compounds,* can be decomposed into simpler substances by chemical means. Other pure substances, called *elements,* cannot be decomposed into anything simpler.

Mechanical mixtures have variable composition. They consist of two or more physically distinct phases. These heterogeneous forms of matter have the properties of the substances that make up the mixtures. The components of a mechanical mixture can be separated by physical means.

A CLASSIFICATION OF SUBSTANCES

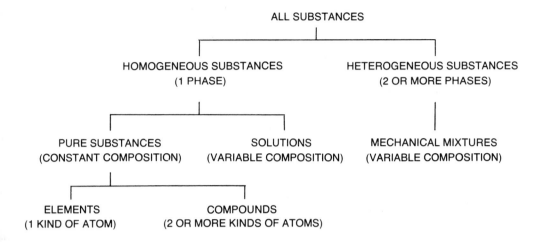

QUESTIONS

1. Distinguish between *elements* and *compounds*. Give three examples of elements and three examples of compounds.

2. Which three elements account for more than 80% of the earth's crust by mass? What are the two most common elements that make up the earth's water? What are the two most common elements in the air?

3. List a few typical properties of (i) metals; (ii) non-metals. Give three examples of each.

4. Explain what is meant by the term *molecule*. Name one pure substance that is made up of molecules.

5. Describe the smallest particles of which a crystal of salt is composed. Is salt a compound or an element?

6. What is an atom?

7. (i) What is a chemical symbol? (ii) What do the following symbols represent? Cl, Co, Ca, C, He, H? (iii) Give the symbol for each of the following: lithium, manganese, phosphorus, tin, boron.

8. What does a chemical formula represent?

9. List the information which each of the following formulas give, (i) H_2O; (ii) HCl; (iii) CO_2; (iv) CH_4; (v) $Ca(OH)_2$.

10. Give the meaning of each number and symbol in the equation:
$H_2 + Cl_2 \rightarrow 2\,HCl$

11. Give two important differences between a compound and a mixture. Give two examples of compounds and two examples of mixtures.

12. Classify the following as elements, compounds, mechanical mixtures, or solutions: (i) pure water; (ii) oxygen gas; (iii) granite; (iv) brine; (v) sugar; (vi) carbon dioxide; (vii) dilute hydrochloric acid; (viii) tomato juice; (ix) nitrogen; (x) concrete; (xi) mercury.

13. How could you separate the component parts of a mixture of sand and salt?

14. How can we prove that the gases collected during the electrolysis of water are oxygen and hydrogen?

15. What is the ratio of the volumes of the two gases produced during the electrolysis of water?

16. If 10 mL of hydrogen and 10 mL of oxygen are placed in a eudiometer tube and sparked, name the gas remaining and find its volume.

17. Repeat question 16 assuming that:
    (i) 5 mL of hydrogen and 10 mL of oxygen are used.
    (ii) 8 mL of hydrogen and 3 mL of oxygen are used.

18. In an experiment to find the percentage composition of water by mass (using the apparatus shown in Fig. 3.5), the following data were obtained:
    Mass of copper (II) oxide and tube before reduction: 682.63 g
    Mass of copper and tube after reduction: 622.63 g
    Mass of drying tube before experiment: 876.32 g
    Mass of drying tube after experiment: 943.89 g
    Calculate the percentage composition of water from this information.

CHAPTER

4

ATOMS AND MOLECULES

4:1   The Law of Conservation of Mass

It has been pointed out earlier (sec. 2:7) that the products obtained from a chemical reaction apparently have the same total mass as the original materials or reactants. This regularity of behaviour found in nature is called the *Law of Conservation of Mass.*

4:2   The Law of Constant Composition

One of the main tasks of chemistry is to study the composition of compounds, and two general methods for doing this have been developed: analysis and synthesis. Illustrations of these

From mighty mountains to the endless ocean, the world of infinite variety is made possible by the invisible world of atoms and molecules.

methods were seen in determining the composition of water (Chapter 3).

The composition of about one million compounds has been determined with the aid of analysis and synthesis. In every compound tested, the percentage by mass of each element present was always found to be constant. This result is summed up in the *Law of Constant Composition* which states that *every pure chemical compound has a constant composition by mass.* Some examples are given in Table 4.1.

TABLE 4.1

Percentage Composition of Some Compounds

Compound	Composition
Water, H_2O	88.8% oxygen, 11.2% hydrogen
Methane, CH_4	75.0% carbon, 25.0% hydrogen
Ethane, C_2H_6	80.0% carbon, 20.0% hydrogen
Methanol, CH_3OH	50.0% oxygen, 37.5% carbon, 12.5% hydrogen

TABLE 4.2

Illustration of the Law of Multiple Proportions

Compound	Parts by mass of oxygen and hydrogen	Ratio of the masses of oxygen that combine with 2.0 g of hydrogen
Water	16 g of O and 2.0 g of H	16 : 32 or 1 : 2
Hydrogen Peroxide	32 g of O and 2.0 g of H	

4:3 The Law of Multiple Proportions

It is not uncommon for the same elements to combine in more than one ratio to form different compounds. For example, 12 g of carbon combine with 16 g of oxygen to form carbon monoxide, and with 32 g of oxygen to form carbon dioxide. It can be seen that the masses of oxygen that combine with a fixed mass of carbon are in the ratio of 16:32 or 1:2.

In all cases there is a simple ratio among the several masses of an element that combine with a fixed mass of another. This fact is summed up in the *Law of Multiple Proportions: If two elements A and B combine to form more than one compound, then the different amounts of A that combine with a fixed amount of B are always in a simple ratio.*

The two compounds, water and hydrogen peroxide, offer another example of the law of multiple proportions. The relationships among the masses involved are shown in Table 4.2.

4:4 A Theory to Explain the Behaviour of Matter and Chemical Change

Surely the laws of chemical combinations presented above must offer some important clue about the ultimate structure of matter and the way in which elements combine to form compounds. Do they answer such questions as: Why can compounds be broken down to elements but elements cannot be broken down into anything simpler? Why is matter not destroyed in chemical change? Why do the products weigh as much as the original reactants? Why do compounds have a definite composition?

About the year 1800, an English schoolteacher attempted to find the answer to these questions by imagining that matter is made up of atoms and that the behaviour of atoms can explain chemical processes.

The main points of *Dalton's Atomic Theory* are the following:

1. All matter is made up of particles called atoms.
2. The atoms cannot be destroyed, or even divided, in a chemical change.
3. The atoms of a particular element have the same properties.
4. When atoms combine with other atoms, they do so in simple ratios, such as 1:1, or 2:1, or 3:2; fractions of an atom never combine.
5. All chemical change is the result of the combination or the separation of atoms.

The first point of the theory is that there are atoms of elements but not of compounds. Dalton's view was that the atom is the smallest particle of an element, and that an atom is indivisible.

Perhaps the most significant idea in the atomic theory is that all chemical change is the union or separation of atoms. When atoms combine they form molecules. If the atoms in the molecules are different, then such molecules account for the existence of compounds. It may happen also that atoms of the same element combine to form molecules. Oxygen is made up of molecules with two oxygen atoms each; hydrogen, nitrogen, and chlorine are similarly made of diatomic molecules. In these gases, each diatomic molecule is separated from other molecules by large distances. Molecules of the element sulfur have eight atoms each. The noble gases, helium, neon, argon, krypton, xenon, and radon consist of molecules which are single atoms.

Thus we can see how Dalton successfully defined elements, compounds, and chemical change in terms of atoms. Can the theory explain the observed laws of chemical combination? Let us see.

4:5   Explanation of the Law of Conservation of Mass

Why is there conservation of mass during a chemical reaction? According to the atomic theory, all chemical change is the combination of atoms with other atoms or the separation of atoms from other atoms. At no time is the mass of the atom itself altered, and there are as many atoms at the end of the reaction as there were at the beginning. They are simply combined differently. Therefore, there is conservation of mass in a chemical reaction.

Explaining the Law of Conservation of Mass with the example of this Chemical Reaction:

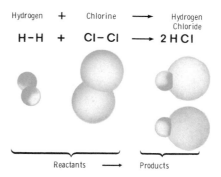

There are 2 atoms of hydrogen and 2 atoms of chlorine first among the reactants, and later among the products. They are respectively the same in number and mass, although differently combined. Hence, conservation of mass.

4:6   Explanation of the Law of Constant Composition

Why do compounds have a definite composition? According to the atomic theory, a compound forms when one (or two or three) atoms of an element A combine with one (or two or three) atoms of element B. But the atoms always combine in the same ratio in forming that compound. Because all the atoms of A are alike, and all the atoms of B are alike, all the molecules of the compound will be alike, each containing the same ratio of atoms of A to atoms of B.

Explaining the Law of Constant Composition with the example of water:

All water consists of water molecules:

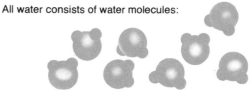

All water molecules are alike consisting of 2 atoms of hydrogen and 1 atom of oxygen:

Therefore, all water has the same composition.
A similar explanation applies to all other chemical compounds.

4:7   Explanation of the Law of Multiple Proportions

How does the atomic theory explain the law of multiple proportions? According to the atomic theory, when a particular element A combines with another element B, one atom of A combines with one atom of B to form a molecule AB. If conditions are altered, it may become possible for the atoms of A and B to combine in a different ratio. For example, two atoms of A might combine with one of B; now a new compound is formed whose molecule is AAB, or A_2B.

On comparing the composition of the two compounds formed out of the same elements A and B; we find that the different masses of A combined with the same mass of B are in the simple ratio of 1:2. This is precisely what had been found by experiment.

Explaining the Law of Multiple Proportions with water and hydrogen peroxide as examples:

The molecule of water has 1 atom of oxygen and 2 of hydrogen:

The molecule of hydrogen peroxide has 2 atoms of oxygen and 2 of hydrogen:

The atoms of oxygen in the respective molecules are in the ratio of 1:2. Hence, multiple proportions.

4:8   Dalton's Dilemma

Unfortunately, Dalton did not know the ratio in which atoms combine, and this was one of the chief weaknesses of the early atomic theory.

It can thus be seen that although Dalton was largely successful in explaining the laws of chemical combination by means of his atomic theory, at least three questions remained unanswered:

(a) If atoms are so small that they cannot be seen, how can we know anything about them? How do they compare to molecules?
(b) How many atoms are in a molecule?
(c) If the atoms of the different elements have different masses, what are these masses?

These are important and difficult questions, and because Dalton did not have the answer to them, the atomic theory met with some criticism and disbelief.

We know today that the atoms of the elements are built up of even more fundamental particles. These subatomic particles, the electron, the proton, and the neutron, are present in every kind of atom. The iron atom, for example, is the smallest particle of the element but it is composed of subatomic particles.

Dalton's view that all atoms are alike is now modified in the light of the discovery of isotopes (Chapter 7). This can hardly be considered a "mistake." It is rather a refinement of the atomic theory. We can say that the essential points of Dalton's atomic theory concerning chemical combination are still valid today.

4:9   Atomic Mass

We have discussed atoms and molecules descriptively. Could they be described quantitatively? Could we say something about their mass? Atoms and molecules are so small that weighing them individually on a balance is out of the question. However, this is hardly necessary. If it is true that the atoms of each element have a certain mass, and that they combine with other atoms in a definite ratio, we could perform an experiment to find out what mass of two given elements combine with each other. If we knew also in what ratio the atoms combine, we could then find the relative mass of the atoms.

A chemical reaction that illustrates such relationships is the combination of carbon with oxygen to form carbon dioxide gas. We can weigh a definite mass of carbon and ignite it. We can determine the mass of carbon dioxide produced by capturing it in some limewater. Then, the mass of oxygen involved in the combination can be calculated by subtracting the mass of carbon used from the mass of carbon dioxide formed.

Such an experiment will permit us to know the respective mass of carbon and oxygen that combine in forming carbon dioxide. However, one other important item of information will be required before the relative mass of the atoms can be established. How many atoms of carbon and oxygen are there in a molecule of carbon dioxide? This is indeed a difficult question. Such was the problem that Dalton could not solve. For our present purpose we will use the now established fact that one atom of carbon combines with two atoms of oxygen to form a molecule of carbon dioxide:

$$C + O_2 \rightarrow CO_2$$

In doing this experiment, the following data are obtained:

Mass of carbon burned:	12 g
Mass of carbon dioxide produced:	44 g
$\therefore$ Mass of oxygen used (44 − 12):	32 g

$$\text{Hence,} \quad \frac{\text{mass of oxygen}}{\text{mass of carbon}} = \frac{32}{12}$$

The result obtained, 32:12, represents the ratio of the mass of oxygen to the mass of carbon that combine, forming carbon dioxide. Now this carbon dioxide is made up of molecules which are all alike. Each molecule of carbon dioxide has 2 atoms of oxygen and 1 atom of carbon. Therefore, the mass of 2 oxygen atoms and the mass of 1 carbon atom are also in the ratio of 32:12. Hence, we may write:

$$\frac{\text{mass of 2 atoms of oxygen}}{\text{mass of 1 atom of carbon}} = \frac{32}{12}$$

$$\text{or} \quad \frac{\text{mass of 1 atom of oxygen}}{\text{mass of 1 atom of carbon}} = \frac{16}{12}$$

Thus we find that the masses of the atoms of oxygen and carbon are in the ratio of

$$O:C = 16:12$$

Although the experimental method of performing the above experiment might be somewhat difficult to carry out, the conclusion reached is fundamentally sound. We have found the relative mass of two atoms.

We could now devise other experiments to find the ratio of other pairs of atoms, until we have such information about as many elements as we please.

To convert our data from comparisons of the mass of atoms to a simpler independent expression of their mass, we need to select an appropriate standard element to whose atom all others may be compared, and an appropriate unit to express atomic mass.

The element chosen in 1961 was carbon, and the atom of its most abundant isotope is the standard to which the mass of all other atoms are compared. To this atom of carbon, a mass of 12 atomic mass units (u) was assigned. Thus the u can be defined as 1/12 the mass of the carbon-12 isotope.

Once the value of 12 u is assigned to carbon, relative values can be assigned to the atoms of the other elements using such data as we found for oxygen. The mass of the oxygen atom is 16 u; the mass of the hydrogen atom is 1 u; etc. The mass of all the atoms of the elements are listed inside the front cover of the book.

A molecule consists of atoms. The mass of the molecule is the sum of the mass of its atoms. The sum is termed the *molecular mass* of the compound. The molecular mass of sulfur dioxide, SO_2, is equal to the sum of the mass of one sulfur atom and two oxygen atoms:

$$(1 \times 32) + (2 \times 16) = 64 \text{ u}$$

Both molecular and atomic masses are based

on the same standard, carbon-12, and are both expressed in u.

The determination of the atomic masses of the elements has helped chemistry to become a quantitative and creative science.

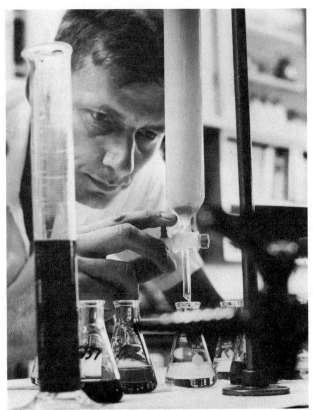

Courtesy Chas. Pfizer and Company, Incorporated

Chemical compounds are created artificially by combining known elements. In a pharmaceutical research laboratory, a scientist separates foreign substances to obtain a pure compound.

4:10   The Size of Atoms and Molecules

With the aid of modern experimental methods, the size of atoms and molecules have been determined. Atoms are very small particles with diameters in the range of 0.2 to 0.5 nm—"nm" stands for the nanometre, equal to 10^{-9} m. Thus if atoms whose diameters are 0.5 nm could be placed side by side, it would require 20 million of them to make up 1 cm. Individual atoms or average-sized molecules are much too small to be seen by the most powerful of microscopes. By means of the electron microscope, however, in which a beam of electrons is used instead of visible light, photographs (more accurately, electron micrographs) of the giant protein molecules of disease-producing viruses have been made. Such giant molecules contain as many as 750 000 atoms.

QUESTIONS

For atomic mass refer to the table inside the front cover of the book.

1. What does the Law of Conservation of Mass *suggest* about the structure of matter?

2. What regularity does the Law of Constant Composition *suggest* about the structure of matter?

3. When an electric current is passed through a molten sample of sodium chloride, sodium metal and chlorine gas are produced at the two electrodes. Is this an example of an analysis or a synthesis? Explain your answer.

4. Iron sulfide, FeS, contains 36.5% sulfur. How much sulfur could be extracted from 1 t of iron sulfide?

5. What does the Law of Multiple Proportions suggest about the structure of matter?

6. Two compounds of tin and oxygen have the following compositions: tin 78.77%, oxygen 21.23%; tin 88.12%, oxygen 11.88%.
    (i) Calculate the mass of oxygen combined with one gram of tin in each of the two compounds.
    (ii) Do these two compounds illustrate the Law of Multiple Proportions? Explain.

7. What do you think prompted Dalton to propose his atomic theory?

8. State the main points of Dalton's atomic theory.

9. Why would the oxygen and mercury obtained from decomposing 10 g of mercury (II) oxide, HgO, together have a mass of 10 g?

10. Use Dalton's atomic theory to explain: (i) the Law of Conservation of Mass; (ii) the Law of Constant Composition; (iii) the Law of Multiple Proportions.

11. List the questions that Dalton's atomic theory did not answer.

12. Suggest some advances that have been made in knowledge about atoms since Dalton's time.

13. Define the following terms: (i) atomic mass; (ii) molecular mass; (iii) atomic mass unit.

14. What is the present standard for atomic and molecular mass?

15. Find the molecular mass of the following substances:
    (i)   hydrogen, H_2;
    (ii)   sodium hydroxide, NaOH;
    (iii)   water, H_2O;
    (iv)   sucrose, $C_{12}H_{22}O_{11}$;
    (v)   hydrogen chloride, HCl;
    (vi)   methane, CH_4;
    (vii)   carbon dioxide, CO_2;
    (viii) sulfuric acid, H_2SO_4;
    (ix)   nitrogen, N_2;
    (x)   ammonia, NH_3.

CHAPTER

5

CHEMISTRY
AND ELECTRONS

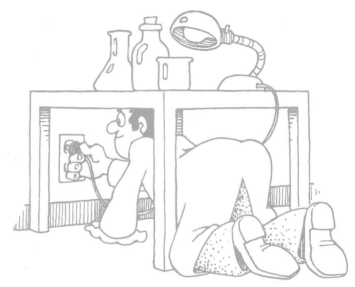

Chemistry is governed by the behaviour of electrons.

5:1   Unanswered Questions

During the first 150 years of scientific chemistry, from about 1750 to 1900, much information about elements and compounds was collected. A number of laws and theories were proposed, but on the whole, many questions could not be answered, such as: Why do atoms combine? Why are certain elements similar to each other? What is an electric current? How does an electric current have the ability to cause chemical change? What is the relationship between matter and electricity?

The answers to these and many other questions came with the discovery that atoms contain electrons. It is really these electrified particles which are responsible for the properties and behaviour of the atoms. Even the electric current was seen to be a stream of electrons. How did this knowledge come about?

5:2   Static and Current Electricity

About 2500 years ago, the Greeks discovered that when amber was rubbed with cloth it attracted small pieces of cotton and straw. The force of attraction was called electricity after the Greek name for amber, *elektron*. Later it was found that whenever two different substances are rubbed together, both acquire electrical charges. Such charges are referred to as *static electricity*.

We can show that electrical charges are of two kinds. If we suspend a glass rod rubbed with silk, it is repelled when a second rod similarly charged is brought near (Fig. 5:1). However, if a hard rubber rod is rubbed with fur and held near the suspended glass rod, the latter is attracted. Two charged rubber rods repel each other. We can thus formulate a simple law: *like charges repel while unlike charges attract.*

Around 1750, Benjamin Franklin, an American statesman and scientist, studied the nature of electricity. He suggested that the two kinds of electricity observed be called *positive* and *negative*.

Then about 1800, Volta and Galvani, two Italian scientists, learned how to produce a continuous electrical current. This was a major discovery, not only in the science of electricity but also in the history of humanity. With the discovery of current electricity, people's level of knowledge in many fields and, indeed their very way of life began to change rapidly.

Later, it was shown that the electrical charges are due to the particles that make up the atoms themselves. The negative charges are due to electrons and the positive charges are due to protons. *Electric current* is the flow of electrons along a metal conductor such as a copper wire or the flight of electrons from the cathode to the anode in a vacuum tube. By knowing the properties of electrons, we learn how to control their motion and how to harness their energy. With the aid of this knowledge we build the hundreds of useful electric appliances so familiar to us.

5:3   The Properties of Electrons

The cathode tube is a glass vacuum tube fitted with two electrodes. A high voltage is applied to the electrodes to give energy to the electrons as they fly from the cathode to the anode; hence the name, *cathode tube.*

The properties of electrons were first studied in the cathode tube from which the television screen was developed. In the picture tube of the television set, electrons travel from a cathode located at the far end, towards an anode placed near the screen. Their motion, controlled through their charge, forms the picture as they strike the screen (Fig. 5.2).

Thomson, an English physicist, and other scientists, found that electrons had the following properties:

1. They carry a negative charge.
2. Their mass is very small. The mass of the hydrogen atom is about 1840 times as great as that of the electron.
3. They are present in the atoms of all the elements.

5:4   Some Electric Terms and Units

An amount of electric charge could be reported as a number of electrons. However, it is customary to

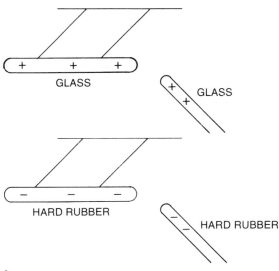
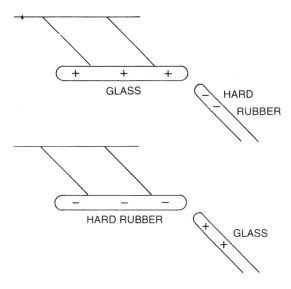

Fig. 5.1:
Electrostatic attraction and repulsion

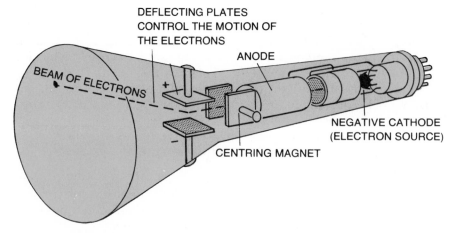

DEFLECTING PLATES
CONTROL THE MOTION OF
THE ELECTRONS

ANODE

BEAM OF ELECTRONS

NEGATIVE CATHODE
(ELECTRON SOURCE)

CENTRING MAGNET

Fig. 5.2:
The television picture tube
The television screen is a modified cathode ray tube, in which direct evidence was first obtained that an electric current is a flow of electrons and that electrons are present in all atoms.

express a quantity of charge in coulombs. One *coulomb* represents 6.24×10^{18} electrons.

The intensity of the electric current, that is, the rate of flow, is measured in amperes. The intensity of the current is one *ampere* when one coulomb passes a given point in the circuit in one second.

Table 5:1 presents a comparison between the flow of water in a pipe and the flow of electricity in a conductor. Pressure must be available to force a certain amount of water through a pipe in a given time. Similarly, a definite amount of electricity can be forced through a conductor in a given time only if a sufficient voltage is available.

5:5   The Charge on the Electron

Millikan, an American scientist, is credited with the first accurate determination of the electron's charge. A simplified version of his apparatus is shown in Fig. 5.3. His general procedure was as follows: he sprayed droplets of oil between charged plates of an electrical apparatus. By watching their rate of fall, he determined their mass. He charged the upper plate of the apparatus positively and the lower one negatively while at the same time, he placed a negative charge on the oil droplets. Thereupon the droplets rose to the upper plate. From the rate of rising he calculated the charge on the droplets.

He found that the charges on the oil droplets were always multiples of the same fundamental value. This he calculated to be 1.60×10^{-19} C*. When charged, the oil droplets acquire one, or two, or three, or some other whole number, of these units. No exception to this rule was found in over 2000 experiments in more than five years by Millikan and his students. Such experiments have been repeated many times since by other scientists, and the results are confirmed. Hence the conclusion that this value must be the charge of one single electron.

$$e = 1.60 \times 10^{-19} \text{ C}$$

*C stands for the coulomb, the unit of electric charge, in SI (metric).

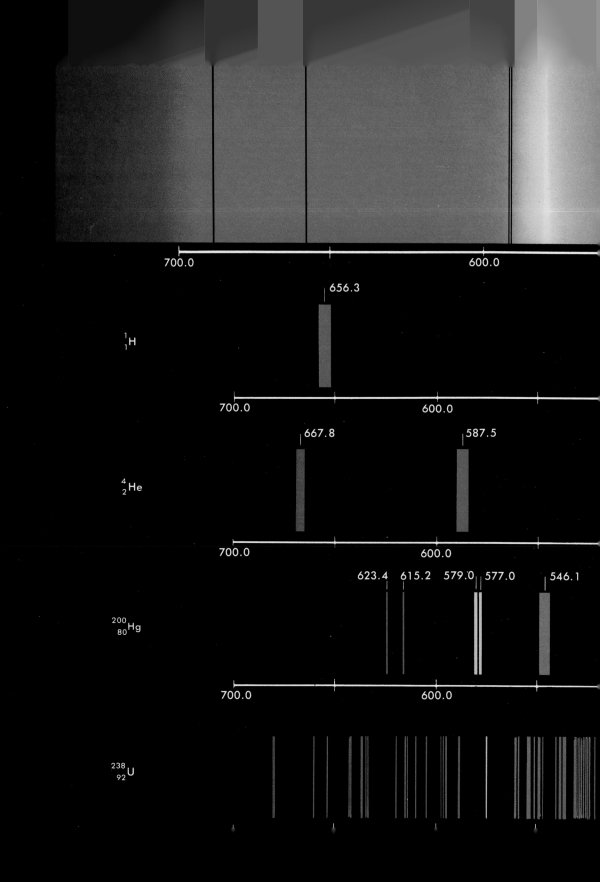

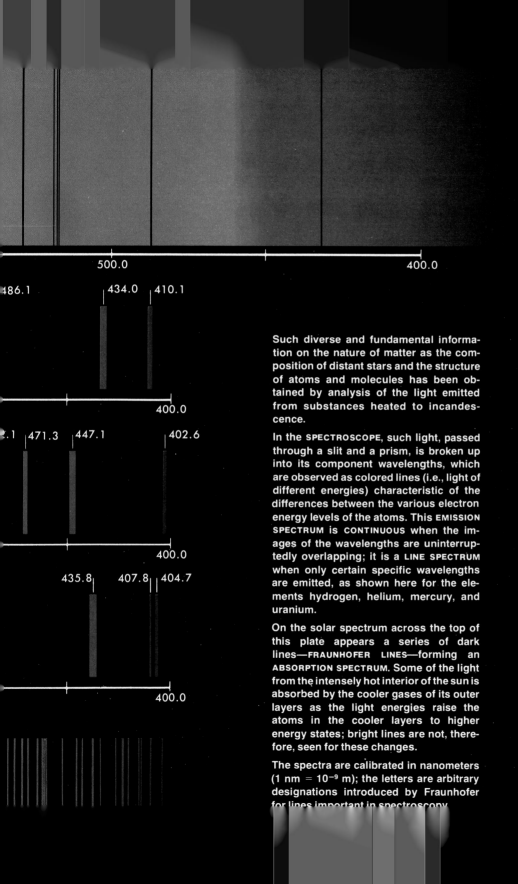

486.1   434.0   410.1

500.0   400.0

400.0

.1   471.3   447.1   402.6

400.0

435.8   407.8   404.7

400.0

Such diverse and fundamental information on the nature of matter as the composition of distant stars and the structure of atoms and molecules has been obtained by analysis of the light emitted from substances heated to incandescence.

In the SPECTROSCOPE, such light, passed through a slit and a prism, is broken up into its component wavelengths, which are observed as colored lines (i.e., light of different energies) characteristic of the differences between the various electron energy levels of the atoms. This EMISSION SPECTRUM is CONTINUOUS when the images of the wavelengths are uninterruptedly overlapping; it is a LINE SPECTRUM when only certain specific wavelengths are emitted, as shown here for the elements hydrogen, helium, mercury, and uranium.

On the solar spectrum across the top of this plate appears a series of dark lines—FRAUNHOFER LINES—forming an ABSORPTION SPECTRUM. Some of the light from the intensely hot interior of the sun is absorbed by the cooler gases of its outer layers as the light energies raise the atoms in the cooler layers to higher energy states; bright lines are not, therefore, seen for these changes.

The spectra are calibrated in nanometers (1 nm = 10^{-9} m); the letters are arbitrary designations introduced by Fraunhofer for lines important in spectroscopy.

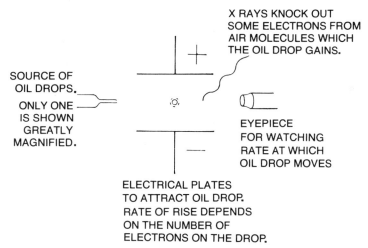

X RAYS KNOCK OUT
SOME ELECTRONS FROM
AIR MOLECULES WHICH
THE OIL DROP GAINS.

SOURCE OF
OIL DROPS.
ONLY ONE
IS SHOWN
GREATLY
MAGNIFIED.

EYEPIECE
FOR WATCHING
RATE AT WHICH
OIL DROP MOVES

ELECTRICAL PLATES
TO ATTRACT OIL DROP.
RATE OF RISE DEPENDS
ON THE NUMBER OF
ELECTRONS ON THE DROP.

Fig. 5.3:
Millikan's Oil Drop Experiment

TABLE 5:1

Analogy Between a Water System and an Electric Current

Quantity Measured	Units used with Water	Units used with Electricity
Amount	litres (L)	coulombs (C)
Rate of flow	litres per second (L/s)	amperes (coulombs per second) (C/s)

5:6   X rays

About the same time that Thomson was studying cathode rays and electrons (1893-5), Roentgen, a German physicist, discovered an unusual form of radiation. Using higher voltages than usual, thereby producing a flow of electrons of high energy, Roentgen found that rays coming out of his apparatus were able to pass through paper, wood, and even flesh, but not as readily through metal and bone. He named this radiation X rays.

X rays resemble light in that they are electrically neutral and travel at the same speed as light. They differ from light by having a shorter wave length and therefore greater frequency and energy. They are important in surgery, medicine, and industry.

The fact that X rays originate in the motion of electrons in the atoms is of great importance to the scientist. Indeed, the wave length and the frequency of the X rays emitted by an element are important clues to the number of electrons in the atom of that element (Chapter 6).

5:7   Radioactivity

Shortly after the discovery of X rays came an even more dramatic disclosure. In 1896, the French physicist Becquerel found that a certain mineral containing uranium gave off extremely powerful radiations even without the application of any energy. Marie Curie, a Polish student working with Becquerel, investigated this phenomenon further and called it *radioactivity*. Working with her husband Pierre Curie, she succeeded in isolating two new elements, radium and polonium, that were even more radioactive than uranium.

Lord Rutherford, a New Zealand physicist, while working at McGill University in Montreal, investigated the radiations emitted by the radioactive elements. He found that three different rays were being emitted. One ray was a stream of positively charged particles later to be identified as the nuclei of helium atoms. This beam was called the *alpha ray*, and the nuclei of the helium atoms were termed *alpha particles*. Another ray was a stream of electrons; this beam was called the *beta ray*. The third ray, called the *gamma ray*, was identified as powerful short-wave X rays. In view of the radiations emitted by the radioactive materials, Rutherford came to the conclusion that *in radioactivity certain atoms were in the process of breaking up*. As they broke up they emitted the various particles observed and thereby changed to atoms of another element.

In the course of his further work on radioactivity, particularly on alpha particles, Rutherford came upon evidence that helped him to form a theory about the structure of the atom.

The discovery of radioactivity in 1896 was the dawn of the nuclear age in which we now live. Similarly, the structure of the atom, suggested by the evidence from radioactivity, marks the beginning of the modern period in chemistry and physics.

QUESTIONS

1. (i) What is static electricity?
   (ii) How can static electricity be produced?

2. (i) Why has it been suggested that there are only two kinds of electrical charges?
   (ii) State the law concerning the attraction and repulsion of electrical charges.

3. What are the fundamental differences between positively and negatively charged bodies?

4. A glass rod is rubbed with silk and becomes positively charged. Do you think that the silk also acquires a charge? If so, what would be the nature of this charge?

5. What particles in atoms are now believed to be responsible for both positive and negative charges?

6. In 1897, J. J. Thomson determined the charge-to-mass ratio (e/m) for an electron using an apparatus very similar to that shown in Fig 5.2. The results that he got convinced others that electrons were particles distinctly different from atoms. Thomson found that $e/m = 1.76 \times 10^8$ Cg^{-1}. What are the other properties that electrons are now known to have?

7. In 1909 Millikan managed to determine the value of e for the electron using the apparatus shown in Fig. 5.3. If $e = 1.60 \times 10^{-19}$ C, determine the mass of the electron in kilograms.

8. Why is the charge on the oil droplet in Millikan's experiment always a certain value or some simple multiple of it?

9. Compare the properties of X rays with the properties of light.

10. Of what use are X rays?

11. What is a radioactive element?

12. Rutherford discovered that the radiation emitted by radioactive atoms was attracted, repelled or left unchanged as it went past a negatively charged plate. Which part of the radiation was attracted, which part was repelled and which part was left unchanged?

CHAPTER

6

ATOMS AND ELECTRONS

6:1   The Nuclear Atom

How do electrons, protons, and neutrons make up the atom and how many of each kind of these fundamental particles are present in the atom? Where are they located? How are they arranged? These questions were first answered by Rutherford, Moseley, and Bohr.

Radioactive atoms are in the process of disintegrating. In this process, some radioactive atoms emit positively charged alpha particles, which are the nuclei of helium atoms. Rutherford wished to determine how alpha particles pass through metal. In 1911 he performed an experiment in which alpha particles from a radioactive source were directed against a thin sheet of gold foil. The alpha particles were detected by means of a screen coated with zinc sulfide, placed around the gold foil. A zinc sulfide screen emits light when struck by an alpha particle, thus showing their whereabouts (Fig. 6.1).

This experiment showed that most of the alpha particles passed through the gold foil. Some were deflected at various angles as they emerged from the gold foil. A few, however, were reflected back into the direction from which they came—a surprising result. Rutherford described it by saying that it was "almost as if you had fired a 15-inch* shell at a piece of tissue paper and it came back and

*37.5 cm

Really, what is chemistry? It is the behaviour of electrons in atoms and molecules.

hit you." Rutherford proposed a possible explanation for the phenomenon: the atom must be largely empty space through which most of the alpha particles can pass easily, but a small heavy nucleus with a positive charge must be present in the centre of the atom. The repulsion between the positive charges on the alpha particle and the atomic nucleus caused the scattering of the alpha particles that was seen (Fig. 6.2).

The idea that the atom consists of a small, dense, and positively charged nucleus surrounded by electrons at relatively great distances is known as the *theory of the nuclear atom.*

6:2   Atomic Numbers

From the scattering of alpha particles, Rutherford was able to prove that the atom consists of a nucleus of positive charge surrounded by electrons, but he did not know how many electrons were present in the atoms of any particular element. This number, called the *atomic number* of the element, was determined by Moseley in 1912.

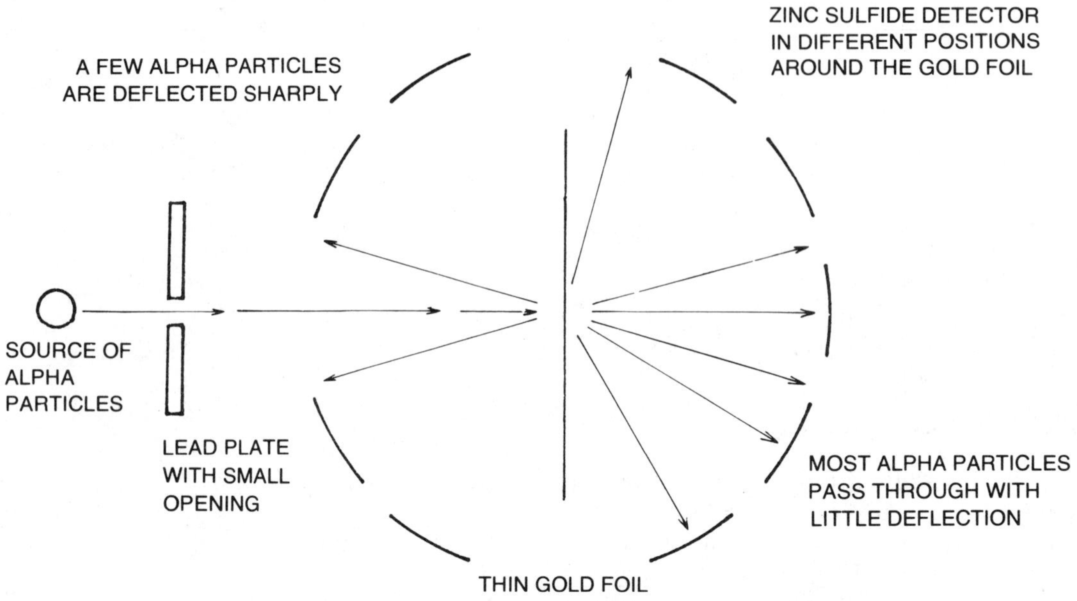

A FEW ALPHA PARTICLES
ARE DEFLECTED SHARPLY

ZINC SULFIDE DETECTOR
IN DIFFERENT POSITIONS
AROUND THE GOLD FOIL

SOURCE OF
ALPHA
PARTICLES

LEAD PLATE
WITH SMALL
OPENING

MOST ALPHA PARTICLES
PASS THROUGH WITH
LITTLE DEFLECTION

THIN GOLD FOIL

Fig. 6.1:
Rutherford's experiment on the scattering of alpha particles

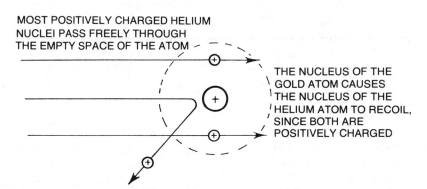

MOST POSITIVELY CHARGED HELIUM
NUCLEI PASS FREELY THROUGH
THE EMPTY SPACE OF THE ATOM

THE NUCLEUS OF THE
GOLD ATOM CAUSES
THE NUCLEUS OF THE
HELIUM ATOM TO RECOIL,
SINCE BOTH ARE
POSITIVELY CHARGED

Fig. 6.2:
Diagram to explain how alpha particles were scattered

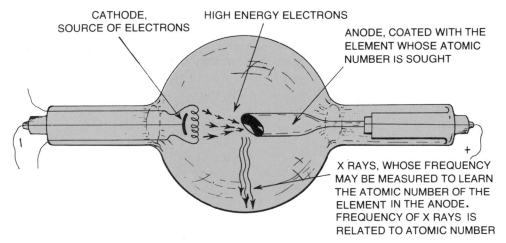

Fig. 6.3:
X rays and atomic numbers

Moseley's method was based on the fact that when an atom is bombarded by high energy cathode rays or electrons, it emits X rays (Fig. 6.3). Moseley found that the frequency of the X rays emitted by an element was related to its atomic number. Since the frequency of the X rays could be found experimentally, the atomic number of an element could be calculated from experimental data.

The number of electrons in an atom is important but their arrangement is even more significant for chemistry. Evidence about the arrangement of electrons in atoms was first deduced from the study of the spectra of the elements.

6:3   Emission Spectra

It has been known for a long time that atoms can absorb or emit light and other forms of radiant energy. When energy is introduced by heating the element to a high temperature, by radiation, or by electrical energy, the atoms absorb energy. When the source of energy is removed, the atoms emit the energy they have absorbed. In some cases, emission occurs while the energy source is still present,

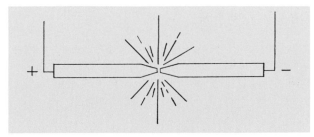

Fig. 6.4:
Electric arc producing light and other forms of radiant energy

as in the case of the light emitted when a high voltage is applied to carbon electrodes, producing an electric arc (Fig. 6.4).

A familiar form of such radiation is light. The light that an element emits is called its *spectrum*, and the study of this phenomenon is known as *spectroscopy*. The instrument used in spectroscopy, called a *spectroscope*, separates light into its component wave lengths. The different wave lengths are then focused as lines on a screen or a film (Fig. 6.5). This is the reason for the name, the *line spectrum*.

Each line corresponds to light of a certain wave

length. The set of lines comprising the spectrum are characteristic for each element. Spectroscopists have learned how to measure the wave lengths of spectral lines with great precision. They have established beyond doubt that every element absorbs and emits only certain wave lengths.

A familiar example of the emission of a particular colour or wave length of light is the reddish light of neon. The gas is placed at low pressure in glass tubes of desired shape. When voltage is applied, thereby introducing electrical energy, the gas glows, giving off the red colour of the neon sign.

Spectroscopists studied the line spectra of atoms with the hope of understanding how atoms can radiate light.

6:4   The Bohr Atom

What is light? It is a form of radiant energy. Other forms of radiant energy include X rays, infrared rays, radio waves, and microwaves used for television reception. All forms of radiant energy travel in a wavelike manner. Their waves differ in size, or *wave length*, and in the number of waves per second, or *frequency*, but all travel at the same velocity of 3.0×10^5 km/s. The colours of light have different wave lengths and frequencies. Red has the longest wave length and violet has the shortest.

It had always been assumed without question that energy could be present in any amounts in any system. This also meant that energy could be added to, or removed from, a system in amounts—large, small, or intermediate. The older idea about energy was that it was continuous. But is light continuous? To Bohr, the fact that the elements absorb or emit light of only certain wave lengths was a contradiction of the "continuous" nature of light. He maintained instead, that atoms absorb or emit light and other forms of radiation in units. These units may be imagined as packets of energy such that the atoms of an element absorb them and emit them entirely or else not at all. If they are not the right "size," the atom must simply pass them up.

The units of radiation that an atom absorbs are called *quanta* (singular, *quantum*). The quantum theory maintains that when atoms, molecules,

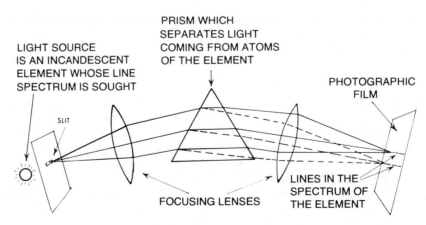

Fig. 6.5:
The line spectrum

ions, or electrons absorb or emit energy they do so only in quanta. This theory had been proposed to explain phenomena other than spectral lines, but it seemed to Bohr that a combination of the ideas of the nuclear atom and the quantum theory might explain how electrons are distributed in atoms.

Waves and Particles

In suggesting that radiation was a stream of quanta, the new theory did not reject entirely the older idea that radiation was also of the wave form; rather the quantum theory brought these two aspects of radiation together by proving that the size of a quantum of energy was proportional to the *frequency* of the radiation. Frequency is a characteristic of wave motion, representing the number of waves per second.

6:5   The Quantum Theory Applied to Atomic Structure

How might electrons be distributed in atoms so that they absorb or emit energy as quanta? To answer this question, Bohr suggested that the electrons must be in orbits of a certain size and moving at a certain speed. The electron would then have a certain energy. If it absorbed energy, the electron would move to an orbit of higher energy further from the nucleus. If it lost energy, the electron would move to another orbit nearer the nucleus.

Thus the quantum theory led to the idea of orbits. The electrons in the orbits had certain amounts of energy, or, in other words, the electrons were said to be at certain *energy levels*.

The spectra of atoms and molecules are signals that help the chemist identify substances.

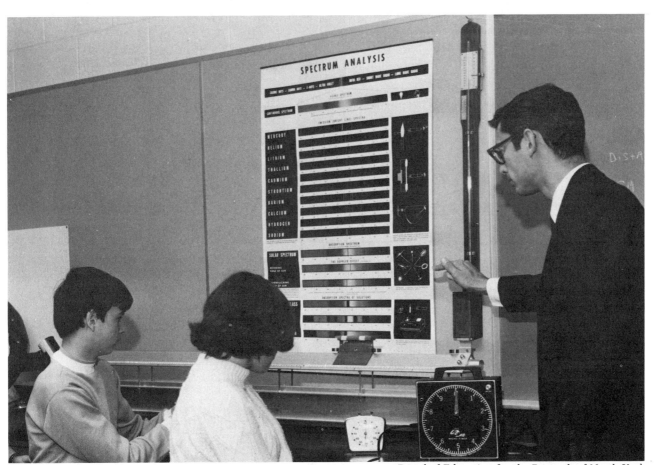

Board of Education for the Borough of North York

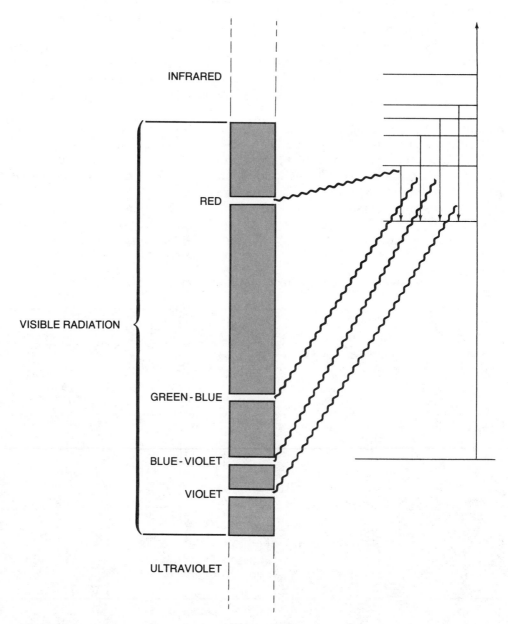

INFRARED

VISIBLE RADIATION

RED

GREEN - BLUE

BLUE - VIOLET

VIOLET

ULTRAVIOLET

Fig. 6.6:
How the hydrogen atom produces its spectrum of lines of different colours
The electron can occupy only certain energy levels. When it falls from one of these to a lower one, a quantum of light is emitted.

Radiation was due to electrons changing from a higher energy level to a lower one. (See Fig. 6.6.)

Bohr applied these ideas to the hydrogen atom and derived mathematically what the frequency of the radiation emitted by hydrogen should be. This was a great triumph. The new theory succeeded in explaining a difficult phenomenon, which the older idea, that light was continuous, could not even begin to explain.

Unfortunately, however, Bohr's theory did not work as well with elements whose atoms are more complex than those of hydrogen.

The New Quantum Theory

Some scientists believed that Bohr's theory became unwieldy with atoms larger than hydrogen because it assumed too much about the electron. The Bohr theory maintained that the electron, supposedly a particle, is at a certain place in the atom and moves at a certain speed. Perhaps, suggested these scientists, the best to be hoped for is an account of where the electrons of any atom or molecule are most likely to be.

As an analogy, the traffic department of a large city could not be expected to know where each individual car is at any moment. Nor is this necessary. It is more concerned with the flow of traffic and the points where traffic is likely to be heaviest at certain times.

Fortunately, to describe the approximate whereabouts of electrons in atoms and molecules proved easier than to establish the exact location of any particular one.

As a result of theoretical and experimental work, a picture of the structure of the atom has been developed which explains chemical phenomena in a satisfactory way. Rather than describing the electron as being found in a sharply defined orbit, the new quantum theory suggests that they exist in regions known as shells. Each shell has the capacity for more than one electron although there is an upper limit that depends on the shell that is being considered. Unlike an orbit, a shell has a more loosely defined location around the nucleus.

QUESTIONS

1. (i)   Describe Rutherford's experiment in which he caused alpha particles to bombard a thin sheet of gold.
    (ii) Why were some of the alpha particles repelled in this experiment?
    (iii) What did this experiment suggest about the structure of the atom?

2. Sketch and label a diagram of the atom as Rutherford imagined it to be.

3. Explain briefly how atomic numbers were determined.

4. What is meant by the term *line spectra*?

5. How did Bohr explain that the energy emitted or absorbed by atoms is in certain definite wave lengths only?

6. How was the Bohr model of the atom different from the Rutherford model?

7. (i) Draw a typical hydrogen atom showing five different orbits that an electron might go into if it received energy and had to leave the lowest orbit.
    (ii) If the electron absorbed enough energy to put it into the sixth orbit, how many different lines might appear in the line spectrum, when the electron returned to the lowest orbit?

8. Name at least one problem encountered with the Bohr model of the atom.

CHAPTER

7

THE STRUCTURE OF THE ATOM

Atoms are the invisible building blocks of the universe, but they also have a structure of their own.

7:1 The Electrical and Nuclear Units of Matter

Electricity is used for a variety of purposes. It supplies the energy for lighting, heating, refrigeration, communication, and for hundreds of useful appliances.

The *electric current* is a flow of charged units called electrons. They are present in all atoms, and are chiefly responsible for the chemical behaviour of atoms, molecules, and ions.

The *electron* carries a negative electric charge and is very light. The mass of the hydrogen atom, the lightest atom, is about 1840 times as great as that of the electron. Indeed, the mass of the electron is so small that it is not ordinarily considered in computing the mass of the atom.

Matter is generally electrically neutral, because the number of positive and negative charges in matter are equal. The particle with a positive charge is the *proton*. This positive particle has almost exactly the same mass as the hydrogen atom which consists of one proton and one electron, and the mass of the electron is negligible.

The *neutron* is another particle in the nucleus of atoms. The name neutron suggests that it is electrically neutral. It carries no negative or positive charge. Its mass is almost the same as that of a proton or a hydrogen atom. Properties of the three important constituents of the atom are summarized in Table 7.1.

TABLE 7.1

Properties of the Fundamental Particles

Particle	Charge	Mass in Atomic Mass Units
Electron	−1	0.000 55 or 1/1840 of the hydrogen atom
Proton	+1	1.0078
Neutron	0	1.0087

7:2 The Atomic Number

In any atom the total number of electrons is equal to that of the protons; so the atom as a whole is electrically neutral. The number of protons or electrons in the atom is called the *atomic number.* Hydrogen has one electron and one proton, and therefore is said to have an atomic number of *one.* Helium has two electrons and two protons, and hence has an atomic number of *two.*

How are electrons situated in an atom? The answer to this question is very important in chemistry because it helps to explain the chemical properties of the elements.

While protons and neutrons are in the nucleus of the atom, the electrons are in motion around the nucleus in shells. Since such motion requires energy, the electrons are said to be at certain energy levels numbered 1, 2, 3, . . . respectively. Often the letter n is used as a symbol for electronic shells. For the first shell, $n = 1$, for the second, $n = 2$ and so forth.

7:3   Imagining the Atom

The nucleus of an atom is extremely small compared to the size of the entire atom. The diameter of the nucleus is about 1/100 000 of the diameter of the whole atom. Yet, nearly all the mass of the atom is concentrated in this region because it contains all the protons and neutrons. The rest of the volume of the atom is occupied by electrons.

By means of the atomic number we can start to build a picture of the atoms. The hydrogen atom, whose atomic number is 1, is the lightest and the simplest of all. It consists of a proton in the nucleus and an electron revolving about it. The atom of helium (atomic number 2) consists of 2 electrons revolving about a nucleus containing 2 protons and 2 neutrons. The first electron shell is now full.

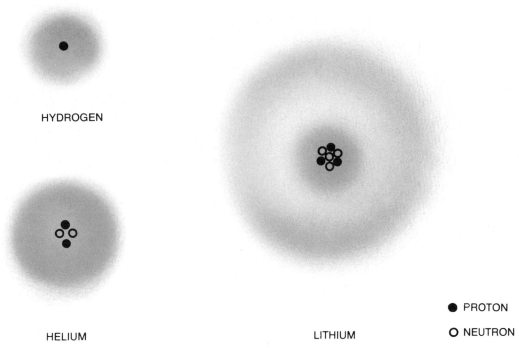

HYDROGEN

HELIUM

LITHIUM

● PROTON

O NEUTRON

Fig. 7.1:
Representation of the first three atoms

TABLE 7:2

Electrons in the Shells of the First Twenty Elements

Elements	Atomic Numbers	Energy Levels and Electrons in the Shells			
		First $n=1$	Second $n=2$	Third $n=3$	Fourth $n=4$
H	1	1			
He	2	2			
Li	3	2	1		
Be	4	2	2		
B	5	2	3		
C	6	2	4		
N	7	2	5		
O	8	2	6		
F	9	2	7		
Ne	10	2	8		
Na	11	2	8	1	
Mg	12	2	8	2	
Al	13	2	8	3	
Si	14	2	8	4	
P	15	2	8	5	
S	16	2	8	6	
Cl	17	2	8	7	
Ar	18	2	8	8	
K	19	2	8	8	1
Ca	20	2	8	8*	2*

The atom of lithium (atomic number 3) consists of 3 electrons. Two of these are in the first shell, and the third electron is in the second shell. The nucleus of lithium consists of 3 protons and 4 neutrons (Fig. 7.1).

Thus lithium's atom has the first electron of the second shell. This shell can hold a maximum of 8 electrons, and with neon, atom number 10, this number is reached. Sodium is atom number 11. Its eleventh electron starts the third shell. The eighteenth electron of argon completes this shell.

Table 7.2 shows how the electron shells, energy levels, and numbers of electrons are interrelated for the first 20 elements.

The First Shell
Hydrogen has only 1 electron and it is located in the first electron shell. Helium has 2 electrons in the first shell; thus the shell is filled completely. All atoms after helium will have 2 electrons in their first shell, plus other electrons in the higher shells.

* Beyond the first twenty elements listed in Table 7:2, the atoms have shells that are able to hold 18 and 32 electrons.

The Second Shell
The lithium atom has 3 electrons in all, 1 of these in the second shell. The 7 next atoms have 2, 3, 4, 5, 6, 7, and 8 electrons respectively in the second shell. Thus we reach neon, atom number 10, with 8 electrons in that shell, now filled completely. All atoms after neon will have 2 electrons in the first and 8 in the second shell.

The Third Shell
Sodium starts the third electron shell with 1 electron in that shell. Once again, the pattern of the previous shell is repeated. The 7 atoms after sodium have 2, 3, 4, 5, 6, 7, and 8 electrons respectively in the third shell.

Resembling the behaviour of neon, argon attains 8 electrons in the third shell, thereby filling it. All atoms after argon will have 2, 8, 8*, electrons in their first 3 shells.

The Fourth Shell
The next element is potassium and its outermost electron starts the fourth shell by having 1 electron in it. Calcium follows with 2.

7:4   The Formation of Ions

In the lithium atom, the single electron in the outer shell may be transferred to another atom. This leaves the original atom with one more proton than it has electrons. Such a particle carries a positive charge and is an example of an ion. The following equation represents a neutral lithium atom becoming a lithium ion by losing an electron:

$$\text{lithium atom} \rightarrow \text{lithium ion} + \text{one electron}$$
$$\text{Li}^\circ \rightarrow \text{Li}^+ + 1\,e^-$$

By contrast, other atoms may easily add one or more electrons to their outer shells. The fluorine atom may easily gain one electron to become the negatively charged fluoride ion:

$$\text{fluorine atom} + \text{one electron} \rightarrow \text{fluoride ion}$$
$$\text{F}^\circ + 1\,e^- \rightarrow \text{F}^-$$

7:5   Isotopes

Atoms of the same element might have different numbers of neutrons despite the fact that they have the same number of electrons and protons. Such atoms have the same atomic number but different atomic mass, and they are called *isotopes*. Remember that the atomic mass is determined by the numbers of protons and neutrons and for this reason different numbers of neutrons would cause such atoms to have a different mass. Since the chemical properties of an element depend on the electrons in the shells, the isotopes of an element have the same chemical properties.

7:6   The Mass Spectrograph

Chemical methods for finding the atomic mass of the elements were used successfully to establish the truth of the atomic theory in the early years of scientific chemistry. In the present century physicists have devised another method for finding atomic mass, based on the mass of the atom as a physical property. The instrument employed in this method is called the *mass spectrograph*.

To illustrate the idea of this method, imagine a few steel balls, each of slightly different mass, which are allowed to roll down a gentle incline. The balls would roll in a straight line from point A to point B. Suppose now, a magnet NS is placed near the path along which the balls roll. It would then be found that the magnetic attraction would cause the balls to be deflected from their paths. The heaviest ball would be deflected to the smallest extent, while the lightest ball would be deflected to

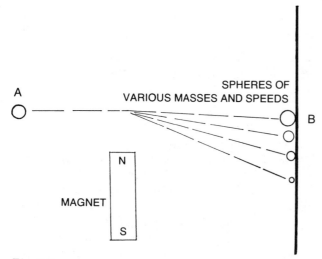

Fig. 7.2:
The mass spectrograph analogy

the greatest extent by the attraction of the magnet (Fig. 7.2).

The spots where the balls strike the target could be noted, and the relative masses of the balls calculated from the extent of their deflection by the magnetic field.

The mass spectrograph works on a similar principle. Instead of steel balls, atoms carrying electrical charges are shot out by electrical energy. These are then deflected by a magnetic field. The atoms of different mass separate and come to rest at different points or lines on a film. From the extent of deflection and the strength of the magnetic field, it is possible to calculate the atomic mass (Fig. 7.3).

When the elements are examined with the spectrograph, it is found that not all the atoms of an element have the same mass. The atoms of chlorine, for example, have masses of 35 u and 37 u. Some elements have as many as 12 atoms of

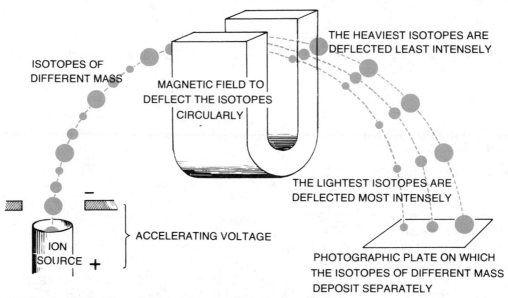

Knowing the accelerating voltage and the magnetic field,
and measuring the deflection of the isotopes, their mass can be calculated.

Fig. 7.3:
Schematic diagram of a mass spectrograph

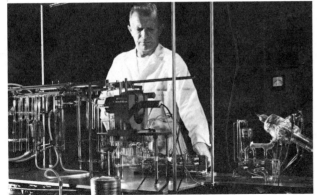

Courtesy Brookhaven National Laboratory

This photo shows a high sensitivity mass spectrometer. This instrument is able to detect as little as one billionth of a cubic millilitre of gas through the difference of the mass of its molecules. The magnet may be seen at the centre of the photo.

different mass. These atoms of the same element that have different mass are called isotopes. The chemical atomic mass is the mass average of the atomic mass of the isotopes of a given element. The atomic mass is constant because any natural sam-

ple of an element always contains the same proportions of its isotopes.

Other methods for determining atomic mass exist and need to be applied in certain cases. Fortunately, all methods for finding atomic mass agree in their results.

7:7   The Isotopes of Hydrogen

Ordinary hydrogen consists of 2 isotopes. The light isotope, of atomic mass 1, makes up 99.98 percent of ordinary hydrogen. The heavier isotope, called deuterium, of atomic mass 2, makes up 0.02 percent. The nucleus of the light isotope, called protium, consists of a single proton, whereas the nucleus of the heavy isotope called deuterium consists of a proton and a neutron.

Still a third isotope of hydrogen is now known, namely tritium. It has 2 neutrons and 1 proton in its nucleus (Fig. 7.4). Tritium is exceedingly rare and occurs merely as traces in water. It can be prepared artificially for research.

It is now known that most elements are a mixture

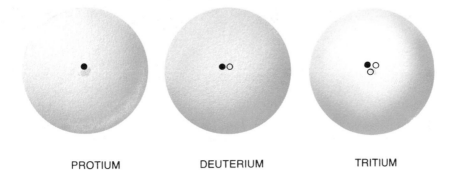

PROTIUM   DEUTERIUM   TRITIUM

● PROTON

O NEUTRON

Fig. 7.4:
The three isotopes of hydrogen

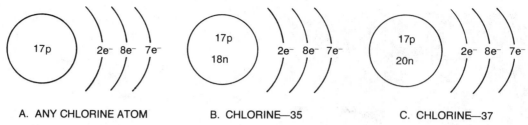

Fig. 7.5:
A schematic way of showing atoms of chlorine

of 2 or more isotopes. The atomic mass of an element is the average mass of its isotopes, according to their abundance. The percentage of each isotope in a naturally occurring element is always the same.

7:8   Useful Representations of Atoms

In order to draw attention to important features in the structure of atoms, a number of special signs and symbols are used. A small ° placed at the upper right of the symbol stresses the fact that the atom is neutral. Thus, in section 7:4 neutral lithium and fluorine atoms were represented by Li° and F°.

Isotopes of an element are shown by having the atomic number below and the mass number* above the symbol. For example $^{35}_{17}Cl$ and $^{37}_{17}Cl$ represent the 2 common isotopes of chlorine. Often we represent them more simply as Cl-35 and Cl-37.

Diagrams similar to those shown in Fig. 7.5 can be used to show the general location of protons, electrons, and neutrons within the atom.

The properties of an element depend on the number of electrons in the shell. More precisely, it is the number of electrons located in the outermost shell of the atom that usually determines its properties. Often we wish to use a simple way to show the outermost electrons. Dots around the symbol of the element are used for this purpose. The atoms of

Fig. 7.6:
Electron dot symbols for the first twenty elements

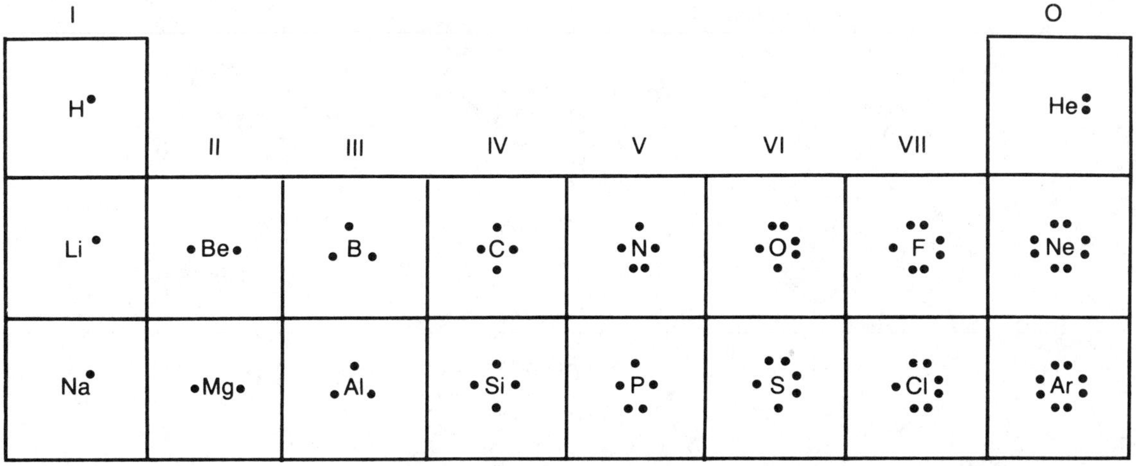

I	II	III	IV	V	VI	VII	O
H•							He:
Li •	•Be•	•B•	•C•	•N•	•O:	•F:	:Ne:
Na•	•Mg•	•Al•	•Si•	•P•	•S:	•Cl:	:Ar:

*Mass number is the sum of the protons and neutrons in the nucleus of an atom.

lithium, magnesium, carbon, chlorine, and neon are represented as follows:

$$\overset{\bullet}{\text{Li}} \quad \overset{\bullet\bullet}{\text{Mg}} \quad \cdot \overset{\bullet}{\underset{\bullet}{\text{C}}} \cdot \quad \overset{\bullet\bullet}{\underset{\bullet\bullet}{:\text{Cl}:}} \quad \overset{\bullet\bullet}{\underset{\bullet\bullet}{:\text{Ne}:}}$$

Here, the symbol of each element represents the nucleus and the filled inner electronic shells. The outer electons are represented by dots.

QUESTIONS

1. Name the three most important "fundamental particles" found in the atoms. Draw a labelled diagram showing their location in the atom.

2. Why is an atom electrically neutral?

3. If a neutral carbon atom contains 12 protons and 14 neutrons, how many electrons does it contain?

4. What is meant by the term *atomic number*?

5. What is the difference between an energy level and an electron shell?

6. What is the electron capacity of the first, second, and third electron shells?

7. What is the essential difference between an atom and an ion?

8. What is the difference between the atomic mass and the mass number of an element?

9. In what way do isotopes of a given element differ from one another?

10. How can the mass number of a given atom be calculated when the number of protons, the number of electrons, and the number of neutrons contained in the atom are known?

11. A given isotope of nitrogen contains 7 electrons, 7 protons, and 8 neutrons. (i) What is its mass number? (ii) What is its atomic number?

12. One isotope of magnesium has a mass number of 25. Which of the following represents this isotope correctly?

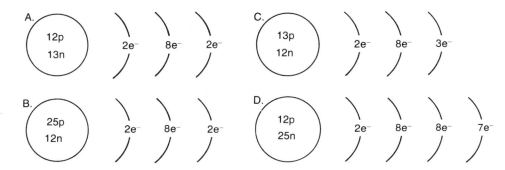

13. The nucleus of an atom contains 10 neutrons and 9 protons. The first 2 shells contain a total of 9 electrons. (i) What is the atomic number of this atom? (ii) What is its mass number? (iii) How many electrons are in the first shell, and how many are in the second shell?

14. If a neutral atom has 11 protons and 12 neutrons, which of the following statements about the atom is correct?
    (i)   It has a mass number of 11.
    (ii) It has an atomic number of 23.
    (iii) It has 11 electrons.
    (iv) It has an atomic mass of 12.

15. Could neutral atoms of the same element have:
    (i)   different mass numbers?
    (ii) different numbers of electrons?
    (iii) different numbers of protons?

16. A neutral atom has 2 electrons in the 1st shell, 8 electrons in the 2nd shell, and 7 electrons in the 3rd shell. From these data, supply the following information if possible:
    (i)   the atomic number;
    (ii) the mass number;
    (iii) the number of protons in the nucleus;
    (iv) the number of electrons in the outermost electron shell of the atom;
    (v)   the number of neutrons in the nucleus.

17. Complete (in your notebook) the following table.

Isotopes	Atomic Numbers	Number of Protons in the Nucleus	Number of Neutrons in the Nucleus	Number of Electrons in the Shells		
				1st	2nd	3rd
Helium-4	2					
Beryllium-9	4					
Carbon-14	6					
Oxygen-18	8					
Neon-22	10					
Potassium-39	19					
Argon-40	18					

18. Using the schematic models shown in Fig. 7.5, draw diagrams representing the following atoms:

$$_6^{12}\text{C}, \quad _{12}^{23}\text{Mg}, \quad _{11}^{23}\text{Na}, \quad _{10}^{20}\text{Ne, and } \quad _{16}^{32}\text{S}.$$

19. Draw diagrams to represent the atoms of the first twenty elements listed in Table 7.2. Show the number of protons and electrons only and use the model shown in Fig. 7.5 (A).

20. Draw diagrams to illustrate the lithium isotopes of mass number 6 and 7. Use the models shown in Fig. 7.5 (B) and (C).

2
ELEMENTS AND COMPOUNDS

This photograph shows the element iron being poured into a mould. The iron can then be reacted with other elements to form compounds such as iron oxide, iron chloride, or iron hydroxide.

Noranda Mines Limited

CHAPTER

8

THE PERIODIC TABLE

Over one hundred elements are known today. When we examine their properties, we find a bewildering array of reactions and compounds. However, it is possible to classify the elements according to resemblances and differences which they display.

8:1   Families of Elements

Many elements can be grouped into families on the basis of their strikingly similar chemical properties. Chlorine and bromine not only react with the same substances, but the molecular formulas of the products formed are similar. With sodium they form the compounds NaCl and NaBr;* both form similar compounds with carbon,

*The names of these compounds are:

NaCl	sodium chloride
NaBr	sodium bromide
CCl_4	carbon tetrachloride
CBr_4	carbon tetrabromide
$HgCl_2$	mercury (II) chloride
Hg_2Cl_2	mercury (I) chloride
$HgBr_2$	mercury (II) bromide
Hg_2Br_2	mercury (I) bromide

The periodic table may be thought to be the natural classification of the elements.

CCl_4 and CBr_4; both react with mercury to form not one but two different compounds: $HgCl_2$ and Hg_2Cl_2, $HgBr_2$ and Hg_2Br_2; and both react with hydrogen to form HCl and HBr.

This generalization is very valuable. Suppose that chlorine is known to react with metallic calcium to form the compound calcium chloride, $CaCl_2$. Then we may predict with reasonable assurance that bromine will also react with calcium, and that the formula of the compound will be $CaBr_2$, not CaBr, $CaBr_3$, or Ca_2Br, but specifically $CaBr_2$.

The existence of families of elements greatly simplifies the task of learning chemistry. If we know the reactions of just one member of a family, we can predict by analogy many of the reactions of the other members of the family.

8:2   Newlands' Octaves

What makes the similarity in chemical and physical properties among the elements of a family even more exciting is that the grouping occurs naturally.

Relationships between the atomic mass of the elements and their properties were first noted by Dobereiner as early as 1817. He suggested that certain elements could be placed in groups of three such as chlorine, bromine, and iodine. Not only did these elements resemble each other, but, in addition the atomic mass of the middle one was the average of the other two.

In 1865, Newlands, an English chemist, suggested that *if the elements are arranged in the order of increasing atomic mass a similar set of properties is displayed by every eighth element.* Omitting hydrogen, the lightest element, (remember that helium and neon were still unknown then), Newlands listed the elements in order of increasing atomic mass as shown in Table 8.1.

Starting from any given element in this arrangement, the eighth element is a kind of repetition of the first, just as the eighth note in an octave of music harmonizes with the first. For this reason, we refer to the arrangement of Newlands as the *Law of Octaves.* Beyond calcium, the Law of Octaves breaks down.

8:3 Mendeleev's Classification

A more accurate arrangement, although still incomplete and imperfect, was proposed by Mendeleev, a Russian chemist, in 1869. Mendeleev's proposal, called the *Periodic Law**, states that the *properties of the elements are periodic functions of their atomic mass.* By the term "periodic functions," we understand the periodic recurrence of similar properties.

The great importance of the Periodic Law is that

TABLE 8.1

Newlands' Law of Octaves

Li	Be	B	C	N	O	F
Na	Mg	Al	Si	P	S	Cl
K	Ca					

it shows clearly that the classification of the elements is completely natural. Simply arrange the elements in order of atomic mass or atomic number and the elements are also arranged in order of their properties. This is an amazing fact. To be able to classify the elements at all, other than in alphabetical order, is surprising enough. To discover that their atomic masses go up regularly,** and indeed their atomic numbers go up one unit at a time, is equally surprising. But to show that both classifications really coincide! That was a truly remarkable discovery. The benefit to chemistry is easy to see. This organizes and simplifies the subject and makes it unnecessary to memorize a limitless amount of detail. Mendeleev's arrangement of the elements is called the *Periodic Table.* A modern form of the table in which the elements discovered since 1869 are included, is presented in Fig. 8.1.

When Mendeleev proposed his classification of the elements, fewer than seventy elements had been discovered. Mendeleev had great faith in the periodic table. Rather than force an element incorrectly into a blank in the table where it did not belong, Mendeleev preferred to leave an empty space and to predict the properties of the element which he believed would someday be discovered to fit into the empty spot.

For example, Mendeleev predicted that an unknown element of atomic mass 72 lying between gallium and arsenic would eventually be found.

---

*The modern statement of the *Periodic Law* is: *The Properties of the elements are periodic functions of their atomic numbers.* The reasons behind this modification become clear when atomic structure is studied.

** It is now known that four pairs of elements do not follow this pattern. They are Ar and K, Co and Ni, Te and I, and Th and Pa. In each case the first element is heavier than the second.

PERIODIC TABLE OF THE ELEMENTS

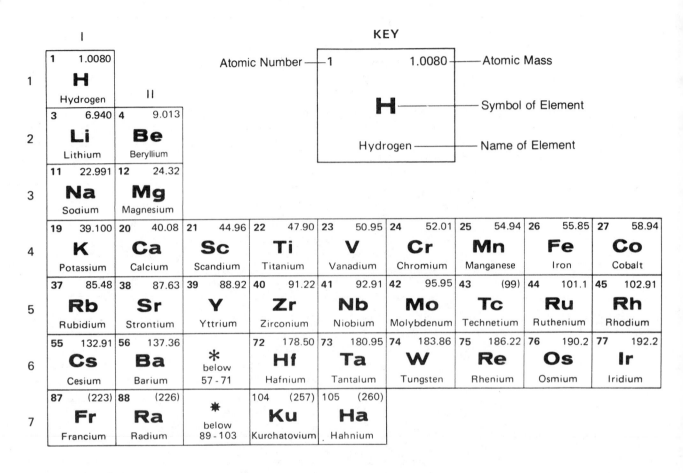

Fig. 8.1:
The Periodic Table

					VIII
					2 4.003 **He** Helium

III	IV	V	VI	VII	
5 10.82 **B** Boron	6 12.011 **C** Carbon	7 14.008 **N** Nitrogen	8 16.0000 **O** Oxygen	9 19.00 **F** Fluorine	10 20.183 **Ne** Neon
13 26.98 **Al** Aluminum	14 28.09 **Si** Silicon	15 30.975 **P** Phosphorus	16 32.066 **S** Sulfur	17 35.457 **Cl** Chlorine	18 39.944 **Ar** Argon

			III	IV	V	VI	VII	
28 58.71 **Ni** Nickel	29 63.54 **Cu** Copper	30 65.38 **Zn** Zinc	31 69.72 **Ga** Gallium	32 72.60 **Ge** Germanium	33 74.91 **As** Arsenic	34 78.96 **Se** Selenium	35 79.916 **Br** Bromine	36 83.80 **Kr** Krypton
46 106.4 **Pd** Palladium	47 107.880 **Ag** Silver	48 112.41 **Cd** Cadmium	49 114.82 **In** Indium	50 118.70 **Sn** Tin	51 121.76 **Sb** Antimony	52 127.61 **Te** Tellurium	53 126.91 **I** Iodine	54 131.30 **Xe** Xenon
78 195.09 **Pt** Platinum	79 197.0 **Au** Gold	80 200.61 **Hg** Mercury	81 204.39 **Tl** Thallium	82 207.21 **Pb** Lead	83 209.00 **Bi** Bismuth	84 (210) **Po** Polonium	85 (210) **At** Astatine .	86 (222) **Rn** Radon

64 157.26 **Gd** Gadolinium	65 158.93 **Tb** Terbium	66 162.51 **Dy** Dysprosium	67 164.94 **Ho** Holmium	68 167.27 **Er** Erbium	69 168.94 **Tm** Thulium	70 173.04 **Yb** Ytterbium	71 174.99 **Lu** Lutetium

96 (248) **Cm** Curium	97 (247) **Bk** Berkelium	98 (249) **Cf** Californium	99 (254) **Es** Einsteinium	100 (253) **Fm** Fermium	101 (256) **Md** Mendelevium	102 (253) **No** Nobelium	103 (259) **Lw** Lawrencium

Because it was in the same family as silicon, but belonged in the space below it, he named it "eka-silicon," meaning "beyond silicon." He predicted its properties solely on the basis of the position it would occupy in the table. He averaged the properties of the elements surrounding it. Mendeleev lived to see his predictions confirmed with uncanny accuracy. In 1886, the German chemist, C.A. Winkler, discovered the element which fitted into that position in the periodic table. He named it germanium. This was triumphant proof of the validity of the periodic table. To see how close the predictions were, compare the predicted and actual properties of germanium as shown in Table 8.2.

8:4 Characteristics of the Periodic Table

In the periodic table shown in Fig. 8.1, the elements are arranged in the order of increasing atomic numbers. The atoms of each succeeding element contain one more electron (and one more proton).

The elements with similar chemical and physical properties are placed under each other in a vertical column called a *group* or *family*. There are eight such main groups designated as groups I, II, III, IV, V, VI, VII, and VIII. The remaining ten vertical columns between groups II and III, represent the "transition" elements wherein resemblances tend to appear among succeeding elements in a horizontal row.

The seven horizontal rows are called *periods*. The first period contains two elements, hydrogen and helium. The second and third periods have eight elements each. The fourth and fifth periods contain eighteen elements each. The sixth period contains thirty-two elements.

Until 1940, the seventh period contained only six elements, ending with uranium. This element

TABLE 8.2

Properties of Germanium ("ekasilicon")

Properties of the Element	"Ekasilicon" (Predicted Values)	Germanium (Actual Values)
Atomic Mass	72 u	72.3 u
Density of the element	5500 kg/m³	5360 kg/m³
Formula of the oxide	EkO_2	GeO_2
Density of the oxide	4700 kg/m³	4700 kg/m³
Formula and properties of the chloride	$EkCl_4$, boiling point a little under 100°C, density 1900 kg/m³	$GeCl_4$, boiling point 86°C, density 1880 kg/m³

has an atomic number of 92, the highest atomic number among the naturally occurring elements. Today there are nineteen elements in the seventh period. The additional thirteen elements have all been synthesized in about thirty years of research in the field of atomic energy. More may be synthesized in the future.

The two large groups of elements placed at the bottom of the table fit into periods six and seven. They are called the lanthanides and the actinides. The elements within these groups have almost identical chemical properties.

The most metallic elements are found on the left-hand side of the periodic table while the most non-metallic elements are on the right-hand side. As we move across a given period from left to right we notice a gradual decrease in the metallic nature of the elements.

8:5   The Noble* Gases

The elements forming group VIII of the periodic table have properties and atomic structures that can help us understand the chemical activity of other elements. The members of this chemical family are the rare or noble gases: helium (He), neon (Ne), argon (Ar), krypton (Kr), xenon (Xe), and radon (Rn).

Discovery of the Noble Gases

In 1892, the English scientist Ramsay became interested in the discovery that nitrogen obtained from the air had a slightly higher density than that prepared by chemical means. After many months of careful investigation, he concluded that the higher density must be due to the presence of an unknown gas. When he separated this gas from the air, he found that it was completely unreactive. He called it argon, the "idle" gas. He soon found also that this gas was really a mixture of gaseous elements, and he isolated helium, neon, krypton, and xenon as well as argon, from this mixture. This was a remarkable achievement when it is considered that these gases are colourless, odourless, and very inert chemically. For over fifty years it was believed that they would not combine with even the most active substances. Today we know that xenon combines with the highly reactive gas fluorine to form XeF_2, XeF_4, and XeF_6. Other noble gas compounds now include KrF_2, KrF_4, RnF_6, and many others.

Some of the Properties and Uses of the Noble Gases

Helium is only one-seventh as heavy as air and therefore has considerable lifting power. Its inactivity makes it safer than hydrogen for use in weather balloons and in toy balloons. It is also used in low temperature research, because it has the lowest boiling point and freezing point of any substance known.

Because argon is an exceptionally good conductor of heat, it is often used in incandescent light bulbs and electronic tubes to conduct heat away from the filament. This permits the filament to be operated at a higher temperature which results in a more efficient bulb. Argon is also used in the welding of magnesium to provide a gaseous atmosphere that excludes oxygen, thereby preventing oxidation of the weld.

When a gas is placed in a tube at low pressure and a high voltage is applied, a spark jumps between the electrodes at each end of the tube, as the gas begins to conduct the electric current. When it does so, it also emits light. By this means neon gives an orange-red light, argon and xenon give a blue light, and helium a cream or pale orange light. The use of mixed gases and dyes in the glass tubes gives us the great variety of signs that are commonly seen today.

Structure and Chemical Stability

The greatest distinctive property of the noble gases is their almost total lack of chemical reactivity. Their inertness is associated with electronic structures that are particularly stable. We know that the outer shells of the noble gas atoms hold eight electrons (two in the case of the helium atom) (Table 8.3). An atom with eight electrons in its outer shell displays a stable electronic structure. Since the outer shell of the helium atom can hold a maximum of only two electrons, and the atom has two electrons, helium is also chemically inert.

How Sodium and Chlorine Atoms Combine

Sodium chloride, table salt, is a very stable chemical compound. The particles that make up the crystals of salt are the positive sodium ions and the negative chloride ions. These ions are present in

---

*The name Noble Gases is used in this book to describe these elements. They are sometimes called the Rare Gases and the Inert Gases. Since some of them are not rare, and others are not inert, these names were rejected here.

TABLE 8.3

Electron Structures of the Noble Gases

Element	Atomic Number	Number of Electrons in the Electronic Shells					
		$n=1$	2	3	4	5	6*
He	2	2					
Ne	10	2	8				
Ar	18	2	8	8			
Kr	36	2	8	18	8		
Xe	54	2	8	18	18	8	
Rn	86	2	8	18	32	18	8

the crystal in the ratio of one to one (Fig. 3.2). What accounts for the great chemical stability of sodium chloride?

Sodium has an atomic number of 11. Therefore, the neutral sodium atom has one more electron than the noble gas neon (atomic number 10) just preceding it. Chlorine on the other hand, with an atomic number of 17, has one electron less than the noble gas argon (atomic number 18) just following it.

In the stable compound sodium chloride, how many electrons do the sodium and chloride ions have? By losing one electron, the sodium atom acquires the stable electronic structure of its nearest noble gas neighbour, the neon atom:

$$Na° \rightarrow Na^+ + 1e^-$$

By gaining one electron, the chlorine atom acquires the stable electronic structure of its nearest neighbour, the argon atom:

$$Cl° + 1e^- \rightarrow Cl^-$$

When sodium and chlorine combine, the sodium atom loses an electron to a chlorine atom. This electron transfer permits both atoms to acquire the stable electronic structures of the noble gases. The reaction between sodium and chlorine can be represented by the following:

$$Na° + \overset{..}{\underset{..}{Cl}}: \rightarrow Na^+ + :\overset{..}{\underset{..}{Cl}}:^-$$

8:6   A Family of Metals: The Alkali Metals

The elements of group I in the periodic table, called the alkali metals, are lithium (Li), sodium (Na), potassium (K), rubidium (Rb), cesium (Cs), and francium (Fr). The alkali metals are all solid

TABLE 8.4

The Alkali Metals—Group I of the Periodic Table

Element	Atomic Number	Electron Configuration							Boiling Point °C	Melting Point °C	Density kg/m³
		$n=1$	2	3	4	5	6	7			
Lithium	3	2	1						1330	108	533
Sodium	11	2	8	1					892	98	970
Potassium	19	2	8	8	1				760	64	860
Rubidium	37	2	8	18	8	1			688	39	1530
Cesium	55	2	8	18	18	8	1		690	29	1900
Francium	87	2	8	18	18	32	8	1	—	(27)	—

*See also Table 7.2.

elements at room temperature. Their melting and boiling points decrease with increasing atomic size. They are soft and may be cut with a knife. They have very low densities, whereas most metals have high densities. The physical properties of the alkali metals along with their electron configurations are summarized in Table 8.4.

Chemically, the alkali metals are extremely reactive. We have seen that sodium and chlorine react readily forming sodium chloride. The two ions formed in the reaction, the sodium ion (Na^+) and the chloride ion (Cl^-), are held together in the crystal (Na^+Cl^-) by mutual electrical attraction. The behaviour of sodium towards chlorine is typical of the alkali metals; they all form stable ionic solids with chlorine.

$$2Li_{(s)} + Cl_{2(g)} \rightarrow 2LiCl_{(s)} \quad \text{(lithium chloride)}$$
$$2Na_{(s)} + Cl_{2(g)} \rightarrow 2NaCl_{(s)} \quad \text{(sodium chloride)}$$
$$2K_{(s)} + Cl_{2(g)} \rightarrow 2KCl_{(s)} \quad \text{(potassium chloride)}$$
$$2Rb_{(s)} + Cl_{2(g)} \rightarrow 2RbCl_{(s)} \quad \text{(rubidium chloride)}$$
$$2Cs_{(s)} + Cl_{2(g)} \rightarrow 2CsCl_{(s)} \quad \text{(cesium chloride)}$$

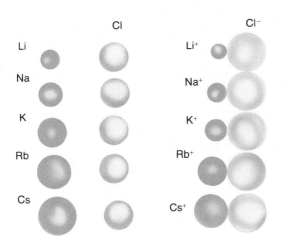

The alkali metals react vigorously with water liberating hydrogen and forming aqueous solutions of their hydroxides. These hydroxides, LiOH, NaOH, KOH, RbOH, CsOH, and FrOH, are all strong bases. Typically the reaction of sodium and water is represented by the following equation:

$$2\,Na_{(s)} + 2\,H_2O_{(l)} \rightarrow 2\,NaOH_{(aq)} + H_2 \uparrow_{(g)}$$

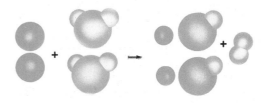

Because of its extreme reactivity, sodium must be kept entirely away from air and water; therefore, it is stored in kerosene. The reaction of sodium with water, and the resultant release of hydrogen may be demonstrated in the laboratory. The amount of sodium used must be very small. If the amount of sodium used is about the size of a match-head, the hydrogen thus given off may be ignited conveniently.

In all their compounds, the alkali metals exist as stable ions with a charge of 1^+. Their atoms have a single electron in their outer shell (Table 8.4) which is removed with relatively little energy, and thus the alkali metals are extremely reactive. By losing one electron, a given alkali metal acquires the stable electron structure of its immediate noble gas neighbour (Fig. 8.2). The larger the atom, the easier it is to remove the outer electron. Furthermore, metals depend on the electrons in the outer shell for bonding or cohesion in the metal state. With only one outermost electron, the alkali metals are held together very weakly; therefore they are soft, and they have low melting and boiling points and low densities.

8:7   A Family of Non-Metals: The Halogens

Another group of elements with strong resemblances includes fluorine (F), chlorine (Cl), bromine (Br), iodine (I),and astatine (At). Called the *halogens*, they form group VII of the periodic table. The word halogen means salt former and these five elements occur in Nature in salts rather than as free elements. Their atoms have seven electrons in the outer shell (Table 8.5), and they readily gain another to become negatively charged ions. The resulting stable ions have the electron configuration of the noble gas atoms just following them. Their great chemical activity depends upon their attraction for electrons. The smaller the atom, the more readily is the electron attracted. For this reason, fluorine has the greatest attraction for electrons and is the most active of the halogens.

The differences in properties of the halogens are themselves interesting, for they demonstrate how differences in size of atoms of similar structure produce gradual differences in other properties.

The melting and boiling points rise as the atomic number increases. At room temperature fluorine is a pale yellow gas, chlorine a greenish-yellow gas, bromine a deep red liquid, and iodine a steel-gray solid. Astatine exists only in trace amounts in nature.

In contrast to the noble gases which exist as single atoms, the halogens form diatomic molecules: F_2, Cl_2, Br_2, and I_2. Apparently, the halogen atoms acquire some of the stable structure of the noble gases by sharing electrons. If two atoms, say of

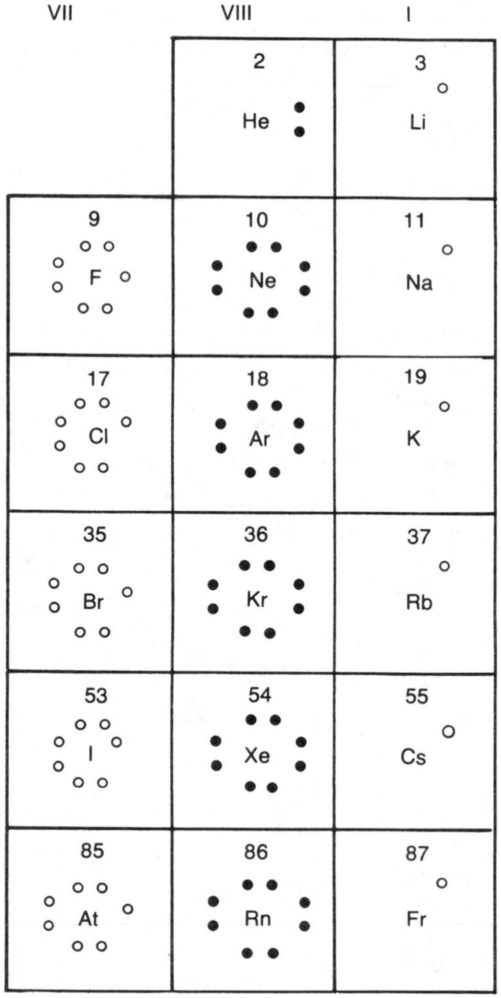

VII	VIII	I
	2 **He**	3 **Li**
9 **F**	10 **Ne**	11 **Na**
17 **Cl**	18 **Ar**	19 **K**
35 **Br**	36 **Kr**	37 **Rb**
53 **I**	54 **Xe**	55 **Cs**
85 **At**	86 **Rn**	87 **Fr**

Fig. 8.2:
The noble gases and their neighbours

TABLE 8.5

The Halogens—Group VII of the Periodic Table

Element	Atomic Number	Electron Configuration						Boiling Point °C	Melting Point °C
		$n=1$	2	3	4	5	6		
Fluorine	9	2	7					−188	−220
Chlorine	17	2	8	7				−35	−101
Bromine	35	2	8	18	7			58	−7
Iodine	53	2	8	18	18	7		183	114
Astatine	85	2	8	18	32	18	7	—	—

Board of Education for the Borough of North York

The Periodic Table is the natural classification of the elements. When we know this, experimental work in chemistry becomes more meaningful.

chlorine, come close together, they might be able to share a pair of electrons:

In the Cl_2 molecule, the shared pair of electrons, may be thought of as belonging to both atoms.

The chemical reaction of chlorine with the alkali metals was noted in the preceding sections. The other halogens react with the alkali metals in a similar manner forming stable ionic compounds. For example:

$2Na_{(s)}$ + $F_{2(g)}$ → $2NaF_{(s)}$ (sodium fluoride)
$2Na_{(s)}$ + $Cl_{2(g)}$ → $2NaCl_{(s)}$ (sodium chloride)
$2Na_{(s)}$ + $Br_{2(g)}$ → $2NaBr_{(s)}$ (sodium bromide)
$2Na_{(s)}$ + $I_{2(g)}$ → $2NaI_{(s)}$ (sodium iodide)

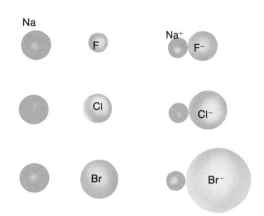

The halogens react with hydrogen at high temperature forming similar hydrides.

$$H_{2(g)} + F_{2(g)} \rightarrow 2\,HF_{(g)} \quad \text{(hydrogen fluoride)}$$
$$H_{2(g)} + Cl_{2(g)} \rightarrow 2\,HCl_{(g)} \quad \text{(hydrogen chloride)}$$
$$H_{2(g)} + Br_{2(g)} \rightarrow 2\,HBr_{(g)} \quad \text{(hydrogen bromide)}$$
$$H_{2(g)} + I_{2(g)} \rightarrow 2\,HI_{(g)} \quad \text{(hydrogen iodide)}$$

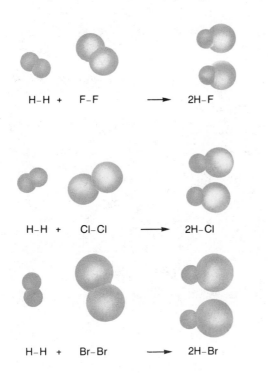

These hydrides are gases at room temperature and are highly soluble in water. When they dissolve in water, they also react with it to form strong acids.

Hydrogen

The chemistry of hydrogen resembles that of both the halogens and the alkali metals. For this reason, hydrogen does not fit well into any group. However because of its single electron, hydrogen is usually placed in group I with the alkali metals.

8:8   The Periodic Table and Atomic Structure

The strongest impression which the study of the periodic table leaves with us is that the atoms of the elements are somehow related despite their differences. If elements resemble one another it is safe to suspect that their atoms must have similar structures. If elements differ regularly in their combining capacity, it is probably because their atoms have structures which differ slightly. For this to be possible the atoms themselves must be composed of still smaller particles. This suspicion likely arose in the minds of chemists when the periodic table was first suggested. It was confirmed with the discovery that all atoms have electrons, units of negative electric charge, and protons, units of positive electric charge. The number of such units, protons or electrons, in an atom is called the atomic number.

The atomic numbers serve to arrange the elements even better than do the atomic mass. Thus you can begin to see the great importance of electrons in chemistry.

QUESTIONS

1. Sodium forms the following compounds: sodium oxide, Na_2O, and sodium hydroxide, NaOH. What would you expect the names and formulas of the corresponding compounds of potassium and rubidium to be?

2. Compare Mendeleev's proposal for the Periodic Law with the modern statement of the same law. Why was a change necessary?

3. What is the difference between periods and groups in the periodic table?

4. Which of the following pairs of elements belong to the same family in the periodic table?
   (i)   oxygen and fluorine

(ii) hydrogen and helium
(iii) sodium and neon
(iv) zinc and gold
(v) helium and krypton

5. (i) List the elements of the second period.
(ii) How does the number of outer electrons vary from element to element in this period?

6. Which of the following statements is true about the elements of a family in the periodic table?
(i) They have similar chemical properties.
(ii) They have the same number of protons in their nuclei.
(iii) They have the same number of electron shells.
(iv) They have the same atomic mass.

7. (i) What led to the discovery of the noble gases?
(ii) What properties do these gases have in common?
(iii) List three uses of these gases.

8. (i) To what do we attribute the lack of chemical activity of the noble gases?
(ii) What is meant when an atom is described as having a stable electronic structure?

9. What happens "electronically" when a potassium atom combines with a fluorine atom?

10. Draw an electron dot diagram to show how cesium and iodine combine.

11. What is the relationship between the melting points of the alkali metals and the size of their atoms?

12. Which of the following statements about the elements of group I is false?
(i) They produce ions having electronic structures similar to those of the noble gases.
(ii) They are called the alkali metals.
(iii) Their melting points show a rising trend with increasing atomic mass.
(iv) They have very low densities, compared to other metals.

13. Write the equations representing the reaction between (i) potassium and water; (ii) lithium and water.

14. Why are the alkali metals stored in kerosene?

15. Write equations showing the formation of the typical ion of each of the alkali metal atoms.

16. The larger the alkali metal atom, the easier it is to remove its outer electron. Suggest a logical explanation for this behaviour.

17. (i) How do halogen atoms acquire noble gas electron configurations?
(ii) How do alkali metals acquire such configurations?

18. Which alkali ion and which halogen ion have an electron configuration similar to that of argon?

19. Write equations representing the formation of typical ions for each of the halogen atoms.

20. (i) What is the relationship between the melting points of the halogens and the size of their atoms?
(ii) Compare this trend among the halogens with that of the alkali metals.

9

AIR:
THE MIXTURE
OF GASES
SURROUNDING
THE EARTH

The air is a vital part of our environment, but it receives most attention when the weather is rough or the pollution is bad.

9:1 Air and Air Pollution

The air necessary for sustaining life is a layer of gases that completely surrounds the Earth, and is commonly referred to as the Earth's atmosphere. It is difficult to describe exactly how extensive the atmosphere is since it changes quite noticeably from the Earth's surface upward. However, it is generally accepted that the atmosphere reaches upward approximately 10 000 km before the gases become so scarce that it is difficult to detect them.

The atmosphere changes in composition, density, and temperature, with increasing distance from the Earth. The first 15 km of the atmosphere contain nearly 90% of the entire air mass. The next 35 km contain a further 9% so that 99% of the air mass is contained in approximately the first 50 out of 10 000 km. There is obviously a very rapid decrease in density as the distance from the Earth increases.

There are also variations in the temperature of the atmosphere. At the Earth's surface temperatures in the range of $-40°C$ to $+40°C$ occur. With increasing distance from the Earth's surface, this temperature drops to about $-55°C$ at 15 km up; then increases to $-10°C$, and finally drops again to $-90°C$ at about 90 km up. All of these variations are caused by the gases that make up the atmosphere, and the ability of these gases to absorb energy from the sun.

The atmosphere is useful in several ways. While it is obviously important as a source of the gases needed for breathing, the atmosphere also protects us from harmful solar radiation. The atmosphere causes solid material from space to burn up as it falls to earth, and it helps to regulate the temperature at the surface of the Earth. With so many vital functions, it is no wonder that there is a growing concern for the stability of the atmosphere.

The atmosphere has not always had the same composition as it has today. About 4.5×10^9 years ago, the atmosphere consisted of water vapour (H_2O), carbon dioxide (CO_2), ammonia (NH_3), and nitrogen (N_2). About 2.5×10^9 years went by before enough oxygen (O_2) existed for plant and animal life to use. There are now fears that human activities could again change the composition of the atmosphere making it unfit for life as we know it.

9:2 What Makes up the Air?

There are several different regions of the atmosphere in which the chemical composition varies considerably. At the Earth's surface, oxygen and nitrogen are the main constituents, but with increasing distance from the Earth, ozone occurs in greater concentrations along with the oxygen and nitrogen up to a height of approximately 320 km. Above this height helium becomes the main gas and beyond 950 km upward, hydrogen is predominant until the atmosphere gradually dissipates into open space.

Of greatest concern to humanity is the atmosphere at the surface of the Earth. This is the layer that all life depends on directly, and which can be affected most easily by human activities. Because the gases that make up the atmosphere are mixed together, and because the chemical composition of these gases varies from point to point, the air is said to be a *mixture of gases*.

TABLE 9.1

Composition of Clean, Dry Air at Sea Level

Chemical	% by Volume
nitrogen	78.09
oxygen	20.94
argon	0.93
carbon dioxide	0.0318
neon	0.0018
helium	0.000 52

More than 16 different gases have been found in the air but only the most common ones have been listed in Table 9.1. Water vapour has not been included in the list since its concentration can vary widely. Water vapour is present in the air to about 3% by volume. Interestingly, it is the water vapour in the air which is the chief factor in determining the weather. Water is responsible for rain, snow, fog, hail, freezing rain, and sleet.

The gases which contribute most to the properties and behaviour of the atmosphere are oxygen, nitrogen, carbon dioxide, and water vapour. For this reason we will concentrate on the importance of these gases and the role they play in the atmosphere.

If each of the gases making up air is separated from the others and tested, then the individual properties of that gas can be determined. When all the results are combined, an overall picture of the properties of air can be described.

9:3 Oxygen

Its Importance and Occurrence
Of the four gases just mentioned, oxygen is the most chemically active component of the atmosphere.

An English clergyman, Priestley, was the first chemist to report the discovery of oxygen and to describe some of the properties of the gas. He found, for example, that a candle burned in the gas had a much brighter flame than in air. Another chemist, Lavoisier, arrived at the conclusion that burning was a chemical change involving oxygen and a combustible substance.

Physical Properties
Oxygen is a colourless, odourless, and tasteless gas. Its density is 1400 kg/m³ at 0°C and 1 atm of pressure. Oxygen is only slightly soluble in water; about 5 mL dissolve in 100 mL of water

Measuring air pollution by taking samples of the smoke coming out of the chimney.

when pure oxygen is bubbled into the water. When air, which is 21% oxygen by volume, is in contact with natural water, only about 0.7 mL dissolve in 100 mL of water. The small amount that dissolves is of great natural importance because it supports the respiration of nearly all life existing in water.

The gills of a fish, for example, are so constructed that they may extract the dissolved oxygen from water. Oxygen condenses to the liquid state at −183°C at the pressure of 101.3 kPa.

Thermal Properties

Oxygen is only moderately active at lower temperatures but much more so at higher temperatures. In many of its reactions with other substances heat and light are produced. Such chemical change is called *combustion*. Oxygen supports combustion but does not burn itself. The test for oxygen is the insertion of a glowing splint into the gas. If the splint bursts into flame, the gas is oxygen. No other odourless gas behaves in this way.

Respiration is a slow combustion of organic compounds in living tissue. Decay is a form of slow combustion of non-living organic tissue by organisms like bacteria or moulds.

9:4   Nitrogen

Its Importance and Occurrence

Nitrogen is often described as an inactive gas because it does not easily react with other chemicals. While nitrogen does not react readily at room temperature it does undergo chemical changes at elevated temperatures and under the stimulus of light.

The fact that nitrogen does not react easily gives it a very important property. The nitrogen in the air dilutes the oxygen to the point where combustion, respiration, and reactions with other chemicals are reasonably slow. In an atmosphere of pure oxygen, all fires would burn at much greater rates and at higher temperatures. All animal life as we know it would cease to exist because all the body processes would speed up, thus causing the body to "burn itself out."

The Nitrogen Cycle

Nitrogen is an essential element in many life processes. Proteins are complex compounds containing mainly carbon, hydrogen, oxygen, and nitrogen. They are essential constituents of all living matter. In addition, nitrogen compounds must be present in animal diets and plant fertilizers since new tissue for growth, repair and maintenance of both plants and animals require proteins.

Unfortunately, the nitrogen of the air cannot be used directly by the majority of plants and animals. Only certain bacteria are able to convert free nitrogen into valuable compounds. They are called the nitrogen-fixing bacteria. These soil bacteria change atmospheric nitrogen to nitrogen compounds in the soil. These compounds are then absorbed by plant roots and used to build proteins which are in turn eaten by humans and animals and absorbed by their bodies. Finally the nitrogen is excreted as animal waste. This is decomposed by other bacteria, thus liberating the nitrogen back into the air and completing the cycle.

The passing of nitrogen from one form to another in the course of natural events may be traced by means of Fig. 9.1.

The Physical Properties of Nitrogen
Nitrogen is a colourless, odourless, and tasteless gas. It is only slightly soluble in water. It is less dense than air, boils at $-196°C$, and freezes at $-210°C$.

The Chemical Properties of Nitrogen
As indicated, nitrogen does not react easily with other chemicals. At high temperatures, nitrogen will combine with some metals, such as magnesium, aluminum, calcium, and iron to form nitrides.

Nitrogen combines with oxygen only when large

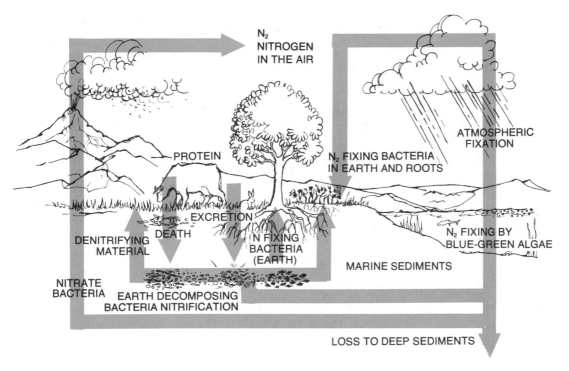

Fig. 9.1:
The nitrogen cycle

amounts of energy are supplied to the gases. In a flash of lightning, the electrical energy supplied by the lightning causes some nitrogen and oxygen to combine to form nitric oxide, NO, and nitrogen dioxide, NO_2.

9:5   Carbon Dioxide

Its Importance and Occurrence
Carbon dioxide gas is the primary "food" of the plant kingdom. From it plants build up sugars and starches with the aid of sunlight in a process known as *photosynthesis*. Animals eat the sugars and starches as part of their diet requirement. Yet, in spite of the great importance of carbon dioxide, it constitutes a mere 0.03% of the air; that is, three volumes in 10 000.

The gas is formed whenever fuels containing carbon are burned. Decay and fermentation also produce it. Exhaled breath contains one hundred times as much carbon dioxide as was inhaled, and the respiration of all living things produces the gas. Metallic carbonates and hydrogen carbonates in the Earth's crust contain vast amounts of chemically fixed carbon dioxide.

The Carbon Dioxide Cycle in Nature
As mentioned, carbon dioxide is used by plants to synthesize sugars and starches. Green plants absorb carbon dioxide and water. Using light energy and the catalyst chlorophyll, (the substance that gives plants their green colour), the plants convert the carbon dioxide and water to glucose (sugar) and starch. Oxygen is given off to the air in the process:

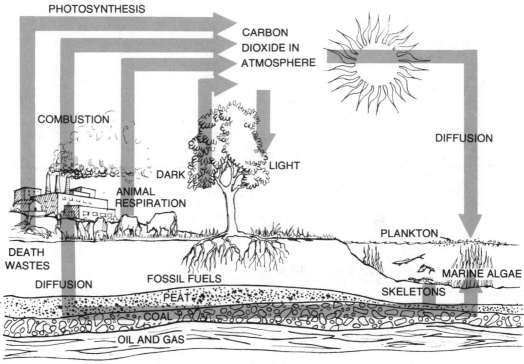

Fig. 9.2:
The carbon cycle

$$6CO_2 + 6H_2O \rightarrow C_6H_{12}O_6 + 6O_2$$
$$\text{glucose}$$

$$nC_6H_{12}O_6 \rightarrow (C_6H_{10}O_5)_n + nH_2O$$
$$\text{starch}$$

From the basic sugar and starch many plant products are formed—these being the ultimate source of food for all living things. At the same time, a proper carbon dioxide level is maintained in the atmosphere. This carbon dioxide cycle not only permits life to exist, but also accounts for the formation in past ages of our resources of coal and oil, since these are mostly residues of materials formed by photosynthetic processes (Fig. 9.2).

Physical and Chemical Properties
Carbon dioxide is a colourless, odourless gas about one and one-half times as heavy as air. At 20°C and a pressure of 70 atm, carbon dioxide condenses to a colourless liquid. If a minimum pressure of 5.2 atm is maintained and the temperature is lowered to −57°C, this liquid solidifies to carbon dioxide snow, known as dry ice, and is compressed into blocks. At one atmosphere pressure this solid sublimes without melting and maintains a temperature of −78°C.

At room temperature and pressure, one volume of water dissolves one volume of the gas. At higher pressures or lower temperatures the gas is much more soluble.

When carbon dioxide dissolves in water, it reacts as follows:

$$H_2O + CO_2 \rightarrow H_2CO_3 \text{ (carbonic acid)}$$

In solution, carbonic acid donates protons to the water molecule to a slight extent; hence it is a weak acid. If a gas comes in contact with calcium hydroxide solution and a white precipitate forms, the gas is carbon dioxide. This is the test for carbon dioxide. Carbon dioxide does not burn; neither does it support combustion. A burning splint would be extinguished in this gas. Carbon dioxide is commonly used in fire extinguishers.

9:6   Air and the Environment

Air has a very important role to play in controlling the energy balance on Earth. Solar energy bombards the Earth constantly. Of the energy that initially enters into the atmosphere, approximately 50% manages to actually get through to the Earth. The portion of the energy that does not make it is either reflected back into space by clouds and particles (35%) or is absorbed by ozone and carbon dioxide (15%) causing the atmosphere to be warmed. The incoming energy is in the form of ultraviolet, visible and infrared radiation. If the atmosphere did not reflect back or absorb the 50% mentioned, the Earth would receive dangerously high amounts of energy. Ultraviolet radiation is a major cause of skin cancer which would be even more common than it is if more solar radiation actually got through to the Earth.

The energy that strikes the Earth is eventually released back into the atmosphere as infrared radiation or by the evaporation of water. The atmosphere absorbs this energy as well. Gradually, all the energy absorbed by the atmosphere is released back into space as infrared radiation.

The cloud of smog over a city

United Nations

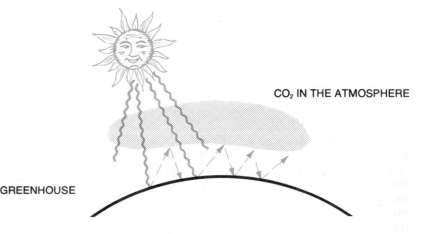

In the greenhouse, solar radiation passes through the glass as light. The resulting heat cannot escape through the glass; thus the temperature rises.

GREENHOUSE

In the atmosphere, solar radiation passes through the carbon dioxide layer as light. The resulting heat cannot escape, however. Again, this causes the temperature to rise.

CO$_2$ IN THE ATMOSPHERE

Fig. 9.3:
The greenhouse effect

9:7   Carbon Dioxide and the Greenhouse Effect

If you have ever stood in a glass greenhouse on a sunny day, you probably noticed how warm it is compared to the outside. Similarly, if you get into a car that has been standing in the sun for some time with the windows closed, the build-up of heat is very obvious. These effects are the result of solar energy, in the form of ultraviolet and visible radiation, passing through the glass and being absorbed by objects inside the greenhouse or car. When the interior absorbs the radiation, it is converted into heat which cannot pass back through the glass, and so it tends to collect on the inside. This is what is known as the *greenhouse effect.*

Carbon dioxide in the atmosphere acts in the same manner as the glass in a greenhouse. The ultraviolet and visible light energy that reaches the Earth is obviously able to pass through the atmosphere, but after being absorbed by the Earth and released as infrared or heat energy, it is absorbed by the carbon dioxide, thus heating up the atmosphere. The atmosphere, then, keeps our planet warmer than it would be without this greenhouse effect. It is estimated that the average Earth temperature at the surface would be approximately 40°C cooler than it is now were it not for the greenhouse effect.

Water vapour and clouds along with carbon dioxide contribute to the greenhouse effect. However, since carbon dioxide is a product of combustion, there has been some concern that the ever increasing burning of fossil fuels could alter the amount of carbon dioxide in the atmosphere causing more warming which may in turn have potentially harmful effects.

9:8   Air Pollution

Air pollution is not new. The Romans complained about air pollution in Rome more than 2000 years ago and England passed laws prohibiting the use of coal that emitted choking fumes as far back as 1273. Furthermore, volcanoes, forest fires, dust storms, and decaying marshes are natural processes that pollute the air.

In former times, populations and cities were smaller, and open spaces were larger, so that artificially induced pollutants could disperse more easily. The natural sources of pollution, severe while they were active, were spread over the globe and were cleaned up by the natural weather cycles.

What is different about the present concern over air pollution is the large scale and the world-wide scope of its occurrence. Never before have population, cities, industry, and transportation been so large as they are today. These modern sources of pollution have also produced substances which do not decompose readily, thus adding to the problem of contamination. We are suddenly forced to realize that we cannot take for granted the 15 kg of pure air we need each day for survival. Up to a point we can be selective and control our food and water intake, but we cannot avoid breathing the air around us regardless of its impurities. Human beings can live for weeks without food and a few days without water, but only a few minutes without air.

In order to understand and control air pollution, we should be able to answer such questions as: What is air pollution? What are the major pollutants? How are they produced? What changes do they undergo in the air? What effects do they have on people, animals and plants? How could they be reported and controlled?

An air pollutant can be defined as any substance in the air that can harm people, animals, vegetation, or materials. This definition shows what a broad subject it is and why it involves so much debate. What is harmful for one person may form part of making a living for another. Would people be willing to give up their cars because they add pollutants to the air? Concerns about air pollution necessitate decisions about the costs and benefits of a particular form of artificially created pollution. We study air pollution in order to be able to make such decisions with understanding.

The main pollutants

a) *Carbon monoxide* is a product of the incomplete combustion of carbon or of carbon compounds:

$$2C + O_2 \rightarrow 2CO$$

Automobile exhaust is the largest source of CO in the outdoor atmosphere in North America.

b) *Hydrocarbons*, compounds of carbon and hydrogen, are obtained from petroleum and coal, and have many industrial uses. Gasoline and other volatile liquids used in paints belong to this class. The variety of effects from such substances is very great. Some are cancer-inducing (carcinogenic), some are irritating, some undergo further chemical change in the atmosphere, while others are harmless. When gasoline in the car is burned incompletely, hydrocarbons escape into the air.

c) *Sulfur dioxide* is probably the most troublesome air pollutant from the point of view of its harmful effect on vegetation and on large numbers of people in urban areas, and the difficulties involved in preventing its discharge into the atmosphere. High SO_2 concentrations have been associated with major air pollution disasters of the type that have occurred in large cities, like London, causing numerous deaths. SO_2 is also responsible for the destruction of vegetation in the areas around smelting furnaces in mining areas. Since sulfur is present in coal and oil as an impurity, SO_2 is released as a pollutant during the combustion of those fuels in winter, and cities may experience SO_2

"alerts." The burning of coal with significant sulfur content to generate steam for electricity in power plants also releases SO_2 to the air.

Once in the atmosphere, SO_2 is oxidized to sulfur trioxide SO_3

$$2SO_2 + O_2 \rightarrow 2SO_3$$

The moisture in the air reacts rapidly with SO_3 to form a mist of sulfuric acid:

$$SO_3 + H_2O \rightarrow H_2SO_4$$

Sulfuric acid is a very corrosive acid that destroys living tissue, clothing and building materials. All three compounds SO_2, SO_3 and H_2SO_4 (as mist) penetrate the lungs to induce a choking feeling accompanied by coughing. If these pollutants persist, severe damage to both throat and lungs can result.

The exhaust gases from the engine of the car are led as a mixture into the converter where they are oxidized to CO_2 and H_2O before leaving.

General Motors of Canada Limited

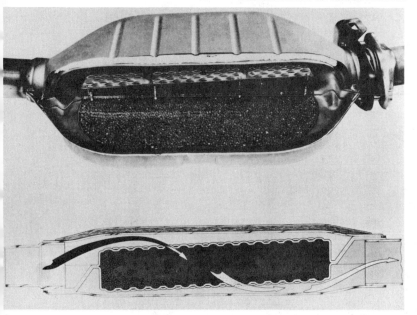

Hydrogen sulfide, H_2S, is another gaseous sulfur compound that has the odour of rotten eggs. This toxic gas brings on nausea and headache when inhaled even in small amounts. Larger amounts can be fatal. Hydrogen sulfide is produced by decomposing sewage and by some industrial and metallurgical processes.

d) The important oxides of nitrogen that occur as air pollutants, nitric oxide, NO, and nitrogen dioxide, NO_2, are present in the exhaust gases of automobiles. They are also produced naturally during lightning storms as the O_2 and N_2 of the air combine under the stimulus of energy released by the lightning.

The effects of the oxides of nitrogen on people, especially in congested urban centers, range from unpleasant odour and mild irritation to serious lung congestions and death. The oxides of nitrogen are also key substances in the chain of chemical reactions that produce "smog."

Particles resulting from a number of processes cause serious air pollution problems. Because these particles are smaller than even the finest sand that can be seen with the naked eye, they can remain suspended in the air for a long time, if not indefinitely. They interfere with the transmission of heat and light from the sun to the Earth. If they accumulate in the course of time, they may cause a serious loss of the sun's energy, thus resulting in a lowering of the average temperature of the Earth and possibly causing another ice age. Particles derived from living sources include pollen grains, bacteria, fungi, moulds, and spores. They are responsible for many effects that are detrimental to human beings. Included among these effects are allergies, bronchial asthma, and various bacterial diseases.

A larger and more diverse group of particles comes from natural and industrial sources. The natural materials include soil particles, salty

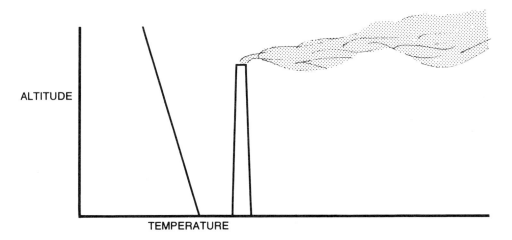

Stable behaviour results when the temperature of the atmosphere decreases with altitude.

THE INVERSION LAYER

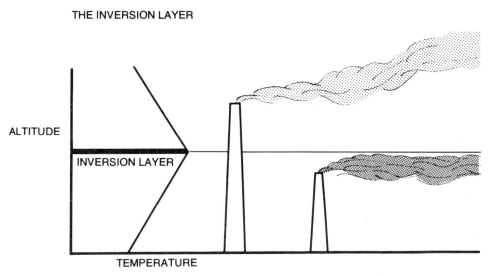

Unstable behaviour results when the temperature of the atmosphere increases with altitude up to a point and then decreases beyond that point, forming an inversion layer which prevents smoke and pollutants from dissipating readily.

Fig. 9.4:
Temperature inversion

droplets near the sea, and volcanic dust. Artificially created particles include smoke from the combustion of fuels, vegetation, and garbage. Mining and metallurgical operations in the production of iron, copper, aluminum, asbestos, uranium, gold, and coal, discharge particulate matter which may be injurious to people and organisms. The people most immediately exposed are the workers in the mines, mills, and factories where these metals, ores, alloys, and other manufactured articles are processed. Government agencies have been alerted to impose protective standards for the employees who come in contact with dangerous industrial pollutants. Non-metallic mineral products such as cement and glass require processes that give off particulate matter. Blasting, drilling, crushing, grinding, mixing, and high temperature decomposition are examples of such processes.

9:9   Air Pollution and Climate

A climatic effect that can intensify air pollution in the modern city is a thermal or *temperature inversion*. Normally, as air rises, it expands and cools. This process, shown in Fig. 9.4, helps to carry away and dissipate any pollutants that may have been in the air. Under some conditions a layer of dense cool air can be trapped under a layer of less dense warm air, termed the warm inverse layer, as shown in Fig. 9.4. The entire process is termed a temperature inversion. Pollutants in the trapped air cannot dissipate as long as the inversion lasts. Instead these pollutants accumulate to dangerous levels as the activity of the city continues to produce them.

Temperature inversions occur more frequently in the fall or winter when the sun's rays do not penetrate enough to warm the air on the ground, and to induce the warm air to rise and push away the trapped cold air. Usually inversions last for only a few hours. Occasionally, when a high pressure weather system persists for days, a serious pollution problem results.

9:10   The Effects of Air Pollution

In the past few years we have begun to realize the extent of air pollution effects, especially in the following five areas:

a) *Effects on the atmosphere*
Air pollution might produce a haze which seems to cover the horizon and to reduce visibility. Pollutants can also affect the weather by helping in the formation of fog and in the reduction of the amount of sunlight reaching the Earth. As was mentioned previously this is the very process that initiates a temperature inversion. Thus a vicious circle starts, often with tragic results.

b) *Damage to vegetation*
Widespread damage to trees, fruits, vegetables, and flowers is caused annually by air pollution. Such effects are seen most intensely in the total destruction of vegetation by SO_2 in the areas surrounding smelters where this gas is produced by the roasting of ores:

$$2CuS + 3O_2 \rightarrow 2CuO + 2SO_2$$

c) *Injury to animals*
The poisoning of animals by fluorides and arsenic has been the most serious effect of air pollution on animals. Some industrial processes give off various fluorine compounds which "fall out" over the fields where cattle graze. A sickness called fluorosis results, showing abnormal calcium deposits in the bones and teeth of the animals and resulting in lameness. The cattle also tend to lose weight and to become listless. Arsenic poisoning has been transmitted by the exhaust gases from smelters.

d) *Direct effects on people*

While much attention has been paid to air pollution disasters resulting from severe temperature inversions, ill-health can be brought on by air pollution in other ways. Almost always, the health effects are seen most clearly in the respiratory tract, the nose, throat and lungs, and in eye irritations. The precise relationships between diseases and air pollution is often difficult to establish because cigarette smoking, itself a powerful air pollutant, is a contributing cause.

e) *Deterioration of materials*

Acidic pollutants are responsible for many damaging effects, such as the corrosion of metals and the weakening of textiles, paper, and marble. Particulate pollutants driven at high speeds by the wind cause erosion of building surfaces. The deposition of dirt on an office building leads to the expense of cleaning and to the wear that results from the cleaning action.

9:11   The Control of Air Pollution

There are two general classes of methods for controlling air pollution at the source: the pollutants are separated from the harmless gases and disposed of in some way other than by discharge into the atmosphere; or the pollutants are somehow converted to harmless products that may then be released to the atmosphere.

a) *Control of pollutants by separation*

Particulate matter may be retained on filters which allow the gas to flow through. Such separations are possible because particles are much larger than gas molecules. For handling large gas streams, the filters are often in the form of cylindrical bags, somewhat like giant stockings, from which the collected particulate matter is periodically shaken out.

Particles may also be electrically charged, and a collecting surface with an electric charge of the

Millions of cars and trucks transport people and goods for work, commerce and recreation. Modern transportation, however, consumes energy, resources and land, and pollutes the air. More efficient systems of rapid transit will have to be developed.

Ministry of Transportation & Communications, Audio Visual Services

opposite sign will attract them. Devices of this sort, called electrostatic precipitators, are used on a very large scale for reducing smoke from power plants that burn fossil fuels.

b) *Control of pollutants by conversion*
By far the most important conversion of pollutants is by oxidation in air. Oxidation is applied most often to pollutant organic gases and vapours, rarely to particulate matter. When organic substances containing only carbon, hydrogen and oxygen are completely oxidized, the products are carbon dioxide and water. The process is often very expensive because considerable energy must be used to keep the entire gas stream hot enough (about 700°C) for complete oxidation to occur. If the pollutant is sufficiently concentrated, its own fuel value may contribute a large part of this energy. Also, the required combustion temperature may be reduced by using a catalyst. The catalytic converter in the exhaust system of new cars changes CO to CO_2 in this way. (See the photograph on page 76.)

QUESTIONS

1. Comment on the possibility of life forms surviving at the various levels of the atmosphere from the surface of the Earth up to 10 000 km above the surface of the Earth.

2. Oxygen is the most "active" constituent of the common gases that make up the atmosphere. What does this mean?

3. At 25°C 100 mL of water can dissolve up to 5 mL of pure oxygen. Explain why natural water usually has only about 0.7 mL/per 100 mL of oxygen in it.

4. "Oxygen supports combustion but does not burn itself." Explain what this statement means.

5. What is the test for oxygen gas?

6. Comment on the role played by nitrogen as it controls events in the biosphere.

7. How are bacteria important in making nitrogen a "useful" chemical?

8. Of what importance is carbon dioxide to plants?

9. What is the test for carbon dioxide?

10. What is meant when we say that the atmosphere keeps an energy balance on the Earth? Discuss with reference to the greenhouse effect.

11. The government constantly monitors the air for pollutants; if the concentration of the pollutants exceeds a certain level, industries may be forced to shut down. Identify and give the possible source of the main pollutants that might be found in the air.

12. In 1952, an air inversion in London, England, contributed to the deaths of 4000 people. What is an inversion and how does polluted air become even more of a problem if there is an inversion?

13. What damage can be done by polluted air? Name the pollutants and the damage they may cause.

14. Is polluted air a necessary evil or can we have our way of life and clean air too?

15. (i) Has the atmosphere always been made up of the same constituent gases?
    (ii) Is it possible for humans to change the atmosphere?

CHAPTER

10

BEHAVIOUR OF GASES AND THE GAS LAWS

Matter exists in three states: gaseous, liquid, and solid. Of these, the gaseous state is the simplest to study. All substances in the gaseous state behave in many strikingly similar ways.

Breathing, flying and many other processes depend on properties of gases. Of special interest to chemistry was the early discovery that all gases behave in remarkably similar ways. This provides more clues about the composition of matter.

10:1 General Characteristics of Gases

(a) Expansion
Gases have no fixed volume. They expand indefinitely to occupy the entire volume available to them. Therefore, gases have no definite shape; they simply assume the shape of their containers.

(b) Compressibility
Gases are easily compressed into a fraction of their original volume. When the service station attendant "fills" the automobile tire, he is compressing air into the volume of the tire.

(c) Pressure
Confined gases exert a force on the walls of their container.

(d) Diffusion
When a gas is introduced into a vessel, it dis-

tributes itself throughout the entire volume. The process, called diffusion, takes place whether the vessel was originally empty or already occupied with another gas. A spray of perfume evaporates easily and soon occupies the entire room with its fragrance. The perfume diffuses throughout the entire space of the room. All gases diffuse readily through one another.

In the remaining sections of this chapter, we will investigate more intensively the properties of gases mentioned above.

10:2 Pressure and Its Measurement

Pressure is the force per unit area of surface that a gas, liquid, or solid exerts.

The instrument used for measuring atmospheric pressure is the *barometer* (Fig. 10.1). A barometer is a glass tube about 80 cm long, sealed at one end,

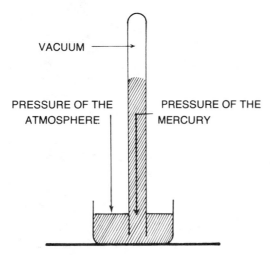

Fig. 10.1:
The barometer

filled with mercury, and inverted in a vessel containing mercury. The mercury column in the tube falls until it exerts the same pressure as the atmosphere around it. As the pressure of the air changes, the level of the mercury moves up or down correspondingly and thus shows the changes of atmospheric pressure. The average barometric reading is 76 cm or 760 mm of mercury at sea level. This is known as standard pressure or one atmosphere. This is often used as a reference pressure.

SI (metric) measures pressure in pascals (Pa). This is equivalent to a force of one newton per square metre (N/m^2). Standard pressure is defined as 101.325 kPa.

The pressure of a gas can be measured with a *manometer* (Fig. 10.2). The gas whose pressure is to be measured is admitted into the left-hand column of the instrument. The curved section of the manometer contains mercury and the right-hand column is open to the atmosphere. Thus, atmospheric pressure is exerted on the right-hand mercury column, while the confined gas exerts pressure on the left-hand column of mercury. The

pressure of the confined gas could be equal to, greater than, or less than the atmospheric pressure. If we let p_g, p_a, and h stand for the pressure of the gas, the pressure of the atmosphere, and the difference in the heights of the columns of mercury, respectively, we obtain for the three illustrated cases (Fig. 10.2):

(a) $p_g = p_a$ (b) $p_g = p_a + h$

(c) $p_g = p_a - h$

(a) Pressure of gas equals pressure of the atmosphere.

(b) Pressure of gas is greater than atmospheric pressure by $+h$.

(c) Pressure of gas is less than atmospheric pressure by $-h$.

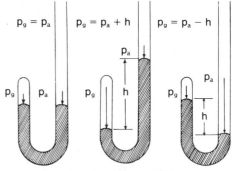

p_g = PRESSURE OF GAS
p_a = PRESSURE OF THE ATMOSPHERE
h = HEIGHT OF MERCURY, EXPRESSED AS PRESSURE

Fig. 10.2:
The manometer

10.3   Boyle's Law

Robert Boyle was one of the first scientists to study the effect of pressure on the volume of a gas. He observed that if the pressure of a gas is doubled while its temperature remains the same, its volume is decreased one-half; and if its pressure is tripled, its volume is decreased to one-third of the original.

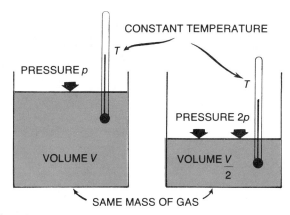

CONSTANT TEMPERATURE

PRESSURE p

T

T

PRESSURE $2p$

VOLUME V

VOLUME $\dfrac{V}{2}$

SAME MASS OF GAS

Fig. 10.3
The volume of a given mass of gas is inversely proportional to the pressure at constant temperature.

Such regularity was found to apply for a large range of pressure changes. Boyle summed up his findings in a statement known as *Boyle's Law: At constant temperature, the volume of a given mass of gas is inversely proportional to its pressure.* (Fig. 10.3).

TABLE 10.1

Relationship Between Pressure and Volume at Constant Temperature

Pressure (p)	Volume (V)	Pressure × Volume (pV)
100	100	10 000
125	80	10 000
150	66²/₃	10 000
200	50	10 000

Table 10.1 gives typical data obtained when a gas is subjected to changes in pressure. The first column lists the pressure readings in kilopascals. The second column lists the volume of gas in millilitres. The temperature is kept constant.

Mathematically, Boyle's Law may be expressed as

Pressure × Volume $= k$

or $\qquad pV = k$

or $\qquad p_1V_1 = p_2V_2$

where the subscripts 1 and 2 refer to the values of pressure and volume at any two readings during the experiment.

Example

The volume of a gas is 415 mL when the pressure is 67 kPa. What will the volume be at 100 kPa pressure if the temperature remains constant?

Solution 1
Boyle's Law states that the volume of a given mass of gas is inversely proportional to its pressure if the temperature remains constant. Therefore, since the pressure has been increased in this problem, the volume will decrease. The new pressure is $\dfrac{100}{67}$ of the original pressure. Therefore, the new volume must be $\dfrac{67}{100}$ of the former volume.

Hence, the new volume will be

$$415 \text{ mL} \times \frac{67 \text{ kPa}}{100 \text{ kPa}} = 278 \text{ mL}$$

Solution 2
The same result would be obtained by using the formula $p_1V_1 = p_2V_2$

In this problem $p_1 = 67$ kPa
$V_1 = 415$ mL
$p_2 = 100$ kPa
V_2 is the unknown

Solving for V_2

$$V_2 = \frac{p_1V_1}{p_2}$$

Substituting, $V_2 = \dfrac{67 \text{ kPa}}{100 \text{ kPa}} \times 415 \text{ mL}$

$$= 278 \text{ mL}$$

10:4   Change in the Volume of a Gas with Temperature

Substances expand when heated and contract when cooled. Gases expand far more than liquids or solids.

A French scientist, Charles, who studied the effect of temperature on the volumes of gases, discovered that all gases expand by the same amount when heated and contract by the same amount when cooled if the pressure remains constant. Such behaviour is in marked contrast to liquids and solids where each liquid and each solid expands at its own individual rate.

Consider the results of an experiment on the expansion of gases upon heating. For greatest simplicity, let us select a volume of 273 mL of a gas at 0°C. When the gas is heated to 1°C at constant pressure, its volume becomes 274 mL; at 2°C, its volume is 275 mL; at 100°C, the volume is 373 mL; and at 273°C, the volume reaches a value of 546 mL. When we cool the original volume of 273 mL from 0°C to −1°C, the new volume is found to be 272 mL; at −2°C, the volume is 271 mL; and at −100°C, it is 173 mL. These data are reported in the first two columns of Table 10.2.

Charles found that the volume of a given sample of gas measured at 0°C increases by 1/273 of its value for every degree rise in temperature. If the gas is cooled, on the other hand, its volume decreases by 1/273 of its value at 0°C for every degree drop in temperature.

10:5   The Absolute Temperature Scale

If the volumes given in Table 10.2 are plotted against the temperatures, the graph shown in Fig. 10.4 is obtained. When the points representing the volumes are joined together, a straight line is obtained. By extending this line so that it intersects the temperature axis, the point of intersection is found to be −273°C. We can deduce that if a sample

TABLE 10.2

Volume of a Gas at Different Temperatures (constant pressure)

Temperature (°C)	Volume (mL)	Temperature (K)
273	546	546
100	373	373
2	275	275
1	274	274
0	273	273
−1	272	272
−2	271	271
−100	173	173

of gas at 0°C could be cooled to −273°C, it would shrink by 273/273 of its original volume; that is, it would occupy no volume at all! Of course, all gases condense into liquids before such a temperature is reached, and remember that liquids do not contract at the same rate as gases. Nevertheless, this temperature, −273°C, is believed to be the lowest possible limit of temperature, and is called *absolute zero*.

For many practical reasons, it is useful to use a temperature scale that begins with absolute zero and has degrees which are the same size as Celsius degrees. Such a scale can be devised by adding 273 to the Celsius reading

$$K = °C + 273$$

Readings on the absolute scale are represented by the symbol K in honour of Lord Kelvin, who proposed the absolute scale.

10:6   Charles' Law

The absolute temperature scale enables us to see the relation between the volume and the temperature of a gas very simply (see Table 10.2 and Fig. 10.4). Charles' Law states that the volume of the gas

THE VOLUME OF A GIVEN MASS OF GAS IS DIRECTLY PROPORTIONAL
TO ITS ABSOLUTE TEMPERATURE

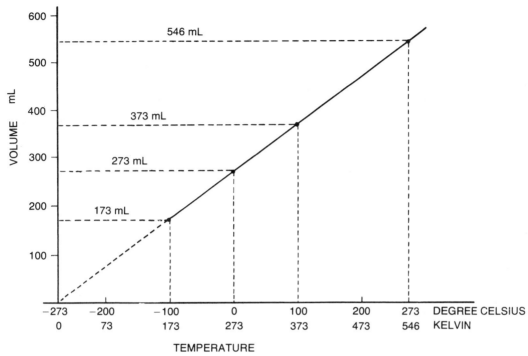

Fig. 10.4:
How the volume of a gas changes with temperature at constant pressure

is proportional to the absolute temperature at constant pressure. For example, if the absolute temperature of a gas is doubled, the volume is doubled. When the absolute temperature is halved, so is the volume. This is *Charles' Law: At constant pressure, the volume of a given mass of gas is directly proportional to its absolute temperature.** (See Fig. 10.5.)

Charles' Law may be expressed by the equation:

$$\frac{V_1}{V_2} = \frac{T_1}{T_2} \text{ (at constant pressure)}$$

where V_1 represents the original volume of a given

mass of gas at a temperature T_1, and V_2 represents the new volume of the gas at a new temperature T_2.

Standard Conditions
In order to provide a uniform basis for comparing gases, we should observe them under similar conditions. Scientists have agreed to specify 0°C (273 K) as the *standard temperature* and 101.325 kPa, as the *standard pressure*. These are known as *standard conditions* of temperature and pressure (STP).

*So far we have assumed that Boyle's and Charles' Laws are exact; they are nearly so for most gases under ordinary conditions of temperature and pressure. Deviations from the gas laws become important, especially at high pressures and at temperatures near the liquefaction point. Special corrections have to be made at such extreme conditions.

Example

The volume of a certain mass of gas is 150 mL at 27°C. What will its volume be at 127°C if the pressure remains constant?

Solution 1
Convert the temperature readings to kelvins: the original temperature is 27°C or 300 K; the final temperature is 127°C or 400 K.

The absolute temperature changes in the ratio of $\frac{400}{300}$.

Therefore, the volume will also increase in this ratio.
Hence the new volume will be

$$150 \text{ mL} \times \frac{400 \text{ K}}{300 \text{ K}} = 200 \text{ mL}.$$

Solution 2
The same result would be obtained by substitution in the formula

$$\frac{V_1}{V_2} = \frac{T_1}{T_2}$$

In this problem $V_1 = 150$ mL
$T_1 = 300$ K
V_2 is the unknown
$T_2 = 400$ K

The expression for V_2 is: $V_2 = \frac{V_1 \times T_2}{T_1}$

Substituting, $V_2 = \frac{150 \text{ mL} \times 400 \text{ K}}{300 \text{ K}}$

$$= 200 \text{ mL}$$

10:7   When Both Pressure and Temperature Change

It is sometimes necessary to find the new volume of a gas when both the temperature and the pressure change. In that event, both temperature and pressure will be responsible for the change in

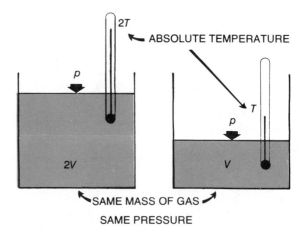

Fig. 10.5:
Charles' Law

volume, according to Boyle's Law and Charles' Law.

In mathematical symbols, the combined effect of pressure and temperature on volume may be expressed by the equation

$$\frac{p_1 V_1}{T_1} = \frac{p_2 V_2}{T_2}$$

where p_1, V_1, and T_1 represent the original pressure, volume, and temperature and p_2, V_2, and T_2 represent the final values. This is sometimes termed the combined gas law equation.

Example

The volume of a gas is 2.00 L at 27°C and 600 kPa pressure. What will the volume be at 227°C and 400 kPa?

Solution 1
The absolute temperature has gone up from 300 K to 500 K; therefore the volume will increase in that ratio. Hence we must multiply the original volume by $\frac{500}{300}$.
The pressure has been decreased from 600 to 400 kPa; therefore, the volume will increase in the ratio of $\frac{600}{400}$.

The final volume will be:

$$2.00 \text{ L} \times \frac{500 \text{ K}}{300 \text{ K}} \times \frac{600 \text{ kPa}}{400 \text{ kPa}} = 5.00 \text{ L}$$

Solution 2

The same result would be obtained by substitution in the formula

$$\frac{p_1 V_1}{T_1} = \frac{p_2 V_2}{T_2}$$

In this problem

$p_1 = 600 \text{ kPa}$ $p_2 = 400 \text{ kPa}$
$V_1 = 2.00 \text{ L}$ V_2 is the unknown
$T_1 = 300 \text{ K}$ $T_2 = 500 \text{ K}$

$$\text{The new volume } V_2 = \frac{V_1 p_1 T_2}{p_2 T_1}$$

$$\text{Substituting } V_2 = \frac{2.00 \text{ L} \times 600 \text{ kPa} \times 500 \text{ K}}{400 \text{ kPa} \times 300 \text{ K}}$$

$$= 5.00 \text{ L}$$

10:8   Partial Pressures of Gases

The presence of different gases in a mixture has no effect on the pressure that any particular gas in the mixture exerts. Each gas exerts the same pressure that it would if it were present alone in the same volume and at the same temperature as the mixture. Each gas contributes part of the total pressure of a mixture. Its contribution is termed the *partial pressure of that gas*. These facts are formulated in *Dalton's Law of Partial Pressures* which states: *In a mixture of gases, the total pressure exerted by the mixture is equal to the sum of the partial pressures exerted by the gases taken separately.* Dalton's Law can be written:

$$p_{total} = p_1 + p_2 + p_3$$

where the subscripts denote the partial pressures of the various gases in the mixture.

Correction for Water Vapour

An important application of Dalton's Law of Partial Pressures is in reporting the pressure of a gas that is collected over water (see Fig. 10.6). The total pressure of the system would be the sum of the partial pressure of the gas plus the pressure of the water vapour. The latter may be found from the table of water vapour pressures.

Appendix 4 gives the values of the vapour pressure of water at different temperatures. Hence, by knowing the temperature and the total pressure, we may find the pressure of the gas by subtracting the water vapour pressure from the total pressure.

Example

Find the volume of a dry gas at standard temperature and pressure if, when collected over water at 20°C and 104.0 kPa pressure, it occupies 100 mL. The vapour pressure of water at 20°C is 2.33 kPa.

Discussion and Solution

The pressure of 104.0 kPa is the sum of the partial pressures of the gas and the water vapour. Now, by Dalton's Law of Partial Pressures:

$$p_{total} = p_{dry \ gas} + p_{water \ vapour}$$

or

$$p_{dry \ gas} = p_{total} - p_{water \ vapour}$$

therefore,

$$p_{dry \ gas} = 104.0 \text{ kPa} - 2.3 \text{ kPa} = 101.7 \text{ kPa}.$$

We need to calculate the volume of a gas at STP corresponding to 100 mL at an original pressure of 101.7 kPa and a temperature of 293 K.

$$\text{The new volume, } V_2 = \frac{V_1 p_1 T_2}{p_2 T_1}$$

$$\text{Substituting, } = \frac{100 \text{ mL} \times 101.7 \text{ kPa} \times 273 \text{ K}}{101.3 \text{ kPa} \times 293 \text{ K}}$$

$$= 93.4 \text{ mL}$$

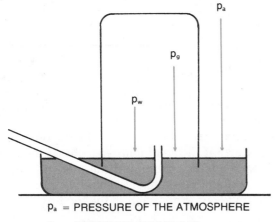

p_a = PRESSURE OF THE ATMOSPHERE

p_g = PRESSURE OF THE GAS

p_w = PRESSURE OF THE WATER VAPOUR

$p_a = p_g + p_w$

Fig. 10.6:
Gas collected over water

10:9   Diffusion of Gases: Graham's Law

When two gases are brought together, they mix by themselves. This process is termed *diffusion*. Graham, a Scottish chemist, discovered that the lighter the gas, the faster it diffuses (Fig. 10.7). He studied the phenomenon carefully, and found that *the rate of diffusion of a gas is inversely proportional to the square root of its density*. This statement is called *Graham's Law of Diffusion*. Stated mathematically, Graham's Law takes the following form:

$$\frac{u_1}{u_2} = \frac{\sqrt{D_2}}{\sqrt{D_1}}$$

where u_1 and D_1 represent the rate of diffusion and the density of one gas, and u_2 and D_2, the corres-

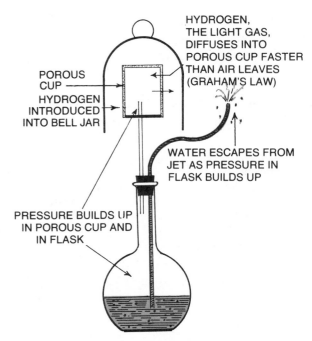

HYDROGEN, THE LIGHT GAS, DIFFUSES INTO POROUS CUP FASTER THAN AIR LEAVES (GRAHAM'S LAW)

POROUS CUP

HYDROGEN INTRODUCED INTO BELL JAR

WATER ESCAPES FROM JET AS PRESSURE IN FLASK BUILDS UP

PRESSURE BUILDS UP IN POROUS CUP AND IN FLASK

Fig. 10.7:
Demonstrating the rapid diffusion of hydrogen

ponding values for a second gas. Both gases must be measured under the same conditions of temperature and pressure.

When this formula is applied to find the relative diffusion rates of hydrogen and oxygen, we obtain:

$$\frac{u_1}{u_2} = \frac{\sqrt{D_2}}{\sqrt{D_1}} = \frac{\sqrt{1.429} \text{ (density of } O_2)}{\sqrt{0.089} \text{ (density of } H_2)} = \frac{4}{1}$$

The result obtained indicates that hydrogen diffuses four times as fast as oxygen when both gases are compared at the same temperature and pressure.

QUESTIONS

1. (i) What is the difference between the expansion of a gas and diffusion?
    (ii) Give an example to illustrate your answer.

2. In a manometer set up as shown in Fig. 10.2, the mercury level is 20 mm higher on the gas sample side. If the atmospheric pressure is 752 mm, what is the pressure of the gas sample?

3. If the atmospheric pressure drops from 745 mm to 732 mm mercury, sketch the barometer before and after the pressure change.

4. What is standard pressure? What causes atmospheric pressure?

5. Plot a graph of p against V using the values in the Table 10.1. What value of p would be required to cause V to become 0 (if this was possible)?

6. (i) In Boyle's Law, what is meant when we say that the volume of a given mass of gas is inversely proportional to its pressure when the temperature remains constant?

   (ii) Why should the pressure value when multiplied by the volume value equal a constant in the situation described in 6(i)?

7. A gas measures 1.00 L at a pressure of 79 kPa. Find its volume at 50 kPa pressure.

8. If a quantity of gas measures 800 mL at 122 kPa, find its volume at 608 kPa.

9. A volume of 400 mL of oxygen is collected at 93.3 kPa pressure. Find its volume if the pressure changes to 101 kPa.

10. A volume of 4.00 L of hydrogen is measured at standard pressure. Find its volume at 104.0 kPa.

11. A tire has a capacity of 60 L when inflated. Find the pressure in the tire if a volume of 240 L of air, measured at atmospheric pressure, is forced into it. Neglect the amount of air in the flat tire.

12. If a volume of 10.0 L of gas at 60.0 kPa pressure is expanded to 12.0 L, find the new pressure.

13. Convert (i) 0°C to K (ii) −50°C to K (iii) 25°C to K (iv) 200 K to °C (v) 50 K to °C (vi) 300 K to °C.

14. What is the significance of absolute zero?

15. If a gas expands, does its temperature remain constant automatically?

16. In Charles' Law, what is meant when we say that the volume of a given mass of gas is directly proportional to its absolute temperature when the pressure is constant?

17. A gas has a volume of 687 mL at 17°C. Find its volume at 30°C.

18. A gas occupies a volume of 1200 mL at 227°C. Find its volume at −173°C.

19. A volume of gas measures 1200 mL at 100°C. To what temperature must it be cooled so that the volume becomes 800 mL?

20. A quantity of gas is measured at 20°C. To what temperature must it be heated so that its volume is doubled?

21. A gas has a volume 22.4 L measured at 20°C and 104.0 kPa pressure. Find the volume at STP.

22. A gas has a volume of 800 mL at 25°C and 72 kPa. Find its volume at 50°C and 80 kPa.

23. A sample of helium measures 100 mL at STP. Find its volume at 125°C and 106.7 kPa.

24. Some carbon dioxide at STP is cooled to 200 K. At the same time the pressure is doubled. If the initial volume of the gas was 400 L, find the new volume.

25. A gas has a volume 20 L at 20°C and 101.3 kPa. To what temperature must it be heated so that the volume doubles and the pressure goes to 192.0 kPa?

26. If a sample of gas is imagined to be a collection of rapidly moving particles, give a possible explanation for Dalton's Law of Partial Pressures.

27. How is the partial pressure of a gas collected over water determined from the total pressure?

28. (i) If, on a day when the barometric pressure is 102.4 kPa, some oxygen gas is collected over water whose vapour pressure is 2.53 kPa, what is the partial pressure of the oxygen gas?

    (ii) A volume of two litres of "wet" oxygen is collected at 102.4 kPa with the water vapour pressure being 2.53 kPa. What would the volume of the oxygen be if the water vapour were removed?

29. A 1.00 L sample of hydrogen is collected over water at 93.3 kPa total pressure and 20°C. What would the volume of the dried hydrogen be at STP?

30. State Graham's Law of Diffusion.

31. Illustrate Graham's Law by reference to the densities and diffusion rates of hydrogen and oxygen.

32. Find the relative rates of diffusion of two gases, sulfur dioxide and methane. Their densities are 2.86 g/L and 0.71 g/L respectively at STP.

33. If some hydrogen were introduced into one end of a glass tube 20 cm long, and some oxygen were introduced into the other end at the same time, where would the two gases meet in the tube?

34. If 1 L of hydrogen will diffuse through a hole in one hour, how long will it take 1 L of oxygen to diffuse through the same hole?

35. A sample of gas is confined to a sealed metal cylinder. Which of the following is true about the pressure exerted by the gas when the absolute temperature is doubled?

    (i) It is halved. (ii) It is doubled. (iii) It is tripled. (iv) It is quadrupled. (v) It remains unchanged.

36. In which of the following cases could the volume of a given mass of gas remain constant?

    (i)   When the temperature is lowered and the pressure is increased.
    (ii) When the temperature is increased and the pressure remains the same.
    (iii) When the temperature is increased and the pressure is decreased.
    (iv) When both the temperature and pressure are increased.

37. Which of the following represent standard conditions?

    (i) 0°C and 10.1 kPa   (ii) 0 K and 101.3 kPa   (iii) 273 K and 101.3 kPa
    (iv) 273°C and 101.3 kPa

38. In which of the following groups are the gases correctly ranked in order of increasing diffusion rate?

    (i) oxygen, hydrogen, helium   (ii) oxygen, helium, hydrogen
    (iii) helium, oxygen, hydrogen   (iv) hydrogen, helium, oxygen

CHAPTER

11

THE KINETIC MOLECULAR THEORY

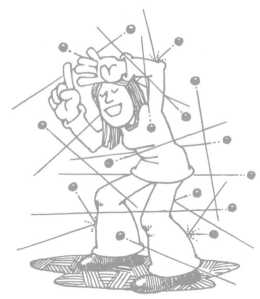

A useful theory even if it is not perfect.

11:1   Some Questions about Gases

The behaviour and properties of gases make one wonder about them. What is a gas? How does it exert pressure? How does it occupy the entire volume of any container in which it is placed? How does it expand so automatically when any external pressure is removed? Why is it possible to compress gases? How do gases diffuse among other gases? Their volumes are affected by temperature and pressure so uniformly that these effects can be expressed as scientific laws. Can this be explained? How does a gas expand when heated? Why do all gases expand by the same amount? Why does the absolute temperature scale express the rate of expansion of gases? What is the difference between a liquid and a gas? Why can a liquid be changed to a gas, and then the gas changed back to a liquid by changing the temperature or pressure?

11:2   The Kinetic Molecular Theory of Gases

An attempt to answer these questions was made by proposing that gases consist of molecules in mo-

tion. Such an idea might be called a model, or a theory. Because of what it proposes, it is called the *Kinetic Molecular Theory*. It has been very useful in explaining gas behaviour, changes of state, and other important phenomena.

The main ideas of the kinetic molecular theory are the following:

1. Gases are made up of exceedingly small particles called molecules.

2. The distances between the molecules are very large compared with the size of the molecules themselves.

3. The molecules are in continuous motion in straight lines and in all directions.

4. The kinetic energy of the moving molecules is proportional to the absolute temperature of the gas.

This energy increases when the gas is heated and decreases when the gas is cooled. The average kinetic energy of the molecules of all gases is the same at a given temperature.

5. The molecules collide with each other and with the walls of their container.

6. The collisions of the molecules among themselves or with the walls of the container are perfectly elastic.

Any molecule that collides with the walls of the container rebounds at a speed that is exactly the same as its speed before collision. When molecules collide among themselves, they rebound with speeds whose sum is the same as that before the collision. Such collisions, in which there is no loss of total speed or momentum, are called *elastic*.

The reason for believing that molecular collisions are elastic is that gases may exist indefinitely, with collisions going on all the time. If the molecules gradually slow down, the gas as we know it ceases to exist.

11:3   A Scientific Model

The above assumptions of the kinetic molecular theory provide us with a *model* which helps us to understand how a gas behaves. Such models are very useful and scientists use them often as an aid to form a mental picture of how some system "works." A model is often an oversimplification, and what it depicts is termed "perfect" or "ideal." The kinetic molecular theory simplifies the behaviour of gases by ignoring any attraction between the molecules. Nevertheless, the assumptions of the theory may be applied to actual gases, especially at low pressure and high temperature, when intermolecular attraction is indeed negligible.

11:4   Explanation of Gas Behaviour by the Kinetic Molecular Theory

The real test of a successful theory is its ability to explain facts. Let us see how the kinetic molecular theory explains the facts of gas behaviour.

Expansion
The expansion of a gas is due to the straight line motion of the molecules, which causes them to "fill" any volume, no matter how large. Upon expansion of the gas, the spaces between the molecules become larger.

Compressibility
The compressibility of a gas is due to the large spaces between the molecules. When outside pressure is applied, the molecules simply crowd together into a smaller volume; the distances between them become smaller.

Pressure
Gas pressure is caused by molecular bombardment of the walls of a vessel by the gas enclosed in it. Since each molecule has mass and velocity, it gives an impulse to the wall upon collision. The total effect of all the collisions of all the molecules with the wall results in pressure.

Diffusion
Diffusion of gases may also be explained by molecular motion. As soon as a vessel containing gas is opened, some molecules escape from it into the adjacent atmosphere. At the same time, molecules of the adjacent air start to fly into the open container. In this way molecular motion causes diffusion and intermingling of gases.

Explanation of the Gas Laws by the Kinetic Molecular Theory

BOYLE'S LAW
If the volume of a gas is compressed, more molecules are present per unit volume (Fig. 11.1). The result is more collisions between the molecules of the gas and the walls of the vessel. Because such collisions are the cause of pressure, it is to be expected that a decrease in volume should produce a corresponding increase in pressure, and vice versa.

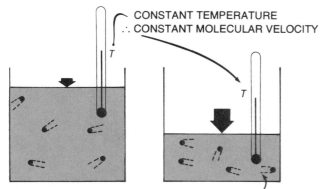

CONSTANT TEMPERATURE
∴ CONSTANT MOLECULAR VELOCITY

SAME NUMBER OF MOLECULES IN SMALLER VOLUME
∴ GREATER PRESSURE

Fig. 11.1:
How the kinetic molecular theory explains Boyle's Law

In this experiment the temperature should remain constant to ensure that the kinetic energy and hence the velocity of the molecules do not change.

CHARLES' LAW

The motion of the molecules of a gas depends on their kinetic energy. In turn, the kinetic energy depends on the absolute temperature of the gas. At a given temperature, the molecules have a definite kinetic energy and move at a definite average speed. When the temperature is raised, the kinetic energy of the molecules is increased, and the molecules move faster than before. Hence, there will be more collisions with the walls of the vessel if the volume is kept the same, and this will cause an increase in pressure.

If the pressure is to be kept constant while the temperature is raised, the molecules must be given a larger volume in which to fly about, so that the number of collisions per unit of wall area will remain the same. Thus we see that the volume would increase at the same rate as the absolute temperature (Fig. 11.2).

DALTON'S LAW OF PARTIAL PRESSURES

So large are the spaces between the molecules of a gas, or a mixture of gases, that the presence of different kinds of molecules does not change the behaviour of the molecules. The pressure of a gas depends on the number of molecules present and their average kinetic energy. These factors are not altered by the presence of molecules of various other gases. Fig. 11.3 illustrates this fact.

The three containers shown have the same capacity. The molecules of gas present in container A exert a pressure of 20 kPa, while the molecules of gas in container B exert a pressure of 10 kPa. When both gases are transferred to the third container C, the combined pressure noted is 30 kPa.

GRAHAM'S LAW OF DIFFUSION

The kinetic molecular theory assumes that the average kinetic energy of the molecules of gases is proportional to the absolute temperature. Furthermore, all gases at the same absolute temperature have the same kinetic energy. From physics, we learn that the kinetic energy, K.E., of a body of mass m and velocity v is given by the equation

$$K.E. = \frac{1}{2} mv^2$$

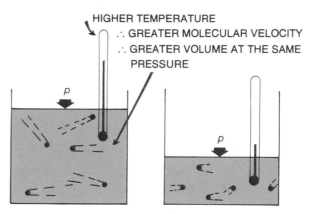

HIGHER TEMPERATURE
∴ GREATER MOLECULAR VELOCITY
∴ GREATER VOLUME AT THE SAME PRESSURE

Fig. 11.2:
How the kinetic molecular theory explains Charles' Law

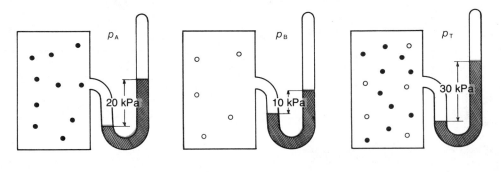

$$p_T = p_A + p_B$$

Fig. 11.3:
Illustration of the Law of Partial Pressures

Different gases have different molecular mass. Therefore, if two gases are to have the same kinetic energy at a given temperature, they must have different velocities. The greater the mass of the molecules of one gas, the slower the speed and the rate of diffusion of that gas compared to another lighter gas.

11:5   The Kinetic Molecular Theory Applied to Liquids and Solids

The kinetic molecular theory can be related to liquids and solids provided slight modifications are made.

In a liquid, the molecules are closer together than in a gas. The molecules of a liquid have enough energy to slide past each other but not enough to overcome the forces of attraction between them.

When applying the kinetic molecular theory to solids, we must keep in mind that the particles making up the solid are not necessarily molecules. These particles can be molecules, atoms, or ions. They are arranged in fixed positions to produce the regular crystalline structure of solids. In all solids, whether molecular, atomic, or ionic, the particles do not move around freely but simply vibrate about their points of location in the crystal structure.

11:6   The States of Matter Viewed in terms of Molecular Motion

Whether a given substance exists as a gas, a liquid, or a solid, depends on whether the molecules are free to fly about, or are prevented from doing so by their mutual attraction. This explains why the temperature and pressure are such important factors in determining the state of a substance.

When the temperature is high and the pressure is low, the molecules have great kinetic energy with large spaces between them for flying about. These conditions favour the gaseous state. Here the kinetic energy of the molecules greatly outweighs the intermolecular attraction and the molecules move about freely as they fill the entire space of the container. Thus, gases have no definite volume and their densities are relatively small. When the temperature is lowered, the kinetic energy of the molecules is less. They move at a greatly reduced speed. If, in addition, the surrounding pressure is high, the molecules come close together and this helps them attract each other. A point is reached where the force of attraction becomes so great as to outweigh the kinetic energy of the molecules. Low temperature and high pressure force the molecules to cling together and the gas condenses to a liquid.

In this state the average distance between molecules is less and the density is greater than in a gas. Furthermore, the liquid has a definite volume and shows an upper surface. One of the forces of attraction between molecules, termed *van der Waals forces*, depends on the kind of molecules between which they are acting as well as the distance between the molecules. They are stronger between molecules of bromine than between those of hydrogen. Between sugar molecules they are stronger still. At a given temperature the average kinetic energy of all molecules is the same. Owing to the difference in the strength of the van der Waals forces, hydrogen is a gas, bromine is a liquid, and sugar is a solid, when all three substances are at room temperature.

11:7 Changes of State in terms of Molecular Motion

It may happen that a certain molecule in a liquid receives more energy than the average through collisions with other molecules. Indeed, collisions may result in the accumulation of enough energy by a molecule to escape from the liquid and enter the air. Molecules of liquids evaporate in this manner. At any temperature, some molecules are able to leave a liquid in this way. As the temperature is raised, the number of collisions between molecules increases. More molecules reach the escape velocity, leaving the liquid as a vapour. Conversely, molecules of vapour may slow down and thus fall back into the liquid. The changes of state from liquid to gas and to liquid are readily explained.

If the temperature of a liquid or gas is lowered sufficiently, the substance will change to the solid state. The forces of attraction overcome the kinetic energy of the molecules. Conversely, when a solid has absorbed sufficient energy to overcome the attractive forces between the molecules, a process called *fusion* or *melting* occurs. The temperature at which this occurs is called the *melting point*.

In a large class of compounds which form solids, the particles are electrically charged atoms or groups of atoms called ions. These are the salts. Here the forces of attraction are even greater than the van der Waals type. As a result, the melting points of salts are relatively high. Thus, the melting of solids to liquids and the freezing of liquids to solids are readily explained by the motion of molecules and ions, and the effect of temperature on such motion.

11:8 The Liquefaction of Air

A gas such as air can be converted into a liquid by lowering the temperature and increasing the pressure. The method used to liquefy air is to compress it and then allow it to expand suddenly. This sudden expansion has a cooling effect whereby the temperature of the air drops. When the air expands, its molecules move farther apart and work is done in overcoming the forces of attraction between the molecules. This work takes heat away from the air and the kinetic energy of the molecules is lowered. The operation is repeated with the cooler gas, each time making it cooler still, until eventually it liquefies. The liquefaction of air is diagrammatically represented in Fig. 11.4.

The Storage of Liquid Air
Because of the low temperature at which liquid air boils, it cannot be stored in an ordinary refrigerator. It can be stored for short periods in

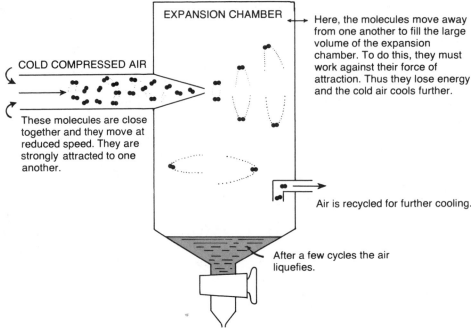

EXPANSION CHAMBER

Here, the molecules move away from one another to fill the large volume of the expansion chamber. To do this, they must work against their force of attraction. Thus they lose energy and the cold air cools further.

COLD COMPRESSED AIR

These molecules are close together and they move at reduced speed. They are strongly attracted to one another.

Air is recycled for further cooling.

After a few cycles the air liquefies.

Fig. 11.4:
Liquefaction of air

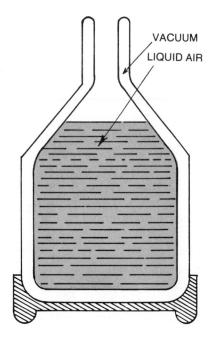

VACUUM

LIQUID AIR

Dewar flasks, which are named after the man who first used them for this purpose. In a Dewar flask, there is a vacuum between the walls (Fig. 11.5) so that heat will not be conducted from the outside to the inside of the flask. The efficiency of the Dewar flask is further improved by silvering so that radiation may be reflected rather than absorbed. It is not possible, however, to stop the passage of all heat into the flask; so the liquid air slowly boils away. Liquid air containers must therefore not be stoppered, because the internal pressure caused by the vaporization of the air might burst the container.

Fig. 11.5:
Dewar flask for storing liquid air

Liquid Air: A Commercial Source for Oxygen
Since industry and hospitals need a large amount of oxygen, a method to produce an ample supply has been devised which separates the oxygen from the other gases of the air by first liquefying the air. Liquid air is a mixture of oxygen (boiling point, −183°C), and nitrogen (boiling point, −196°C). To separate the gases, the more volatile nitrogen is allowed to boil off first; then the oxygen comes off as a gas and is stored in steel cylinders. The separation just described is based on the fact that the liquids mixed have different boiling points. The process is called *fractional distillation*.

QUESTIONS

1. Tabulate the main points of the kinetic molecular theory.

2. (i) Suggest a reason why a real gas does not behave exactly as an ideal gas would.
   (ii) Why might real gases vary more from the ideal behaviour at high pressures and low temperatures?

3. In terms of the kinetic molecular theory explain why:
   (i) gases fill their containers;
   (ii) gases are compressible;
   (iii) gases exert pressure;
   (iv) gases are miscible.

4. By means of the kinetic molecular theory, explain why:
   (i) letting air out of a tire reduces the pressure;
   (ii) the pressure exerted by a gas increases as it is heated;
   (iii) 2 g of oxygen gas in a given container exerts twice the pressure of 1 g of oxygen in the same container at the same temperature;
   (vi) hydrogen diffuses faster than oxygen when the two gases are at the same temperature.

5. Do the molecules of two different gases at the same temperature have the same average velocity? Explain.

6. A container has a certain number of molecules of oxygen and three times as many molecules of nitrogen. The partial pressure exerted by the oxygen is 150 kPa. If the pressure depends on the number of molecules, what is the total pressure exerted by the mixture of gases?

7. What would happen to a gas if the collisions between its molecules and the walls of its container were not perfectly elastic?

8. Why does the air under pressure in a tire become cool as it escapes?

9. Distinguish between gases, liquids, and solids, in terms of the kinetic molecular theory.

10. Under what conditions will a gas condense into a liquid?

11. Explain why condensation is a heat evolving process.

12. Suggest a reason why liquids are practically incompressible.

13. How do liquids evaporate?

14. Explain how the compression and sudden expansion of air causes its temperature to drop.

15. Once the temperature drops low enough to liquefy air, how is the oxygen separated from the nitrogen portion?

16. Does the separation of the oxygen and nitrogen in liquid air involve a chemical or physical change?

17. How does a Dewar flask maintain low temperature?

Questions 18, 19, 20, and 21 relate to the following points of the kinetic molecular theory:
1. Gases are made of molecules with large spaces between them.
2. The molecules move about at high speeds.
3. The collisions between molecules are perfectly elastic.
4. The molecules have kinetic energy which increases directly with absolute temperature.

Which of the above statements best explains:

18. Charles' Law?
    (i) 1   (ii) 2   (iii) 3   (iv) 4

19. Why gases are compressible?
    (i) 1   (ii) 2   (iii) 3   (iv) 4

20. How gases exert pressure?
    (i) 1   (ii) 2   (iii) 3   (iv) 4

21. How gases diffuse?
    (i) 1   (ii) 2   (iii) 3   (iv) 4

CHAPTER

12

THE PRINCIPLE OF AVOGADRO

Avogadro discovered the clue that made chemistry a quantitative science.

12:1　The Molecule-Atom Problem

Physical changes, such as the compression and expansion of gases and changes of state, are explained by supposing that gases consist of molecules in motion, according to the kinetic molecular theory.

Chemical changes, such as the formation of compounds from the elements, are explained by supposing that the elements consist of atoms, according to the atomic theory. Both the atom and the molecule are so small that they cannot be seen. Are molecules and atoms the same, or are they different? If atoms combine to form molecules, how are we to find out how many atoms there are in a molecule? In what proportion do atoms combine in any given case? What evidence have we that in the water molecule there are two atoms of hydrogen and one of oxygen? Why not one of hydrogen and one of oxygen?

A similar difficulty arises even in the case of certain elements. For example, since oxygen is a gas, the molecular theory maintains that it is composed of atoms. Since oxygen is an element, the atomic theory maintains that it is composed of atoms. Are the molecules of oxygen the same as the atoms of oxygen, or are they different? If they are different, what is the difference?

Even if we know that atoms combine in the ratio of one to one (or two to one) to form a certain molecule, how can we provide equal numbers of atoms to react with one another? Surely we cannot count them out one by one because they are not visible and they would be too numerous. There must be some other way to provide the required numbers of atoms and molecules in chemical reactions. How can such problems be solved?

12:2　A Clue to the Solution of the Problem

At about the time that Dalton proposed the atomic theory, the French scientist Gay-Lussac became interested in a special feature of reactions between gases. As we have seen in Chapter 3, when water is decomposed by electrolysis, the volume of hydrogen obtained is exactly double that of the oxygen liberated at the same time. The volumes of hydrogen and oxygen evolved are in the simple ratio of 2:1. Similarly, when water is synthesized from

Ambassade de France, Ottawa

Gay-Lussac, famous French chemist, whose Law of Combining Volumes led to our understanding of the difference between molecules and atoms.

hydrogen and oxygen, the volumes of these gases are in the same ratio of 2:1.

Gay-Lussac wondered whether this ratio was a feature of this chemical reaction alone, or whether it was true for all reactions involving gases. He found that when hydrogen and chlorine combine to form hydrogen chloride, the volumes of the hydrogen and chlorine are equal, and the volume of hydrogen chloride produced is exactly double that of either of the combining gases. Similarly, when carbon monoxide reacts with oxygen to form carbon dioxide, the volume of carbon monoxide required is twice that of the oxygen. The volume of carbon dioxide produced is the same as the volume of carbon monoxide used up. In similar experiments, he found that whenever gases react, the volumes are in a simple ratio of small whole numbers.

The chemical reactions described above can be summarized in the following equations:

(a)	hydrogen	+	oxygen	→	steam
	(2 vol.)		(1 vol.)	→	(2 vol.)

(b)	hydrogen	+	chlorine	→	hydrogen chloride
	(1 vol.)		(1 vol.)		(2 vol.)

(c)	carbon monoxide	+	oxygen	→	carbon dioxide
	(2 vol.)		(1 vol.)		(2 vol.)

Gay-Lussac summed up his findings in the *Law of Combining Gas Volumes*, which states that *volumes of gases which combine or which are produced in chemical reactions are always in the ratio of small whole numbers.*

12:3   Avogadro's Principle

In 1811, the Italian scientist Avogadro realized that the Law of Combining Gas Volumes contained a clue to the problem of how to obtain more precise information about atoms and molecules. Here was a chance to discover the secret of the mass, the number, and the composition of molecules. There might even be some way of proving that the molecule of an element was not the same as an atom of that element. Avogadro suggested that the reason why the volumes of reacting gases are always in a simple ratio is that *equal volumes of all gases at the same temperature and pressure contain the same number of molecules.* This statement is termed Avogadro's Principle.

As you will see, the Avogadro Principle accomplished much for chemistry:

1. It explained Gay-Lussac's Law of Combining Gas Volumes.

What is seen experimentally:

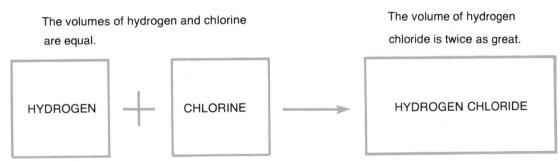

The volumes of hydrogen and chlorine are equal.

The volume of hydrogen chloride is twice as great.

HYDROGEN + CHLORINE → HYDROGEN CHLORIDE

Fig. 12.1:
The hydrogen-chlorine reaction

2. It distinguished between the idea of the atom and that of the molecule.

3. It proved that the molecules of some gaseous elements contained two atoms.

4. It provided a method for finding the mass of molecules and atoms.

5. With the aid of molecular and atomic mass, molecular formulas became possible.

6. With molecular formulas, chemical equations became possible.

Thus you can see why it is said that Avogadro helped to change chemistry, in the early years of that science, from a confusing mass of details into a quantitative study with its own exact and dependable language.

Nevertheless, despite its possibilities, Avogadro's Principle remained unnoticed for nearly fifty years. In 1860 a congress of chemists was called to consider the confusing molecule-atom problem. Cannizzaro, another Italian chemist, revived Avogadro's ideas and proved beyond doubt the validity of the principle. A German chemist present at the congress remarked: "It was as if the scales fell from my eyes; doubt vanished, and was replaced by a feeling of peaceful clarity."

Let us see how reasonably the Avogadro principle explains the Law of Combining Gas Volumes.

It is an experimental fact that one volume of hydrogen combines with one volume of chlorine to produce two volumes of hydrogen chloride gas (Fig. 12.1).

What must happen here, said Avogadro, is that each molecule of hydrogen reacts with one molecule of chlorine, the first molecule of hydrogen with the first of chlorine, the second with the second, the nth with the nth, the last with the last. Now all the molecules of hydrogen have reacted, each with a molecule of chlorine. The reaction is over. All the molecules are "used up." But so too are the equal volumes of hydrogen and chlorine. There must be some relationship between the equal numbers of reacting molecules and the equal volumes of reacting gases, thought Avogadro. The simplest possible connection is that equal volumes of all gases must have the same numbers of molecules at the same temperature and pressure.

What are we to conclude about the "double" volume of hydrogen chloride that was produced? It must contain twice as many molecules of hydrogen chloride as there were of hydrogen or of chlorine in their original "single" volume. The above ideas are shown in Fig. 12.2.

But why was it necessary to say that equal volumes of gases contained the same number of molecules and not of atoms? Would it not have been possible to give the above explanation in

What is seen:

A volume of hydrogen reacts with an equal volume of chlorine to yield a double volume of hydrogen chloride.

What is imagined:

1. That the equal volumes of the gases contain equal numbers of molecules at the same temperature and pressure.

2. That each molecule of chlorine reacts with one molecule of hydrogen to yield two molecules of hydrogen chloride.

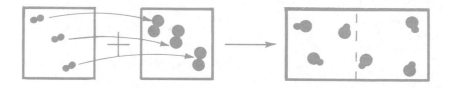

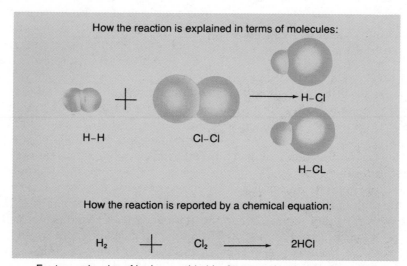

For two molecules of hydrogen chloride, 2 atoms of hydrogen are needed,

∴ the molecule of hydrogen has 2 atoms. Similarly, the molecule of chlorine has 2 atoms.

Fig. 12.2:
The hydrogen-chlorine reaction

terms of atoms instead of molecules, keeping in mind that chemical reactions take place between atoms? The atomic theory maintains, for example, that hydrogen chloride is formed when atoms of hydrogen combine with atoms of chlorine.

12:4   How the Difference between Molecules and Atoms Was Established

In the reaction between hydrogen and chlorine, the volume of the hydrogen chloride produced is twice as great as that of either the hydrogen or the chlorine. Avogadro therefore assumed that twice as many molecules of hydrogen chloride were formed as there were of either hydrogen or chlorine originally. This would mean that *one molecule of hydrogen and one molecule of chlorine combine to form two molecules of hydrogen chloride.*

Each of the molecules of hydrogen chloride contains one atom of hydrogen and one of chlorine. Therefore, Avogadro concluded that each hydrogen particle had been split into two halves, one for each of the two molecules of hydrogen chloride. In the same way each of the particles of chlorine must have been split into two halves to supply the chlorine for the two hydrogen chloride molecules (Fig. 12.2).

Since atoms could not be divided by chemical means, Avogadro reasoned that *the particles that make up hydrogen gas could not be simple atoms but must contain two atoms. Such particles are the molecules of hydrogen.* Similarly, the particles that make up chlorine gas could not be simple atoms, but must also be molecules that contain two atoms. The *molecule* is the smallest particle that can exist physically and yet retain the composition of the original pure substance. The *atom* is the smallest particle of an element able to enter chemical reaction. "*I have shown*," wrote Avogadro, "*that the physical molecule and the chemical atom are not the same.*"

12:5   The Molecules of Hydrogen, Chlorine, Oxygen, and Nitrogen Each Have Two Atoms

To prove that the molecules of hydrogen and chlorine have two atoms each, we noted that one volume of hydrogen combines with an equal volume of chlorine to form a double volume of hydrogen chloride. The same argument may be given to prove also that the molecules of oxygen and nitrogen have two atoms each.

In the reaction between oxygen and hydrogen to form steam, one volume of oxygen gas is responsible for the formation of a volume of steam twice as great. According to Avogadro's Principle, one molecule of oxygen helps to form two molecules of water vapour. The molecule of oxygen must have divided into two halves, one for each molecule of steam. This proves that the molecule of oxygen contains two atoms (Fig. 12.3).

Nitrogen combines with hydrogen to form ammonia. In this reaction, the volume of ammonia produced is twice as great as the volume of the original nitrogen used. Reasoning as before, the conclusion is reached that the molecule of nitrogen contains two atoms (Fig. 12.4).

12:6   Consequences of Avogadro's Principle

Avogadro's main purpose in suggesting that equal volumes of gases contained the same number of molecules was to explain the Law of Combining Gas Volumes in terms of the atomic and molecular theories. The principle did this very successfully, as we have seen. It also accomplished much

What is seen:

A double volume of hydrogen reacts with a single volume of oxygen to yield a double volume of steam.

What is imagined:

1. That there are twice as many molecules in the double volume of hydrogen as in the single volume of oxygen.

2. That each molecule of oxygen reacts with 2 molecules of hydrogen to yield 2 molecules of steam.

How the reaction is explained in terms of molecules:

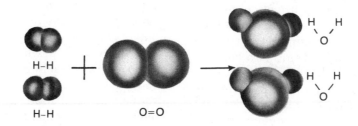

How the reaction is reported by a chemical equation:

$$2\,H_2 \quad + \quad O_2 \quad \longrightarrow \quad 2\,H_2O$$

For two molecules of water, 2 atoms of oxygen are needed,

∴ the molecule of oxygen has 2 atoms.

Fig. 12.3:
The hydrogen-oxygen reaction

more. It provided a clear distinction between the "physical molecules" and the "chemical atoms" by showing that even a simple molecule might be composed of two atoms.

What is seen:

A triple volume of hydrogen reacts with a single volume of nitrogen to yield a double volume of ammonia.

What is imagined:

1. That there are three times as many molecules in the triple volume of hydrogen as in the single volume of nitrogen.

2. That each molecule of nitrogen reacts with 3 molecules of hydrogen to yield 2 molecules of ammonia.

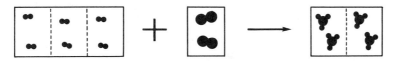

How the reaction is explained in terms of molecules:

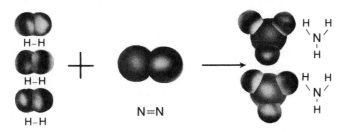

How the reaction is reported by a chemcial equation:

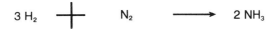

$$3\,H_2 \quad + \quad N_2 \quad \longrightarrow \quad 2\,NH_3$$

For 2 molecules of ammonia, 2 atoms of nitrogen are needed,

∴the molecule of nitrogen has 2 atoms.

Fig. 12.4:
The hydrogen-nitrogen reaction

Perhaps the most far-reaching result of the principle is that it gave to chemistry a method of finding the relative mass of the molecules and atoms. Thus it helped to make chemistry a quantitative science, as was mentioned before.

12:7   Avogadro's Number and Avogadro's Law

Since Avogadro's time, scientists have been able to determine the actual number of molecules in a given volume or mass of gas. Thirty-two grams of oxygen have been found to contain 6.02×10^{23} molecules. This number is called *Avogadro's Number*. It is also referred to as *one mole* of particles.

Two famous physicists, Perrin and Millikan, stated that it is possible to calculate the number of molecules in a gas as accurately as one can determine the population of a city like New York. Many chemists and physicists have worked on the calculation of Avogadro's number, and because their final results are in very close agreement, confidence has been established in the accuracy of this number. So great is this confidence that Avogadro's Principle is now accepted as a law.

QUESTIONS

1. (i) Apply the Law of Combining Volumes to the decomposition of water and to the union of hydrogen and oxygen.
   (ii) Discuss this law in reference to the reactions between (i) hydrogen and chlorine (ii) carbon monoxide and oxygen.

2. (i) According to Avogadro's Principle, what is true about the number of molecules contained by 2.0 L samples of hydrogen and oxygen at 25°C and 100 kPa?
   (ii) What led to the development of this principle?

3. Explain why the size of the molecules in a gas has little to do with its volume.

4. Outline a proof showing that the molecule of hydrogen and the molecule of chlorine each contains two atoms. Do the same for nitrogen and oxygen.

5. Distinguish between the terms *atom* and *molecule*.

6. When may the terms *atom* and *molecule* be used interchangeably?

7. What is Avogadro's number? What does it signify with respect to oxygen?

8. What is a *mole* of particles?

9. How many molecules are there in 1 g of oxygen at STP?

10. What is the importance of Avogadro's Principle?

CHAPTER

13

THE MOLE

One mole of any substance contains 6.023×10^{23} particles.

13:1   Method for Finding Molecular Mass of Gases

Finding the mass of a single molecule or atom on a balance is impossible. It is a fairly simple matter, however, to find the mass of equal volumes of different gases at the same temperature and pressure. In effect, this is the same as finding the mass of equal numbers of molecules of the various gases. In this way, Avogadro's law spares us the need of having to find the mass of single molecules on a balance in order to find the relative mass of molecules.

If, for example, a certain volume of gas A contains X molecules, then an equal volume of gas B would also contain X molecules at the same temperature and pressure. Suppose that the mass of A is twice as great as that of B. Then the mass of one molecule of A must be twice as great as one of B. This illustrates how Avogadro's law enables us to find the relative mass of molecules.

As a more realistic example, suppose that the mass of a certain volume of oxygen at 0°C and 101.3 kPa pressure is 32 g. The mass of the same volume of hydrogen under the same conditions is only 2 g. If the number of oxygen molecules is X, the number of hydrogen molecules would also be X. Since the mass of X molecules of oxygen is sixteen times as great as X molecules of hydrogen, therefore, the mass of one molecule of oxygen is

sixteen times as great as one molecule of hydrogen.

We have already seen that the molecules of oxygen and hydrogen have two atoms each. We may now conclude that the mass of the atom of oxygen is sixteen times as great as the mass of the atom of hydrogen. (See Fig. 13.1.)

13:2   Standard for Atomic and Molecular Mass

The above idea has been used by chemists to find the relative mass of molecules of gases, and of the atoms which form such molecules. To apply the method, we choose an atom to which all other atoms and molecules could be compared. We have already indicated in Section 4:9 that the atom of the most common isotope of carbon was chosen for this purpose. It has been assigned a value of exactly 12.000 atomic mass units (u). On the same scale, the atomic mass of oxygen is 15.9994 u to an accuracy of 99.996 percent. For convenience, the atomic mass of oxygen will be taken as 16 u and other atomic masses also will be rounded out.

13:3   The Atomic Mass Unit (u)

The standard for atomic mass is the carbon-12 isotope. The most abundant isotope is assigned a mass of 12.000 atomic mass units (u)*. Thus, 1 u is 1/12 the mass of the "standard" isotope of carbon. With the atomic mass unit, we can assign units to the atomic and molecular mass of the elements and compounds. To illustrate, the atomic masses of oxygen and hydrogen, in round numbers, are 16 and 1 u respectively, while their molecular masses are 32 and 2 u. The molecular mass of the water molecule is $(2 \times 1) + 16 = 18$ u.

13:4   The Mole: A Practical Chemical Unit for Handling Atoms and Molecules

When we wish to carry out a reaction, we cannot find the mass of individual atoms or molecules or count them because of their tiny size. Remember, too, how numerous they are. What we need is some way to link up a number of molecules or atoms with mass. We can then simply find the mass of our sample, and automatically know the number of particles in it. Our concern about knowing the number of molecules or atoms in a sample is easy to understand. Chemical reactions take place between one (or two, or three) atoms or molecules of reactant A, and one (or two, or three) of reactant B.

The quantity of substance that always contains the same number of particles is the mole. If you wish to study a reaction between two substances, A and B, in which one particle of A combines with one of B, you would measure out one mole of A and one of B, or two moles of each, depending on the amount of product you wish to obtain. The moles of A and B are easy to measure for practical purposes because their mass can be found on a balance. The individual atoms or molecules of these substances cannot be handled in this way.

The mole of an element or compound is the mass represented numerically by the symbol or formula of the substance in gram amounts. For carbon, the symbol C represents one atom with a mass of 12 u. Automatically, the mole of carbon is 12 g. Similarly, the formula for sulfur, S, represents 32 u. The mole of sulfur has the mass of 32 g. In 12 g of carbon and in 32 g of sulfur, the same number of atoms are present. This is so because the masses of the respective moles are in the same ratio as the masses of the respective atoms of carbon and sulfur.

13:5   What the Mole Represents

The mole of all substances contains the same number of particles. That number is very important and is named in honour of Avogadro, the scientist who gave chemistry its first method for finding molecular and atomic mass. The Avogadro Number is 6.02×10^{23} particles.

A mole of any pure substance has a mass in grams equal numerically to the atomic or molecular mass of the substance. When the atomic mass of an element is expressed in grams, it is called also the molar mass of the element. Similarly, the molar mass of a substance is its molecular mass expressed in grams. One mole of any pure substance contains 6.02×10^{23} particles.

The concept of the mole is one of the most

---

* At one time H = 1 was the standard because it is the lightest element known. Oxygen was then chosen, because it forms compounds with both metallic and non-metallic elements, while hydrogen does not. In 1961, C = 12 was adopted as a standard because it is easier to obtain the pure isotope of carbon-12 than that of oxygen-16. Changes in standards of atomic masses do not alter the theory of how atomic masses were found; neither do they seriously change the numerical values of the atomic masses.

important ideas in chemistry. It is widely used in the solution of problems about the mass of reactants and products in chemical changes.

The mole represents:
(a) the molar mass of an element;
(b) the number of atoms in the atomic mass;
(c) the molar mass of any substance;
(d) the number of molecules in a molar mass;
(e) the molar volume (section 13.6) of a gaseous substance at STP;
(f) the number of particles in the molar volume of a gaseous substance at STP.

"A mole of atoms" and "a mole of molecules" should not be confused. In a mole of oxygen gas, there is one mole of molecules and two moles of atoms. Unless specified, a mole of gas refers to the number of molecules.

13:6   The Molar Volume

To simplify the task of finding the molar mass of a gas, the volume can be calculated from the molar mass of oxygen and its density of 1.43 g/L at STP. If 1.43 g of oxygen occupy 1 L at STP, then, 32.00 g of oxygen occupy:

$$\frac{1\ L}{1.43\ g} \times 32.00\ g = 22.4\ L$$

This volume, 22.4 L, occupied by the molar mass (1 mol) of oxygen at STP is called the molar volume.

The molar volume of any gas at STP weighs the molar mass of that gas (Table 13.1). Since it is feasible to weigh 22.4 L of a gas at STP, it is possible to find the molar mass, and from this, the molecular mass of that gas. In practice, it is not even necessary to weigh a volume of exactly 22.4 L at 0°C and 101.3 kPa of pressure. Any volume at any pressure and temperature will do, for the data can be converted to the standard values with the aid of gas laws.

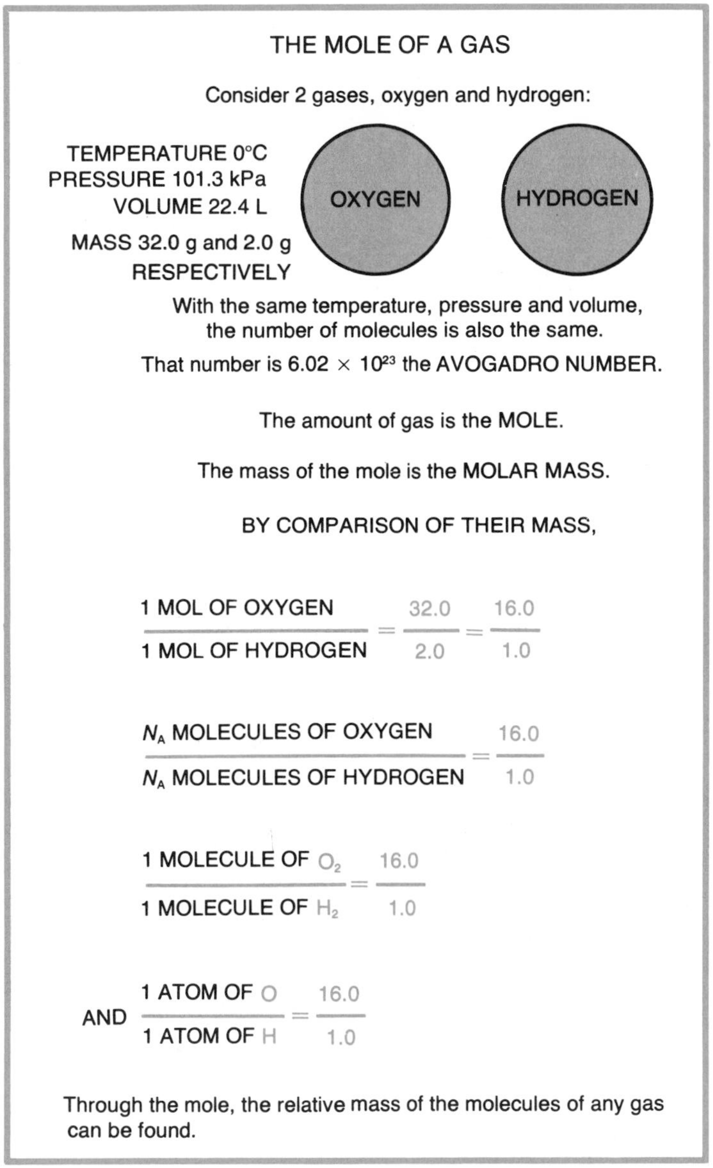

THE MOLE OF A GAS

Consider 2 gases, oxygen and hydrogen:

TEMPERATURE 0°C
PRESSURE 101.3 kPa
VOLUME 22.4 L

MASS 32.0 g and 2.0 g
RESPECTIVELY

With the same temperature, pressure and volume, the number of molecules is also the same.

That number is 6.02×10^{23} the AVOGADRO NUMBER.

The amount of gas is the MOLE.

The mass of the mole is the MOLAR MASS.

BY COMPARISON OF THEIR MASS,

$$\frac{1\ \text{MOL OF OXYGEN}}{1\ \text{MOL OF HYDROGEN}} = \frac{32.0}{2.0} = \frac{16.0}{1.0}$$

$$\frac{N_A\ \text{MOLECULES OF OXYGEN}}{N_A\ \text{MOLECULES OF HYDROGEN}} = \frac{16.0}{1.0}$$

$$\frac{1\ \text{MOLECULE OF } O_2}{1\ \text{MOLECULE OF } H_2} = \frac{16.0}{1.0}$$

$$\text{AND} \quad \frac{1\ \text{ATOM OF } O}{1\ \text{ATOM OF } H} = \frac{16.0}{1.0}$$

Through the mole, the relative mass of the molecules of any gas can be found.

Fig. 13.1:
Comparing equal volumes of gases

TABLE 13.1

The Molar Volume and the Molar Mass

Molar Volume	Molar Mass of Some Common Gases		Molecular Mass of Their Molecules	
	Oxygen	32.0 g	O_2	32.0 u
	Hydrogen	2.0 g	H_2	2.0 u
22.4 L contains	Helium	4.0 g	He	4.0 u
6.02×10^{23} molecules	Carbon Dioxide	44.0 g	CO_2	44.0 u
termed 1 mol at STP	Ammonia	17.0 g	NH_3	17.0 u
	Hydrogen Chloride	36.5 g	HCl	36.5 u
	Any Gas X	x g	Molecule of X	x u

13:7   Examples

Example 1
The density of a hydrocarbon gas is 2.54 g/L at STP. Find its molar mass.

Solution
The molar mass of a gas is the mass of 22.4 L at STP. Therefore, the molar mass

$$= 2.54 \frac{g}{L} \times 22.4 \frac{L}{mol}$$

$$= 56.9 \frac{g}{mol}$$

Note that the units of the molar mass are grams per mole ($\frac{g}{mol}$) and of the molar volume are litres per mole ($\frac{L}{mol}$).

Example 2
One litre of ammonia weighs 0.71 g at a pressure of 104 kPa and a temperature of 27°C. Find its molar mass.

Solution
The first step is to calculate the volume that the gas would occupy at STP. Using the equation $\frac{p_1V_1}{T_1} = \frac{p_2V_2}{T_2}$ where the subscript 1 refers to the original conditions and the subscript 2 refers to the final standard conditions, we may solve for the volume at STP,

$$V_2 = \frac{V_1 p_1 T_2}{p_2 T_1}$$

$$= 1.00 \text{ L} \times \frac{104 \text{ kPa}}{101.3 \text{ kPa}} \times \frac{273 \text{ K}}{300 \text{ K}}$$

$$= 0.94 \text{ L}$$

The next step is to calculate the mass of 22.4 L at STP.

Thus, the molar mass

$$= \frac{0.71 \text{ g}}{0.94 \text{ L}} \times 22.4 \frac{L}{mol}$$

$$= 17.0 \frac{g}{mol}$$

Alternatively, keeping in mind how changes in pressure and temperature affect volumes according to Boyle's and Charles' laws, we may say:

The volume at STP

$$= \begin{array}{c} \text{present} \\ \text{volume} \end{array} \times \begin{array}{c} \text{temperature} \\ \text{change} \end{array} \times \begin{array}{c} \text{pressure} \\ \text{change} \end{array}$$

$$= 1.00 \text{ L} \times \frac{273 \text{ K}}{300 \text{ K}} \times \frac{104 \text{ kPa}}{101.3 \text{ kPa}}$$

$$= 0.94 \text{ L}$$

The next step is to calculate the mass of 22.4 L at STP.

0.94 L at STP weighs   0.71 g

$$\therefore 22.4 \text{ L at STP weighs } \frac{0.71 \text{ g}}{0.94 \text{ L}} \times 22.4 \frac{\text{L}}{\text{mol}}$$

$$= 17.0 \frac{\text{g}}{\text{mol}}$$

Example 3

The molar mass of carbon dioxide is 44.0 g. Find the mass of 3.00 L of this gas at STP.

Solution

One mole (22.4 L) of carbon dioxide weigh 44.0 g at STP. Therefore, the mass of 3.00 L is

$$\frac{3.00 \text{ L}}{22.4 \text{ L}} \times 44.0 \text{ g}$$

$$= 5.90 \text{ g}$$

Alternatively

22.4 L of the gas weighs 44.0 g

$$\therefore 3.00 \text{ L weighs } \frac{44.0 \text{ g}}{22.4 \text{ L}} \times 3.00 \text{ L}$$

$$= 5.90 \text{ g}$$

13:8   The Ideal Gas Equation

From the laws of Boyle, Charles, and Avogadro, we learn that the volume of a gas depends on three factors, the pressure p, the absolute temperature T, and the number of molecules or the number of moles n. Thus,

Boyle's Law: $V \propto \frac{1}{p}$, (const T, n)

Charles' Law: $V \propto T$, (const p, n)

Avogadro's Law: $V \propto n$, (const T, p)

Combining these, $V \propto \frac{nT}{p}$

$$or \ V = constant \times \frac{nT}{p}$$

The constant in this equation is called the gas constant because it applies to all gases. It is represented by R. Now the equation becomes

$$V = \frac{RnT}{p}$$

$$or \ pV = nRT$$

This is called the Ideal Gas Equation. To evaluate R we may write

$$R = \frac{pV}{nT}$$

and then substitute values for p, V, n and T. Thus, for any gas at STP,

If $n = 1.00 \text{ mol}$,
            $p = 101.3 \text{ kPa}$
            $T = 273 \text{ K}$
then $V = 22.4 \text{ L}$

Therefore $R = \frac{101.3 \times 22.4}{1.00 \times 273}$ or $8.3 \frac{\text{kPa·L}}{\text{mol·K}}$

Example

(a) The volume of a gas measures 10.0 L at 50.66 kPa and 27.0°C. How many moles of gas are present?

Solution

From $pV = RnT$

$$n = \frac{pV}{RT}$$

$V = 10.0$ L, $T = 300$ K and $p = 50.66$ kPa

$$R = \frac{8.3 \text{ L·kPa}}{\text{mol·K}}$$

Substituting, $n = \dfrac{50.66 \times 10.0}{8.3 \times 300} \times \dfrac{\text{kPa} \times \text{L}}{\dfrac{\text{L·kPa}}{\text{mol·K}}} \times \text{K}$

$$= 0.20 \text{ mol}$$

(b) If the mass of the above gas is 15.0 g, what is its molar mass?

Solution

0.20 mol has a mass of 15.0 g

1 mol has a mass of $\dfrac{15.0}{0.20} = 75.0$ g

The molar mass is 75.0 u or 75.0 g/mol.

The use of the ideal gas equation $pV = nRT$ to calculate molar mass of gases:

The number of moles n of gas may be expressed by dividing the mass m by the molar mass M.

$$n = \frac{m \text{ grams}}{M \text{ grams/mole}} = \text{moles}$$

When this value of n is substituted into the ideal gas equation, the result is

$$pV = \frac{mRT}{M}$$

and the molar mass is given by

$$M = \frac{mRT}{pV}$$

This equation makes it possible to find the molar mass in one calculation.

(c) 3.00 g of gas is present in 2.50 L at 27.0°C and 50.66 kPa pressure. What is the molar mass of the gas?

Solution

Using $M = \dfrac{mRT}{pV}$

where $m = 3.00$ g,

$T = 300$ K,

$V = 2.50$ L

$R = 8.3 \dfrac{\text{L·kPa}}{\text{mol·K}}$

and $p = 50.66$ kPa

we obtain

$$M = \frac{3.00 \times 8.3 \times 300}{50.66 \times 2.50}$$

$$= 59.1 \text{ g/mol}$$

QUESTIONS

1. Explain clearly why the mass of identical volumes of different gases under the same conditions are in the same ratio as the mass of their individual molecules.

2. (i) Define the terms atomic mass, atomic mass unit, molecular mass, molar mass, mole.
   (ii) How many moles of nitrogen gas are there in 42 g of the element?
   (iii) How many grams are there in 0.52 mol of helium?

3. Why was hydrogen originally chosen as the standard for atomic and molecular mass?

4. (i) What is the present standard for atomic mass?
   (ii) Why was this standard chosen?

5. What can a mole represent?

6. Define the term molar volume. Explain its importance.

7. Outline the method used to calculate the molar mass of a gas.

8. Find the molar mass of a gas if 1 L of it weighs 0.09 g at STP.

9. If 340 mL of a gas weighs 0.70 g at STP, what is its molar mass?

10. Find the mass of 3.00 L of ammonia, NH_3, at STP.

11. Calculate the mass of 400 mL of oxygen at STP.

12. What volume would be occupied by 10.0 g of hydrogen at STP?

13. Find the volume occupied by 4.00 g of carbon dioxide, CO_2 at STP.

14. What is the molar mass of a gas if a volume of 200 mL of it at 20°C and 104 kPa pressure has a mass of 0.28 g?

15. What is the mass of 300 mL of oxygen at 25°C and 80 kPa?

16. Calculate the density (g/L) of methane gas, CH_4, at STP.

17. How are the atomic masses of the elements conclusive evidence for the atomic theory?

18. What mass of sulfur will combine with 10.0 g of oxygen to form sulfur dioxide, SO_2?

19. Calculate the number of atoms in (i) 5.00 g of carbon; (ii) 5.00 g of oxygen.

20. How many moles of oxygen and carbon atoms are there in 10.0 g of carbon dioxide?

21. Find the mass in grams of (i) 0.50 mol of sodium; (ii) 1.50 mol of silver.

22. How many grams of iron will combine with 12.0 g of sulfur to form iron (II) sulfide, FeS?

23. Using the Ideal Gas Equation, find the pressure exerted by 0.25 mol of gas in 6.25 L at 127°C.

24. Solve problems 8 to 15 inclusive, using the Ideal Gas Equation.

CHAPTER
14

CHEMICAL FORMULAS

14:1　Symbols

Each element is represented by a symbol which stands for the element, its atom, and its atomic mass (Chapter 3). Thus, C stands for carbon, for the atom of carbon, and for the atomic mass of 12. When speaking of the atom of carbon, its mass is in u (C = 1 u); when speaking of the mole of carbon, its mass is in grams (C = 12 g).

The chemical formula of a compound is instant information about its composition.

The formula of a compound shows the atomic composition of its molecule, or, if the compound is ionic, the atomic composition of its ions.

14:2　The Composition of Compounds

How can the composition of a compound be represented? We might report the mass of the elements in it. For instance, in the case of water, we can say that 1 g of hydrogen combines with 8 g of oxygen to form 9 g of water. Another way of reporting the composition of water is to say that it is 11.2% hydrogen and 88.8% oxygen. This is called the *percentage composition of water*.

With the help of atomic symbols, the composition of a compound can be represented in a much more significant way; namely, by showing how many atoms of each element are present in the molecule. Even when atoms form ions, it is possible to show the ratio of atoms in the compound.

14:3　Deriving the Molecular Formula

Let us derive the formula of water. The molecular mass of water is 18 u and the percentage composition is 11.2% hydrogen and 88.8% oxygen. The atomic mass of its elements are H = 1 u and O = 16 u in round numbers. To find the molecular formula, the reasoning is as follows:

The molecule of water weighs 18 u. Of this mass, hydrogen is 11.2%; therefore, the hydrogen in the molecule weighs 18×0.112 or 2 u. Since the atom of hydrogen weighs 1 u, there must be two atoms of hydrogen in the molecule of water.

Oxygen makes up 88.8% of the mass of the molecule. The mass of oxygen in the molecule would be 18×0.888 or 16 u. The atom of oxygen

TABLE 14.1

The Molecular Formula of Water (18 u)

The Elements in Water	Percentage in Compound	Mass in Molecule	Number of Atoms	
Hydrogen (1 u)	11.2%	11.2% of 18 u = 2 u	$\dfrac{2\ u}{1\ u} = 2$	∴ formula H_2O
Oxygen (16 u)	88.8%	88.8% of 18 u = 16 u	$\dfrac{16\ u}{16\ u} = 1$	

weighs 16 u; therefore there is one atom of oxygen in the molecule of water. Thus the molecule of water consists of two atoms of hydrogen and one of oxygen. Hence, its formula is H_2O (Table 14.1).

In the case of methane, the molecular mass is 16 u and the percentage composition is 75% carbon and 25% hydrogen. The mass of carbon in the molecule is 75% of 16 u which equals 12 u and since the mass of an atom of carbon is also 12 u there is one atom of carbon in the molecule of methane. The mass of hydrogen is 25% of 16 u which equals 4 u. Since the mass of hydrogen's atom is 1 u, it is evident that there are four atoms of hydrogen in methane's molecule. With one atom of carbon and four of hydrogen, methane has the molecular formula CH_4.

A general method for finding formulas may be worked out using these ideas.

14:4   Simplest and Molecular (or True) Formulas

Some compounds are composed of molecules, others are made up of ions. For molecular compounds, it is possible to find the number of the different kinds of atoms in the molecule and, thus, express the molecular, or true, formula. To do this, the percentage composition, atomic mass of its elements, and molecular mass of the compound are needed.

Ionic compounds, on the other hand, are represented by formulas which show only the ratio of the atoms in the compound. Such representation is called the *simplest* or *empirical* formula.

14:5   Examples

Example 1
Sodium chloride is 39.3% sodium and 60.7% chlorine. What is its simplest formula?

Solution
In 100 g of sodium chloride there are 39.3 g of sodium and 60.7 g of chlorine.
The number of moles of sodium is

$$\frac{39.3\ g}{23.0\ g/mol} \text{ or } 1.71\ mol$$

The number of moles of chlorine is

$$\frac{60.7\ g}{35.5\ g/mol} \text{ or } 1.71\ mol$$

The ratio of moles of sodium to chlorine is thus 1.71:1.71 or 1:1. This is also the ratio of their atoms in the compound; therefore, the simplest formula is NaCl.

Example 2
A pure compound was found on analysis to contain 31.9% potassium, 28.9% chlorine, and 39.2% oxygen. Calculate its simplest formula.

Solution
From the percentage composition, it follows that 100 g of the compound contain 31.9 g of potassium, 28.9 g of chlorine, and 39.2 g of oxygen. To find the number of moles of each element in this sample, we divide the mass of each element by its molar mass.

The number of moles of K $= \dfrac{31.9 \text{ g}}{39.1 \text{ g/mol}} = 0.815$ mol

The number of moles of Cl $= \dfrac{28.9 \text{ g}}{35.5 \text{ g/mol}} = 0.815$ mol

The number of moles of O $= \dfrac{39.2 \text{ g}}{16 \text{ g/mol}} = 2.45$ mol

The molar ratio of K to Cl to O is $0.815 : 0.815 : 2.45$. To simplify this we divide all three of these numbers by the smallest.

$$K = \dfrac{0.815}{0.815} = 1, \; Cl = \dfrac{0.815}{0.815} = 1, \; O = \dfrac{2.45}{0.815} = 3$$

The simplest formula of the compound is, therefore, $KClO_3$.

Example 3
Ethane is 80.0% carbon and 20.0% hydrogen. Its molecular mass is 30.0 u. What is its (a) simplest formula (b) molecular formula?

Solution
In 100 g of ethane there are 80.0 g of carbon and 20.0 g of hydrogen.

The number of moles of C $= \dfrac{80.0 \text{ g}}{12.0 \text{ g/mol}} = 6.66$ mol

The number of moles of H $= \dfrac{20.0 \text{ g}}{1.00 \text{ g/mol}} = 20.0$ mol

The molar ratio of C to H is $6.66 : 20.0$ or $1 : 3$. Therefore the simplest formula is CH_3.
This has a formula mass of 15.0 u.
The molecular mass of the ethane is 30.0 u; therefore, the molecular formula is $(CH_3)_2$ or C_2H_6.

Example 4
A certain organic compound contains 26.7% carbon, 2.24% hydrogen and 71.1% oxygen. Its molecular mass is 90.0 u. What is its molecular formula?

Solution
In 100 g of the compound there are 26.7 g of carbon, 2.24 g of hydrogen and 71.1 g of oxygen. The number of moles of each element in this sample are:

Carbon, $\dfrac{26.7 \text{ g}}{12.0 \text{ g/mol}} = 2.24$ mol

Hydrogen, $\dfrac{2.24 \text{ g}}{1.00 \text{ g/mol}} = 2.24$ mol

Oxygen, $\dfrac{71.1 \text{ g}}{16.0 \text{ g/mol}} = 4.45$ mol

Therefore the atomic ratio of C to H to O is $2.24 : 2.24 : 4.45$. This is closest to $1 : 1 : 2$.
Therefore the simplest formula is CHO_2.
Since CHO_2 has a formula mass of $12 + 1 + 32 = 45$ u and the organic compound one of 90.0 u, the molecular formula is twice CHO_2 or $C_2H_2O_4$.

14:6   What the Chemical Formula Expresses

A great deal of information obtained by careful experimentation is represented by the chemical formula of a compound. The basic things expressed by the formula are:

The atomic composition of molecules or ions
The elements whose symbols appear in the for-

mula are the only ones present in the compound. Their atoms have combined in the ratio shown in the formula.

The composition by mass of the compound
The formula reports the composition of the compound in terms of the number of atoms. But atoms have mass. Hence it is possible to calculate the composition by mass of the compound.

The molecular mass and the formula mass
From the formula and the atomic mass, the molecular mass for molecular compounds and the formula mass for ionic compounds can be calculated. The term *formula mass* is used when referring to ionic substances. Such compounds do not contain molecules. The mole of sodium chloride contains one mole of sodium ions and one mole of chloride ions. Its formula mass is the sum of Na, 23.0 u, and Cl, 35.5 u. for a total of 58.5 u.

The information to calculate gas volumes and masses
In the case of gases, the molar mass fills the molar volume at STP. The molecular formula of a gas enables us to calculate what volume a certain mass of gas will occupy, or alternatively, how much a certain volume of a given gas will weigh.

14:7   Calculations Based on Formulas

Example 1
The molecular formula of butane is C_4H_{10}. What is its molecular mass?

Solution
The molecule is composed of four atoms of carbon and ten of hydrogen. Their mass is $(4 \times 12.0) + (10 \times 1.0) = 58.0$ u. Therefore the molecular mass of butane is 58.0 u.

Example 2
What is the percentage composition of butane?

Solution
The mass of carbon is 4×12.0 or 48.0 u out of 58.0. The mass of hydrogen is 10×1.00, or 10.0 u out of 58.0. The percentages of carbon and hydrogen are:

$$\text{Carbon,} \frac{48.0 \text{ u}}{58.0 \text{ u}} \times 100 = 82.8\%$$

$$\text{Hydrogen,} \frac{10.0 \text{ u}}{58.0 \text{ u}} \times 100 = 17.2\%$$

Example 3
What volume does 10.0 g of butane occupy at STP?

Solution
Because butane is a gas, the mole (58.0 g) occupies the molar volume at STP. The reasoning now is as follows:

$$58.0 \text{ g occupy } 22.4 \text{ L}$$

$$10.0 \text{ g occupy} \frac{22.4 \text{ L}}{58.0 \text{ g}} \times 10 \text{ g} = 3.94 \text{ L}$$

Alternative Solution
Since the volume is proportional to the mass, we may find the new volume x by means of the ratio:

$$\frac{x \text{ L}}{22.4 \text{ L}} = \frac{10.0 \text{ g}}{58.0 \text{ g}}$$

$$\text{and } x = \frac{10.0 \text{ g}}{58.0 \text{ g}} \times 22.4 \text{ L}$$

$$= 3.94 \text{ L}$$

Example 4
What is the density of butane at STP?

Solution
22.4 L of butane weigh 58.0 g. Therefore, 1 L of butane

weighs $\frac{58.0 \text{ g}}{22.4 \text{ L}}$ or 2.58 g at STP (or 2580 kg/m³).

Example 5
What is the formula mass of Na_2SO_4?

Solution
The formula mass, the sum of the mass of the atoms in the formula, would be

$$(2 \times Na) + (1 \times S) + (4 \times O)$$
or $(2 \times 23.0 \text{ u}) + (1 \times 32.2 \text{ u}) + (4 \times 16.0 \text{ u})$

which adds up to 142.2 u.

14:8   Structural Formulas

While the molecular formula gives much information about the composition of a compound, it does not show how the atoms are linked to each other. The structural formula does this. The difference between a molecular formula and a structural formula is important. To draw an analogy, it is not enough to describe a car by reporting how much steel, glass, rubber, and plastic it contains; we want to know how these are arranged in the finished car. In other words, we are interested in the "structure" of the car. Similarly, we are interested in knowing the structure of molecules, and structural formulas have been devised to attempt to show how the atoms are linked together to form the molecule.

The structural formulas for some simple compounds are shown in the diagram below. Structural formulas, like molecular formulas, are based on experimental evidence.

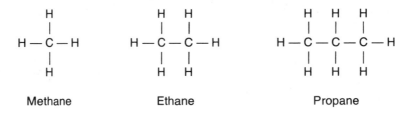

Methane   Ethane   Propane

QUESTIONS

For atomic mass refer to the table inside the front cover of the book.

1. List three things which a chemical symbol represents.

2. What is the difference between the simplest formula and the molecular formula of a substance?

3. Report the composition of benzene, C_6H_6, as
   (i)   a ratio of the mass of the elements involved;
   (ii) a percentage composition;
   (iii) a ratio of atoms present in the molecule.

4. Is NaCl a molecular formula? Give reasons for your answer.

5. What information is required to calculate the simplest formula of a compound?

6. Find the simplest formula of a salt whose composition is 85% silver and 15% fluorine.

7. Calculate the simplest formula of a salt with composition 27.4% sodium, 1.2% hydrogen, 14.2% carbon, and 57.2% oxygen.

8. What is the simplest formula of a compound composed of 32.4% sodium, 22.5% sulfur, and 45.1% oxygen?

9. Calculate the simplest formulas of the compounds whose percentage compositions are listed below:
   (i) 29.5% calcium, 23.5% sulfur, 47.0% oxygen;
   (ii) 26.5% potassium, 35.4% chromium, 38.1% oxygen.

10. What minimum information is required to calculate the molecular formula of a compound?

11. The simplest formula of a compound is CH_2O, and its molecular mass is 180 u. Find its molecular formula.

12. (i) Calculate the simplest formula of a compound consisting of 47.48% sulfur and 52.52% chlorine.
    (ii) If the molecular mass of this compound is 135 u, find its molecular formula.

13. Calculate the molecular formula of a compound that is composed of 27% carbon and 73% oxygen with molecular mass 44 u.

14. A compound contains 92.25% carbon and 7.75% hydrogen. What is its molecular formula, if 1.0 L of its vapour at STP has a mass of 3.48 g?

15. The composition of a compound is 2% hydrogen, 33% sulfur, and 65% oxygen; its molecular mass is 98 u. Find its molecular formula.

16. Calculate the molecular mass or the formula mass of the following:
    (i) H_2SO_4 (ii) H_3PO_4 (iii) NaOH   (iv) $Ca(OH)_2$ (v) $Al(OH)_3$
    (vi) $Ca_3(PO_4)_2$ (vii) $C_6H_{12}O_6$ (viii) $C_{12}H_{22}O_{11}$ (ix) O_3 (x) $MgSO_4.7 H_2O$

17. How many atoms are there in each of the formulas represented in question 16?

18. Find the percentage composition of calcium carbonate, $CaCO_3$.

19. Find the percentage composition of sodium sulfate, Na_2SO_4.

20. What is the percentage of chromium in chrome alum, $KCr(SO_4)_2.12H_2O$?

21. What is the percentage of water in gypsum, $CaSO_4.2H_2O$?

22. Determine the maximum mass of mercury that could be obtained from 10.0 kg of cinnabar, assuming that it is 100% pure HgS.

23. Find the volume occupied by 6.0 g of hydrogen at STP.

24. Find the volume occupied by 6.0 g of carbon dioxide, CO_2, at STP.

25. At STP, 2.20 g of a gaseous compound occupies 1 100 mL. Find its molar mass.

26. At STP, 2.8 L of sulfur dioxide weigh 8.0 g. Find the molar mass of sulfur dioxide.

27. Find the mass of 6.0 L of hydrogen measured at STP.

28. What is the mass of 10.0 L of carbon dioxide measured at STP?

29. How much aluminum could be obtained from 100 kg of bauxite that contains 80% of pure alumina, Al_2O_3?

30. Find the mass of 3×10^{23} molecules of chlorine.

31. Find the mass of 1.5 mol of nitrogen gas.

32. The density of nitric oxide, is 1.34 g/L at STP. Find its molecular mass. Given that the ratio of nitrogen to oxygen atoms in nitric oxide is 1:1, what is its molecular formula?

33. Find the density of sulfur dioxide, SO_2, at STP.

CHAPTER

15

$$2Na_{(s)} + Cl_{2(g)} \rightarrow 2NaCl_{(s)}$$

ELEMENTS, COMPOUNDS AND CHEMICAL EQUATIONS

The chemist represents elements and compounds by means of symbols and formulas. Chemical reactions are also summarized in expressions called chemical equations. In this chapter, we will investigate methods for writing correct formulas easily and for setting up chemical equations. We will also explore the relationships among masses and volumes of reactants and products shown in chemical equations.

15:1 Common Ions and Their Charges

It would be a difficult task to memorize the formulas of thousands of compounds. However, the study of a number of experimentally determined formulas reveals that elements have a definite combining power. For example, sodium, magnesium, aluminum, and tin combine with chlorine forming the compounds:

| NaCl | MgCl$_2$ | AlCl$_3$ | SnCl$_4$ |
| sodium chloride | magnesium chloride | aluminum chloride | tin (IV) chloride |

Chemistry has an alphabet and a language consisting of symbols for the elements, formulas for the compounds, and equations for the chemical reactions.

Obviously the combining capacities of these metallic elements are different. The sodium atom combines with only one chlorine atom, while the magnesium atom can combine with two. Aluminum and tin can combine with three and four atoms of chlorine respectively.

This combining ability that atoms have is associated closely with their electronic structures. When atoms combine, they may gain, lose, or share electrons. Since electrons are negatively charged, their gain or loss results in the electrical charges associated with ions.

We have already mentioned (Chapter 8) that the alkali metals with one electron in their outer shell readily form stable ions with a charge of 1 + : Li$^+$, Na$^+$, K$^+$, Rb$^+$, Cs$^+$, and Fr$^+$. The halogens on the other hand readily gain an electron, forming stable ions with a charge of 1 − : F$^-$, Cl$^-$, Br$^-$, I$^-$, and At$^-$.

We can refer to the periodic table to generalize our ideas on the formation of ions. The elements of groups I, II, and III have 1, 2, and 3 electrons respectively in the outer shell of their atoms. If we assume that these atoms may lose their electrons, the resulting ions will have charges of $1+$, $2+$, and $3+$, (Fig. 15.1). The atoms of the non-metallic elements of groups V, VI, and VII may acquire 3, 2, and 1 electrons respectively. The ions formed will then have charges of $3-$, $2-$, and $1-$. When the transition metals lose electrons they commonly form ions with a charge of $2+$ or $3+$. It is uncommon for atoms to gain or lose larger numbers of electrons.

A number of elements form more than one type of ion depending on what reactions take place. For example, copper, mercury, chromium, and iron may form the following ions: Cu^+, Cu^{2+} Hg^{2+}, Hg_2^{2+}, Cr^{2+}, Cr^{3+}, Fe^{2+}, and Fe^{3+}.

In many compounds, there are groups of atoms bonded together, carrying an electric charge. The group behaves as if it were a single atom in chemical reactions. Examples of such groups, called *polyatomic ions* or *radicals*, are: the ammonium ion, NH_4^+; the hydroxide ion, OH^-; the nitrate ion, NO_3^-; the carbonate ion, CO_3^{2-}; the sulfate ion, SO_4^{2-}. A list of common ions and their charges is shown in Table 15.1.

15:2 Valence

Valence was once regarded as the study of how atoms combine. With rapid growth of our knowledge of atomic structure, the ideas of valence have also changed rapidly. So extensive is the modern study of atomic bonding, that it is best to use more meaningful words than valence to describe particular aspects of bonding. Three ideas stand out in a definition of valence:

(a) The capacity of an atom to combine with other atoms.
(b) The electrical charges which some atoms may obtain.
(c) The bond between atoms.

Valence as Combining Capacity
As was seen in section 15.1, elements have different combining capacities. This must relate to the combining ability of atoms. What is true in the formation of chlorides, is also evident when atoms of various elements combine with different num-

PERIODIC TABLE OF THE ELEMENTS SHOWING GROUP NUMBER AND CHARGE

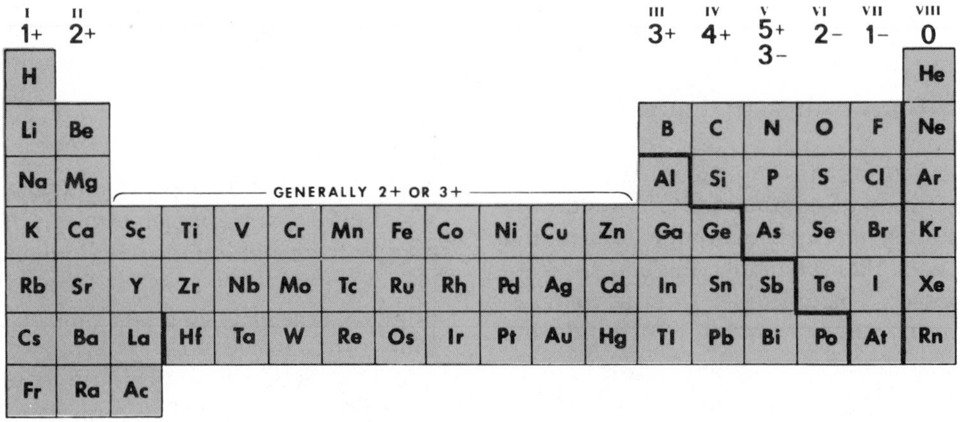

Fig. 15.1:
Group number vs. ionic charge

TABLE 15.1

Common Ions and Their Charges

Ammonium	NH_4^+	Barium	Ba^{2+}	Aluminum	Al^{3+}
Copper (I)*	Cu^+	Calcium	Ca^{2+}	Antimony	Sb^{3+}
Hydrogen, hydronium	H^+, H_3O^+	Chromium (II)	Cr^{2+}	Bismuth	Bi^{3+}
Lithium	Li^+	Copper (II)	Cu^{2+}	Chromium (III)	Cr^{3+}
Mercury (I)**	Hg_2^{2+}	Iron (II)	Fe^{2+}	Iron (III)	Fe^{3+}
		Lead	Pb^{2+}		
		Magnesium	Mg^{2+}		
Potassium	K^+	Mercury (II)	Hg^{2+}		
Silver	Ag^+	Zinc	Zn^{2+}		
Sodium	Na^+				
Acetate	CH_3COO^-	Carbonate	CO_3^{2-}	Nitride	N^{3-}
Bromide	Br^-	Chromate	CrO_4^{2-}	Phosphate	PO_4^{3-}
Chlorate	ClO_3^-	Dichromate	$Cr_2O_7^{2-}$		
Chloride	Cl^-	Oxide	O^{2-}		
Chlorite	ClO_2^-	Sulfate	SO_4^{2-}		
Fluoride	F^-	Sulfide	S^{2-}		
Hydrogen carbonate		Sulfite	SO_3^{2-}		
or bicarbonate	HCO_3^-				
Hydrogen sulfate					
or bisulfate	HSO_4^-				
Hydrogen sulfite					
or bisulfite	HSO_3^-				
Hydroxide	OH^-				
Hypochlorite	ClO^-				
Iodide	I^-				
Nitrate	NO_3^-				
Nitrite	NO_2^-				
Perchlorate	ClO_4^-				
Permanganate	MnO_4^-				

* When an element has ions with more than one possible charge, the ion is named with a Roman numeral indicating the charge. For example, copper (I) is the Cu^{1+} ion.

** The mercury (I) ion is unique in that it always bonds to a second mercury (I) ion as follows: $Hg^{1+} - Hg^{1+}$ forming the Hg_2^{2+} ion.

bers of hydrogen atoms. This may be seen from the formulas of the following compounds:

HCl	H_2O	NH_3	CH_4
Hydrogen Chloride	Water	Ammonia	Methane

In the molecule of hydrogen chloride, an atom of chlorine is combined with only one atom of hydrogen. In the other molecules shown, the atoms of oxygen, nitrogen, and carbon are combined with two, three, and four hydrogen atoms, respectively.

So it is apparent that the combining abilities of chlorine, oxygen, nitrogen, and carbon differ.

From this point of view, the "valence" of an element is the number of hydrogen or chlorine atoms with which one atom of that element will combine. This definition stresses valence as combining capacity.

Valence as electrical charge

This is due to the gain or loss of electrons. Since electrons are negatively charged, their gain or loss results in the electrical charges that are commonly associated with valence. *Ionic charge* is a better term than valence to describe this electrical property of ions.

Valence as a bond

Atoms may be bonded together by sharing electrons. The shared electrons are referred to as a "*chemical bond*," and this form of bonding is called *covalence*. Covalent bonds between atoms are oriented in certain directions. Therefore, molecules formed by atoms united through covalent bonds have definite shape, as discussed in Chapter 19.

In this book the terms combining capacity, ionic charge, and chemical bonding will be used, rather than the vague term "valence."

15.3   Writing Formulas of Compounds

Formulas for many compounds can be correctly written using our knowledge of the charges of the ions listed in Table 15.1. When a positive metallic ion is combined with a negative non-metallic ion, the total positive charges must equal the total negative charges, so that the algebraic sum of the charges in the compound is zero. It is customary to place the symbol of the metallic element first when writing the formula. A few examples will illustrate these practical rules.

The formula for sodium chloride is NaCl; the single positive charge of the sodium ion just balances the single negative charge of the chloride ion. However, two chloride ions are needed to equal the charge of a calcium ion; therefore, the formula for calcium chloride is $CaCl_2$. Aluminum sulfate is composed of aluminum ions, Al^{3+}, and sulfate ions, SO_4^{2-}. The total positive charges of two aluminum ions will be balanced by the total negative charges of three sulfate ions: $Al_2(SO_4)_3$. Notice that when a polyatomic ion or radical is taken more than once, it is enclosed in parentheses and the proper subscript is placed just outside to the right. Since iron may form two different ions, Fe^{2+} and Fe^{3+}, two different compounds will result when chlorine reacts with iron: iron (II) chloride, $FeCl_2$, and iron (III) chloride, $FeCl_3$.

The above rules permit us to write the formulas of compounds by inspection. Remember that formulas must be checked by experiment. What is so gratifying about the rules is that the formulas they predict always check with experimental results.

15.4   Naming Compounds

Compounds containing two elements are called binary and those with three elements are ternary.

Binary Salts

Binary salts consist of a metallic and a non-metallic element combined together. The name of a binary salt is made up of the name of the metal followed by the name of the non-metal whose ending is changed into -ide.

> NaF, sodium fluoride
> $ZnCl_2$, zinc chloride
> PbS, lead sulfide
> Mg_3N_2, magnesium nitride

Oxides

Oxides are binary compounds containing the element oxygen. They are named in a similar fashion to binary salts.

BaO, barium oxide
CO, carbon monoxide
CO_2, carbon dioxide
FeO, iron (II) oxide (ferrous oxide)
Fe_2O_3, iron (III) oxide (ferric oxide)
SO_2, sulfur dioxide

Notice that prefixes are sometimes used to indicate the number of atoms present. The prefixes mono-, di-, tri-, tetra-, penta-, etc., indicate that 1, 2, 3, 4, 5, etc. atoms of a given element are present. When metallic elements exhibit different ionic charges, these are indicated by a Roman numeral placed in brackets after the name of the metal. For example, iron in FeO and Fe_2O_3 exhibits a charge of 2+ and 3+ respectively. The names of these two oxides are therefore iron (II) oxide and iron (III) oxide. Older names for these are still used: ferrous oxide and ferric oxide. The suffixes -ous and -ic refer to the lower and higher charges respectively.

Peroxides
Some oxides possess one more oxygen atom than ordinary oxides. The prefix per- is used to designate such substances.

H_2O_2, hydrogen peroxide
Na_2O_2, sodium peroxide
BaO_2, barium peroxide
K_2O_2, potassium peroxide

Binary Acids
All binary acids consist of hydrogen along with another element. Therefore, the name of a binary acid consists of the prefix *hydro-* for the hydrogen, a short form of the name of the element with which the hydrogen is combined in the acid, and the ending -ic. When these compounds are in the gaseous state rather than in solutions their names end with -ide.

gaseous compounds
HF, hydrogen fluoride
HCl, hydrogen chloride
HBr, hydrogen bromide
HI, hydrogen iodide
H_2S, hydrogen sulfide

acid solutions
HF, hydrofluoric acid
HCl, hydrochloric acid
HBr, hydrobromic acid
HI, hydriodic acid
H_2S, hydrosulfuric acid

Ternary Acids
These compounds contain hydrogen, oxygen, and a third element. They are always named after this third element. The common ternary acids end with -ic. Sometimes other acids exist that have one more oxygen atom than the -ic acid; the prefix per- is then added. Other acids still, may have one or two atoms of oxygen less than the common -ic acid. The -ic ending is then changed into -ous in one case and both the suffix -ous and the prefix hypo- are used in the other case.

HNO_3 nitric acid
$HClO_3$, chloric acid
H_2SO_4, sulfuric acid
H_3PO_4, phosphoric acid
H_2CO_3, carbonic acid
$HClO_4$, perchloric acid
$HClO_3$, chloric acid
$HClO_2$, chlorous acid
HClO, hypochlorous acid

Ternary Salts
A salt is the product formed when a metallic element replaces the hydrogen of an acid. The names of the ternary salts are derived from the names of the corresponding acids. An -ic acid gives an -ate salt. An -ous acid gives an -ite salt, etc. The following examples illustrate these rules:

$NaNO_3$, sodium nitrate
$NaClO_3$, sodium chlorate
Na_2SO_4, sodium sulfate

Na_2CO_3, sodium carbonate
Na_3PO_4, sodium phosphate
$NaClO$,   sodium hypochlorite
$NaClO_2$, sodium chlorite
$NaClO_3$, sodium chlorate
$NaClO_4$, sodium perchlorate

Bases
Common bases contain the hydroxide (OH^-) ion. They are all called hydroxides:

$NaOH$, sodium hydroxide
NH_4OH, ammonium hydroxide
$Ca(OH)_2$, calcium hydroxide
$Al(OH)_3$, aluminum hydroxide

Acid Salts
An acid salt is formed when only part of the replaceable hydrogen of an acid is displaced by a metal. Here are a few examples of such salts and their names:

$NaHSO_4$, sodium hydrogen sulfate or sodium bisulfate
$KHCO_3$, potassium hydrogen carbonate or potassium bicarbonate

15:5   Chemical Equations

Chemical equations are so important in the study of chemistry that they had to be introduced near the very beginning of the book (Chapter 3) and have had to be used in nearly every chapter since. We are now in a position to appreciate their meaning and use more thoroughly.

In the chemical equation, the left-hand side shows the substances that react. These are termed the *reactants*. The right-hand side shows the new substances resulting from the change, and these are termed the *products*.

Perhaps you have noticed the following points about the chemical equations used thus far:

1. A chemical equation represents a reaction that really takes place. The mere writing of symbols and formulas does not make up a chemical equation unless they report an actual chemical reaction.

2. Every chemical equation is "balanced," which means that there are the same number of atoms of each element on both sides of the equation. This is done because every chemical reaction complies with the Law of Conservation of Mass.

15:6   Writing and Balancing Chemical Equations

A chemical equation is more than a mathematical exercise. Make it a policy to understand the chemical reaction when you write its equation. To write and balance a chemical equation correctly, we must:

a. Know what substances react and are produced during the reaction;

b. Know the correct formulas of all the substances involved;

c. Account for every atom before and after the reaction.

To illustrate the method for writing and balancing equations, let us consider a few common reactions.

Example 1
The reaction between magnesium and oxygen may be reported by the word or name equation:

Magnesium + oxygen → Magnesium oxide
(Rule *a*)

If we use the chemical formula for each substance instead of the name, we obtain the beginnings of a chemical equation:

$Mg + O_2 \rightarrow MgO$ (Rule *b*)

We thus observe the second rule about chemical equations. We must use formulas which represent the substances correctly. Thus Mg, the symbol for magnesium, stands for the atom of that metallic element. This is justified because metals consist of atoms rather than molecules. O_2 is the true formula for oxygen, an element which occurs as molecules with two atoms. MgO is the simplest formula for magnesium oxide. This is an example of a compound where we can report only that the ratio of magnesium atoms to oxygen atoms is 1:1. Because magnesium oxide does not form molecules, a true molecular formula is not possible.

In a chemical reaction there is no loss or gain in the total number of atoms involved (Rule c). Since each molecule of oxygen is known to contain two atoms, it follows that for every molecule of O_2 used up, two "molecules" of MgO will be formed. For these, two atoms of Mg will be required. The balanced chemical equation is thus:

$$2Mg + O_2 \rightarrow 2MgO$$

The numbers that are placed before the formulas in the balanced equations are called the coefficients of the equation. Indeed this equation is valid because it is *both* balanced and correct. The formulas represent the composition of the substances.

To write $Mg + O \rightarrow MgO$ is unacceptable despite the fact that the equation is balanced. Oxygen occurs as O_2 not as O.

Similarly $Mg + O_2 \rightarrow MgO_2$ is no better. The formula for magnesium oxide is MgO, not MgO_2.

Example 2

It can easily be established experimentally that zinc reacts with hydrochloric acid to produce zinc chloride and hydrogen gas. Experiments have also proved that the formula for hydrochloric acid is HCl and for zinc chloride, $ZnCl_2$. Of course, we would arrive at the same formulas by applying the generalizations made in the earlier sections of this chapter concerning the ions and their charges. We know that hydrogen gas exists as diatomic mole-

cules. With this information, we are ready to set up the following skeleton equation:

$$Zn_{(s)} + HCl_{(aq)} \rightarrow ZnCl_{2(aq)} + H_{2(g)} \uparrow$$
$$\text{(not balanced)}$$

This skeleton equation may be read: solid zinc reacts with hydrochloric acid to produce zinc chloride that remains in solution and hydrogen that escapes as a gas. This skeleton equation, however, does not satisfy the Law of Conservation of Mass. Two atoms of chlorine and two atoms of hydrogen are shown on the right-hand side while only one atom of each of these elements is represented on the left-hand side. If we could tamper with the formulas for zinc chloride and hydrogen gas, we might write ZnCl, and H for these substances. This is not permissible, however, because it would contradict experimental facts. We can simply "balance" the equation by doubling the number of molecules of HCl, thus doubling the number of hydrogen and chlorine atoms represented on the left-hand side:

$$Zn_{(s)} + 2HCl_{(aq)} \rightarrow ZnCl_{2\ (aq)} + H_{2(g)} \uparrow$$

We see that an equation can be balanced by adjusting the coefficients placed in front of the formulas of the substances involved in order to obtain the same number of atoms of each element on each side of the equation.

Example 3

When potassium chlorate is strongly heated it is decomposed into potassium chloride and oxygen gas. The skeleton equation with formulas only representing this reaction is:

$$KClO_{3\ (s)} \rightarrow KCl_{(s)} + O_{2\ (g)} \uparrow$$
$$\text{(not balanced)}$$

In the equation, three atoms of oxygen are present in $KClO_3$, and two atoms of oxygen are present in O_2. The lowest common multiple of three and two is six. Three divides into six twice, and two divides into six three times. Two becomes the coefficient of $KClO_3$, and three becomes the coefficient of O_2. KCl, according to the same reasoning, receives the same coefficient as $KClO_3$. Thus the equation is written:

$$2KClO_3{}_{(s)} \rightarrow 2KCl{}_{(s)} + 3O_2{}_{(g)} \uparrow$$

In many equations, there are certain atoms or ions which are more significant than the rest. These are helpful in balancing the equation, since the problem becomes one of finding the lowest common multiple for those on both sides of the equation. This point was illustrated with oxygen in the above equation.

Example 4
The following equation is also instructive:

$$NaOH + H_2SO_4 \rightarrow Na_2SO_4 + 2H_2O$$
(not balanced)

This illustrates the difficulty of attempting to balance an equation without knowing the chemistry that it represents. Without such knowledge, the equation looks strange, and balancing it is more or less pointless. If, however, we recognize that this reaction is the neutralization of a base, NaOH, by an acid, H_2SO_4, then we readily see that the OH^- of the base and the H^+ of the acid are the "significant reactants."

Since NaOH provides one OH^-, and H_2SO_4 provides two H^+, we obtain the lowest common denominator of one and two, namely two. Thus the coefficient of NaOH is two, and that of H_2SO_4 is one, and the equation is balanced accordingly:

$$2NaOH{}_{(aq)} + H_2SO_4{}_{(aq)} \rightarrow Na_2SO_4{}_{(aq)} + 2H_2O{}_{(l)}$$

15:7   The Quantitative Meaning of Equations

In addition to reporting a chemical change, the chemical equation states what masses and volumes of substances react and how much product

is formed. The importance of such relationships becomes apparent when we realize that they enable the chemist to calculate the actual amounts of reactants required to produce a desired amount of a product.

Let us consider an example to see how many facts are implied in a chemical equation. The products of combustion when methane gas burns are carbon dioxide and water:

$$CH_4{}_{(g)} + 2O_2{}_{(g)} \rightarrow CO_2{}_{(g)} + 2H_2O{}_{(l)}$$

Besides stating qualitatively that methane combines with oxygen producing carbon dioxide and water, this equation may be interpreted quantitatively as follows:

a. 1 molecule of methane combines with 2 molecules of oxygen forming 1 molecule of carbon dioxide and 2 molecules of water;

b. 1 mol of methane combines with 2 mol of oxygen forming 1 mol of carbon dioxide and 2 mol of water;

c. 16 g of methane combine with 64 g of oxygen forming 44 g of carbon dioxide and 36 g of water;

d. 22.4 L (STP) of methane combine with 44.8 L (STP) of oxygen forming 22.4 L (STP) of carbon dioxide and 36 g of water.

Note that water cannot be reported as a gaseous volume here because it would be either a liquid or a solid (ice) at STP.

These facts are summarized on page 129.

15:8   Calculations Based on Equations

The quantities of reactants and products of a chemical reaction can easily be found from the equation. Problems about such quantities can easily be solved if a few simple steps are observed.

1. Make sure that all formulas in the equation are correct and that the equation is balanced.

	$CH_{4(g)}$	+	$2O_{2(g)}$	→	$CO_{2(g)}$	+	$2H_2O_{(l)}$
(a)	1 molecule (16 u)	+	2 molecules (64 u)	→	1 molecule (44 u)	+	2 molecules (36 u)
(b)	1 mol (6×10^{23} molecules)	+	2 mol (12×10^{23} molecules)	→	1 mol (6×10^{23} molecules)	+	2 mol (12×10^{23} molecules)
(c)	16 g	+	64 g	→	44 g	+	36 g
(d)	22.4 L (STP)	+	44.8 L (STP)	→	22.4 L (STP)	+	36 g

2. Think and reason through what is required and what is given in the problem. These quantities must be in the same ratio as that represented by the equation.

3. From the equation, note how many moles of each reactant and product are involved. From this information, the mass of reactants and products may be found.

4. The ratio and proportion of the various quantities used will be seen more easily if these are written directly below and above the equation.

15:9 Mass Relationships in Chemical Reactions

Example
What mass of oxygen is needed for the complete combustion of 25.0 g of methane?

Solution
We will solve the problem by following the steps mentioned in the previous paragraph.

Step 2:   25.0 g   x g
Step 1: $CH_4 + 2O_2 \rightarrow CO_2 + 2H_2O$
Step 3:   16.0 g   64.0 g

From the equation, we know that 16.0 g of methane requires 64.0 g of oxygen for complete combustion. Then,

25.0 g of methane will require $\dfrac{25.0}{16.0}$ times as much oxygen. Therefore,

Step 4:   Mass of oxygen $= \dfrac{25.0 \text{ g}}{16.0 \text{ g}} \times 64.0 \text{ g} = 100.0 \text{ g}$

Alternate Solution

In 25.0 g of methane there are $\dfrac{25.0 \text{ g}}{16.0 \text{ g/mol}} = 1.56$ mol of the gas. We can then write:

Step 2:   1.56 mol   x mol
Step 1: CH_4 + $2O_2$ → $CO_2 + 2H_2O$
Step 3:   1 mol   2 mol

Since 1 mol of methane requires 2 mol of oxygen, then 1.56 mol of methane will require 3.12 mol of oxygen. Because 1 mol of oxygen weighs 32.0 g, the mass of oxygen needed in grams is:

Step 4: Mass of oxygen = 32.0 g/mol × 3.12 mol = 99.8 g

15:10 Mass-Volume Relationships in Chemical Reactions

In many reactions the reactants and/or the products are in the gaseous state. Remember that in such cases, the formula of a gaseous compound shown in an equation represents not only the molar mass of the substance but also the molar volume, i.e. 22.4 L at STP occupied by one mole of the gas. This fact enables us to solve problems involving volumes of gases in chemical reactions.

Example
What volume of oxygen measured at 27°C and

80 kPa is required for the complete combustion of 25.0 g of methane?

Solution

Since we are interested in a *volume* of oxygen we will let the formula for oxygen in the equation stand for a volume and we will calculate the volume needed at STP.

Step 2:   25.0 g   x L (STP)
Step 1: CH_4 + $2O_2$ → CO_2 + $2H_2O$
Step 3:   16.0 g   2 × 22.4 L (STP)

We see that 44.8 L of oxygen measured at STP are needed for the combustion of 16.0 g of methane. For the combustion of 25.0 g of methane, $\frac{25.0}{16.0}$ times as much oxygen will be needed. The volume of oxygen obtained at STP can then be converted, by applying the gas laws, into the volume it would occupy at 27°C and 80.0 kPa.

Volume of oxygen at STP = $\frac{25.0 \text{ g}}{16.0 \text{ g}}$ × 44.8 L = 70.0 L

Volume at 27°C and 80.0 kPa would be

$$V_2 = \frac{V_1 p_1 T_2}{p_2 T_1}$$

$$= \frac{70.0 \text{ L} \times 101.3 \text{ kPa} \times 300 \text{ K}}{80.0 \text{ kPa} \times 273 \text{ K}}$$

$$= 97.4 \text{ L}$$

15:11   Volume—Volume Relationships in Chemical Reactions

When gaseous volumes only are involved, the problems are simplified by the fact that single moles of all gases at the same conditions of temperature and pressure occupy the same volume.

Example

What volume of carbon dioxide measured at STP will be formed if 50.0 L of methane, measured at STP, are completely burned?

Solution

The equation shows that 1 mol of methane produces 1 mol of carbon dioxide. The volume of carbon dioxide formed is always equal to the volume of methane consumed when both gases are measured under the same conditions.

Step 2:   50.0 L   x L
Step 1: CH_4 + $2O_2$ → CO_2 + $2H_2O$
Step 3:   22.4 L   22.4 L
          (1 vol)   (1 vol)

Step 4:   Volume of carbon dioxide at STP =

$\frac{50.0 \text{ L}}{22.4 \text{ L}}$ × 22.4 L = 50.0 L

QUESTIONS

1. What is the meaning of the terms *copper (I)* and *copper (II)*?

2. What "rule" must be observed when a formula for a compound made of a metallic ion and a non-metallic ion is written?

3. What is meant by the term *polyatomic ion*? Give a few examples of such ions.

4. Write the formula and the name for the compound formed when each of the following pairs of ions combine:

    (i) K^+ and CO_3^{2-} (iii) Al^{3+} and O^{2-}
    (ii) Ca^{2+} and NO_3^- (iv) Mg^{2+} and SO_4^{2-}

(v)	K^+	and	MnO_4^-		(viii)	Ba^{2+}	and	OH^-
(vi)	Cu^{2+}	and	Cl^-		(ix)	Zn^{2+}	and	PO_4^{3-}
(vii)	NH_4^+	and	SO_3^{2-}		(x)	Ag^+	and	Cl^-

5. Name the following compounds:

   (i) $MgBr_2$ (vi) $KClO$ (xi) $KClO_3$

   (ii) H_2SO_4 (vii) KOH (xii) $NaHCO_3$

   (iii) H_2SO_3 (viii) HCl (xiii) HgO

   (iv) $Al(NO_3)_3$ (ix) Na_2S (xiv) $MgSO_3$

   (v) K_2O_2 (x) Na_2SO_4 (xv) CO

6. Give the formulas for the following:

   (i)   magnesium oxide   (vi)   carbonic acid

   (ii) sulfur trioxide   (vii) calcium hydroxide

   (iii) nitric acid   (viii) hydrogen iodide

   (iv) zinc sulfate   (ix)   iron (II) sulfide

   (v)   sodium hydroxide   (x)   potassium hydrogen sulfate

7. Distinguish between *reactants* and *products*.

8. What do upward and downward-pointing arrows used in chemical equations signify?

9. Outline a method of writing and balancing a chemical equation.

10. Balance each of the following equations:

   (i) $Fe + O_2 \rightarrow Fe_2O_3$

   (ii) $AgNO_3 + MgCl_2 \rightarrow AgCl\downarrow + Mg(NO_3)_2$

   (iii) $HgO \rightarrow Hg + O_2\uparrow$

   (iv) $Na + H_2O \rightarrow NaOH + H_2\uparrow$

   (v) $Mg + O_2 \rightarrow MgO$

   (vi) $Zn + HCl \rightarrow ZnCl_2 + H_2\uparrow$

   (vii) $Fe + H_2O \rightarrow Fe_2O_3 + H_2\uparrow$

   (viii) $Na_2SO_4 + BaCl_2 \rightarrow BaSO_4\downarrow + NaCl$

   (ix) $C_{10}H_{16} + Cl_2 \rightarrow HCl\uparrow + C$

   (x) $CaO + H_2O \rightarrow Ca(OH)_2$

11. One volume of hydrogen combines with one volume of fluorine to produce two volumes of hydrogen fluoride.

   (i)   Write the equation for this reaction.

   (ii) How many moles of fluorine are necessary to produce 4 mol of hydrogen fluoride?

   (iii) How many molecules of hydrogen are required in the formation of 4 molecules of hydrogen fluoride?

12. Sodium reacts with chlorine to produce sodium chloride.

   (i)   Write the equation for this reaction.

   (ii) How many moles of sodium chloride will be formed from one mole of sodium?

   (iii) How many grams of sodium chloride will be formed from 23 g of sodium?

13. From the reaction $CH_{4(g)} + 2O_{2(g)} \rightarrow CO_{2(g)} + 2H_2O_{(l)}$, calculate:

   (i)   the number of moles of water produced from 5 mol of methane;

   (ii)   the volume of carbon dioxide at STP produced from 5 mol of methane;

   (iii) the number of grams of oxygen necessary for the combustion of 5 mol of methane.

14. Find the mass of magnesium oxide formed from the complete oxidation of 6.25 g of magnesium according to the equation:

$$2Mg_{(s)} + O_{2(g)} \rightarrow 2MgO_{(s)}$$

15. Zinc reacts with sulfuric acid according to the following equation:

$$Zn_{(s)} + H_2SO_{4(aq)} \rightarrow ZnSO_{4(aq)} + H_2\uparrow_{(g)}$$

What mass of zinc sulfate will be formed when 2 mol of zinc react with excess acid?

16. How many grams of calcium oxide will be produced by heating 75.0 g of calcium carbonate according to the following equation?

$$CaCO_{3(s)} \rightarrow CaO_{(s)} + CO_2\uparrow_{(g)}$$

17. How many moles of hydrogen chloride will be formed when 12 mol of hydrogen combine with excess chlorine?

18. In an electrolysis experiment 9.0 g of water were electrolyzed by a current producing hydrogen and oxygen.
(i) What volume of hydrogen measured at STP was produced?
(ii) What volume would this hydrogen occupy at 27°C and 50.7 kPa?

19. How many moles of carbon dioxide are produced by the complete combustion of 660 g of carbon?

20. Potassium chlorate decomposes into potassium chloride and oxygen when heated: $2KClO_{3(s)} \rightarrow 2KCl_{(s)} + 3O_2 \uparrow_{(g)}$. What volume of oxygen measured at STP can be obtained when 49.0 g of potassium chlorate is strongly heated?

21. Find the mass of sodium carbonate that is required to prepare 50.0 L of carbon dioxide measured at STP. The equation for this reaction is:

$$Na_2CO_{3(s)} + 2 HCl_{(aq)} \rightarrow 2 NaCl_{(aq)} + H_2O_{(l)} + CO_2\uparrow_{(g)}$$

22. What volume of hydrogen will combine with 33.6 L of oxygen in the synthesis of water? What will be the mass of the water formed?

23. The complete combustion of acetylene is represented by the following equation:

$$2C_2H_{2(g)} + 5O_{2(g)} \rightarrow 4CO_{2(g)} + 2H_2O_{(l)}$$

(i) What volume of oxygen is needed for the combustion of 100 L of acetylene, both gases being measured at STP?
(ii) What volume of carbon dioxide measured at 23°C and 98.9 kPa pressure is produced?

CHAPTER

16

WATER AND THE ENVIRONMENT

16:1   The Abundance of Water

Water is one of the most important compounds.

Water is the most widespread and common substance on Earth. It covers three-quarters of the Earth's surface as oceans, lakes, and rivers. Vast quantities are locked as snow and ice in the polar regions and on high mountains. Large quantities of water occur below the ground in liquid form, and are also found combined chemically in rocks.

All the water in the world is interconnected in a great flow through the biosphere. This movement, called the *hydrologic cycle*, is made possible by solar energy that evaporates the water from lakes, seas, rivers and vegetation. The water vapour rises in the atmosphere and condenses to form clouds. Winds drive the clouds over the land, and eventually the water falls back to earth as rain or snow depending on the temperature.

The hydrologic cycle is an important factor in the world's climate. It is also the process by which water purifies itself.

The atmosphere contains large masses of water vapour. It has been estimated that in the summer as much as 18 000 t* of water vapour can cover one square kilometre of the Earth's surface. Water present in the atmosphere condenses and is precipitated in various forms.

*t is the SI symbol for the tonne, equal to 1000 kg.

Plants and all living beings store great quantities of water in their tissues. The human body contains approximately 70% of water by mass. The water content of milk is 87%, that of meat is 74%, and that of tomatoes is more than 90%.

Since water is such an abundant substance, why should we worry about it? Why should we fear water shortages? To begin with, even though water is indeed plentiful, most of it cannot be used directly. Of all the Earth's water resources, about 97% is found as saltwater in the oceans. Another 2% is locked in ice caps. Only a small percentage of the total amount is fresh water.

16:2   The Vital Importance of Water

Water is an essential substance for plant and animal growth. Without water, there would be no vegetation and no life on Earth.

We use water on a large scale for domestic, industrial, and agricultural purposes. It has been

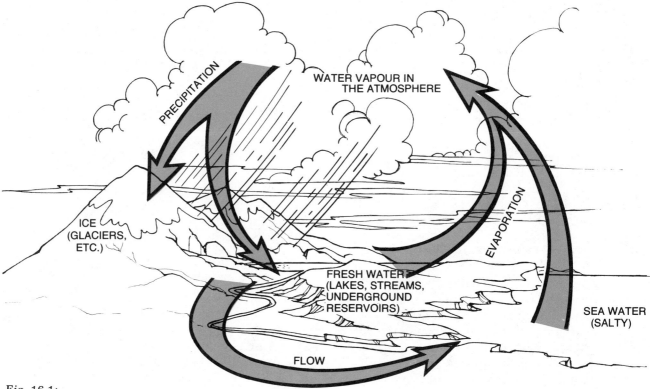

Fig. 16.1:
The Earth's water or hydrologic cycle

Table 16.1

Domestic Daily Water Needs (estimated in litres)

Drinking	2
Flushing toilets	40
Personal washing	10
Waiting for water to run hot	10
Baths	40
Washing dishes	40
House cleaning	10
Washing clothes	38
Cleaning car	10
Total	200

estimated that in North America since 1900 the consumption of water per capita has tripled. The consumption today is about 200 L per person per day for domestic purposes alone. The daily supply of fresh water for each person in the developing countries is as little as 12 L.

The uses of water are multiple and varied. Some of the domestic uses include drinking, washing, cooking, sewage disposal, heating, and air-conditioning. (See Table 16.1.)

Industrial demands for water are much greater than domestic needs. Industrial water consumption represents about 5 000 L per person per day. Industries require water for washing, cooling, condensing, and as a mechanical and chemical agent.

Literally rivers of water are poured down the drains by industries every day. For example, about 200 000 L of water are used to produce one automobile. Such a large amount stems from the fact that the steel that is necessary to build the automobile requires the use of water at almost every stage of steelmaking. Iron ore and coal are mined and cleaned with water. The blast furnace where the iron is extracted from the ore is cooled by water. The steel itself is washed and quenched with water.

Most of the water needed for agricultural purposes is used for irrigation. The water needed for agricultural uses is about 3000 L per person per day.

Other large consumers of water include: hydroelectric power stations, commercial fishing establishments and navigational transportation.

16:3   How Long Will the Supply of Fresh Water Last?

It is often assumed that fresh and pure water is a free resource; we think we have an endless supply of it. Of course, a great deal of the water we use can be recycled. However, in the process, the level of pollution steadily increases to an alarming degree.

As the world population increases at a frightening rate, it is becoming more and more difficult to find adequate fresh water supplies. Already, many heavily populated and industrialized areas are faced with serious water shortages and pollution problems.

Concerted drastic action on the part of governments, industries, and municipalities is needed to conserve the Earth's water resources and restore used waters to a favourable condition of purity.

16:4   Physical Properties of Water

Chemically pure water is colourless, odourless, and tasteless. Any odour or taste that water may have is caused by the presence of dissolved matter. The water in a lake or other large body appears blue because of the reflection of light from the sky.

British Columbia Government Photograph

A non-polluted lake

Although we think of water as a liquid, we should remember that its state depends on its temperature and pressure. Water freezes at 0°C and below this temperature it assumes the solid state of ice or snow. As water cools, its volume contracts and its density increases until it reaches its greatest density (1 g/mL) at 4°C. Below this temperature, water expands a little until it reaches its freezing point. At a pressure of one atmosphere (101.325 kPa), water boils at 100°C.

The expansion of water just before freezing is an unusual property which is of great importance in preventing large bodies of water from freezing completely.

At the lowest depths water has the greatest density and is, consequently, at 4°C above the freezing temperature. Therefore, while the surface of a lake or a river may freeze, the deeper water remains unfrozen, leaving acquatic life undisturbed.

Since ice has a density of 0.9 g/mL, compared with the 1.0 g/mL density of water at 4°C, there must be considerable expansion when water freezes. This expansion is the cause of burst water pipes and automobile radiators in freezing weather, as well as the chipping off of layers of rock and pavement in which water has been trapped.

The ice that forms during the winter freeze-up remains at the surface of a lake or river. As the cold dense water contracts, it breaks away from the frozen ice surface, and thus a layer of air remains between the ice and the water. This supply of air is a further aid to the survival of the fish through the winter.

16:5 Natural Waters

Water is often called a "universal solvent" because it can dissolve many substances. As a result of the solvent action of water, natural waters contain a variety of substances in solution. Atmospheric oxygen and carbon dioxide dissolve to a small extent when in contact with water. These two dissolved gases are essential for aquatic life.

When rain water strikes the ground, it immediately starts to dissolve soluble materials from

A polluted lake

Department of Transport Photo

the soil, rocks, and vegetation. Consequently, lakes and rivers will carry varying amounts of organic compounds, particles, gases, minerals, and ions. Much of this eventually reaches the ocean causing the mineral-salt content to rise to about 3.5%.

Rain water may penetrate deep into the soil and emerge later as a spring or well after having been naturally filtered in the ground. It may be clear and sparkling but it will still contain minerals dissolved from the soil. Most of the time this water is good drinking water. If this water contains a high concentration of calcium and magnesium ions it is known as *hard water*. Hard water is objectionable because it reacts with soap forming an insoluble curd before a lather can be produced. It also leaves a deposit of scale in steam boilers and pipes, thus causing clogging and a waste of fuel.

Natural waters found in populated, heavily industrialized areas contain literally hundreds of impurities in addition to the substances enumerated above. In such cases the municipal water supplies have to be thoroughly treated to turn them into safe tap water.

16:6 Water Pollution

People have always relied on fresh natural water supplies for drinking, washing, growing food, and raising animals. Ancient communities were established near lakes and rivers for this reason. These ancient peoples were familiar with the problems of water pollution. They made sure that waste water was kept separate from clean water. They dumped their sewage downstream from their community and let nature take care of the problem. Indeed, for a long time nature did this quite well by purifying the wastes and diluting them until they were harmless. But with constant growth in world population and industry, one city's waste water becomes the next city's water supply. Natural purification processes are no longer effective and aquatic life is endangered. In addition, the water

Table 16.2

Types of Water Pollutants

1. Microorganisms
2. Organic wastes
3. Plant nutrients
4. Sediments
5. Heavy metals
6. Pesticides
7. Chemicals
8. Radioactive wastes
9. Heat

acquires foul odours and can transmit disease-producing bacteria.

Natural water is never completely pure. As was mentioned above, it always carries small amounts of organic compounds, gases, particles, minerals, and salts. When the nature and concentration levels of these substances are considered to be "safe," then the water can be used for human consumption. In recent decades, thousands of lakes and rivers have become increasingly polluted by human activities.

The sources of water pollution today are numerous and varied. To help in a systematic study of water pollutants, we classify them into types such as those enumerated in Table 16.2 and discussed below.

(a) *Microorganisms*. Raw or inadequately treated sewage discharged into rivers or lakes is the main source of microorganisms capable of transmitting cholera, typhoid, dysentery, and hepatitis.

(b) *Organic Wastes*. Decaying organisms (plants and animals), animal waste, domestic sewage, effluents from slaughterhouses and food processing plants are some of the main sources of organic wastes. The carbon content of organic wastes is slowly oxidixed to carbon dioxide:

$$\underset{\substack{\text{in organic} \\ \text{wastes}}}{C} \quad + \quad \underset{\substack{\text{disolved} \\ \text{in water}}}{O_2} \quad \rightarrow \quad CO_2$$

This reaction leads to a depletion of dissolved oxygen and makes the water unfit for fish and aquatic plants. This slow oxidation of organic wastes is accomplished by *aerobic* bacteria, that is, by bacteria that need oxygen. When the dissolved oxygen level becomes too low, the aerobic bacteria are replaced by *anaerobic* ones that do not require oxygen to live. Anaerobic bacteria transform organic wastes into foul-smelling and poisonous substances such as methane, hydrogen sulfide, and ammonia that make the water putrid.

(c) *Plant Nutrients*. Plants require a number of chemical elements such as nitrogen, phosphorus, and oxygen for their growth. When nitrates and phosphates contained in detergents, fertilizers, and animal wastes enter a body of water such as a lake or a river, the growth of algae and other aquatic plants is speeded up. This uses up the biotic resources of a lake which eventually turns into a swamp, a process called *eutrophication*.

(d) *Sediments*. Excessive sedimentation can be caused by improper landscaping and agricultural malpractices. These pollutants also arise from strip mining activities that greatly increase erosion in a given area. As a result of excessive sedimentation, domestic water supplies are impaired, aquatic life is destroyed, light penetration into water is reduced and the cost of treating water is increased.

(e) *Heavy Metals*. The toxicity of heavy metals has been known for years but attention has been focussed on this fact only recently when it was discovered that mercury was being diffused into the environment on a big scale. Mercury, for example, is used in the manufacture of a plastic substance called polyvinyl chloride (PVC) and in the pulp and paper industry.

Since 1960 some 900 people in the Japanese village of Minamata have shown symptoms of mercury poisoning after eating fish that had been contaminated by the mercury wastes discharged into Minamata Bay from a local chemical plant. Fifty people died as a result of this poisoning and twice as many remained crippled for life. Since then it has been found that fish in many other areas

Table 16.3

Sources and Health Effects of Some Heavy Metals

Metal	Source	Effects
Mercury	Pulp and paper industry; plastic industry	Chromosomal abnormalities; kidney and nerve damage
Cadmium	Zinc mining; certain metal pipes	Cardiovascular diseases; high blood pressure
Lead	Automobile exhaust; lead-base paints	Brain, kidney, and liver damage
Nickel	Diesel oil; coal; certain steel alloys	Lung cancer

around the world are also contaminated by alarming levels of mercury and this includes fish in many Canadian rivers and lakes.

Besides mercury, other heavy metals such as cadmium, lead, nickel, and arsenic can cause serious health problems. Some of the sources and effects of these metals are listed in Table 16.3.

It is the process of *biological magnification* that causes these heavy metals to be dangerous. By this

This must not be allowed to happen.

Ron Johnson, Ont. Dept. of Energy and Resources Management Information Services

process, heavy metals from prey organisms that are already contaminated are concentrated in predators' bodies. The concentration along links in a food chain (plankton → large fish → humans) gradually increases.

(f) *Pesticides.* Pesticides, such as DDT that are used on farmland to control insect population, are washed by rain into rivers and lakes. Here, they enter the food chain and cause biological harm to animals and humans. DDT has recently been banned from widespread use.

(g) *Chemicals.* This class of water pollutants consists of inorganic salts, mineral acids, and metallic compounds that enter waterways as a result of mining, smelting, and metallurgical activities. It also includes the thousands of synthetic chemicals developed in the last few decades. The long term effects of these chemicals on health are mostly unknown.

(h) *Radioactive wastes.* These pollutants may leak from nuclear reactor plants or they may come from the wastes from the mining of uranium-containing radioactive compounds. The absorption of these pollutants by people can produce leukemia, cancer, and genetic damage.

(i) *Heat.* Hot water discharges from industrial plants and power-generating facilities gradually increase the temperature of large bodies of water. This may seriously affect the ecological balance in Nature. The heat reduces the oxygen content of the water and as a result fish and plant life decrease. Long term climatic changes may also result.

16:7 The Purification of Water

Every community is faced with the serious problem of obtaining an adequate supply of good drinking water. In most cases this supply has to be purified by one or more methods depending on the nature of the impurities present in the water.

(a) *Sedimentation.* In this process the water is

stored in large settling tanks where the coarser suspended matter slowly settles on the bottom.

(b) *Coagulation* (alum treatment). A turbid or coloured water supply is treated with aluminum sulfate which causes the formation of a jelly-like precipitate that settles to the bottom carrying with it the colouring matter, suspended matter, and some bacteria.

(c) *Filtration*. Beds of sand are usually used for filtering the water. In this method, most of the remaining suspended particles are removed from the water along with some bacteria.

(d) *Chlorination*. After sedimentation and filtration any bacteria present in the water are destroyed by the addition of chlorine. Liquid chlorine is usually added in small quantities. Chlorine reacts with water liberating atomic oxygen which destroys the microorganisms by oxidation.

Before the use of chlorine, epidemics of typhoid fever and other water borne diseases could bring disaster to a city.

16:8 Waste-Water Treatment

When a small quantity of sewage is dumped into a river, the water dissolves it and renders it harmless. A few kilometres downstream, the water may be pure again. However, when large amounts of sewage are discharged into the same river, the purifying bacteria may be killed and the water loses its purifying power. Many rivers the world over have become loaded with incredible amounts of sewage as population and industrial activities increase. It is a fact today that most of the sewage of civilization is dumped into rivers, lakes, and oceans without having been properly treated.

Most of the waste-water plants now in use utilize crude purification techniques based on natural processes that are accelerated by means of simple devices.

(a) *Screens*. The waste water may be passed through screens that will retain large particles.

(b) *Settling tanks*. The waste water is allowed to remain in huge settling tanks where solid matter drops to the bottom and can later be removed.

(c) *Skimmers*. The scum and greases floating on top of the waste water can be removed by means of skimming devices.

(d) *Trickling basins*. The waste water is allowed to trickle through beds of rocks in large open-air basins. In these basins, the oxygen of the atmosphere comes in contact with the organic matter which is oxidized by the microorganisms present in the water and on the rocks.

(e) *Activated sludge tanks*. Pure oxygen or simply air can be bubbled through the waste water kept in these big tanks. Aerobic bacteria work on the waste, breaking it down into harmless forms.

(f) *Anaerobic digesters*. The sludge that accumulates in settling tanks can be transferred into other tanks that are completely sealed off from the air. In these digesters, anaerobic microorganisms can transform organic matter without the assistance of oxygen.

In some regions, raw sewage is subjected to a *primary treatment* only before being discarded into waterways. This waste water is screened, skimmed, and allowed to settle. Then the water is released into rivers or lakes. The sludge can be burned, or used as fertilizer, or anaerobically destroyed.

In many places, especially in highly populated areas, after raw sewage has been given a primary treatment, it undergoes a *secondary treatment*. The organic matter still present is oxidized and broken down by bacteria in trickling basins. This waste water is subjected to further treatment in anaerobic digesters and is then chlorinated before being discharged. The chlorination process kills microorganisms and disease-producing bacteria.

Obviously, the secondary treatment of waste water is more effective than the primary treatment, although both leave much to be desired. Both types

Official U.S. Coast Guard Photograph

Building seas whipped by high wintry winds broke the SS Argo Merchant in half on Dec. 21, 1976, in spite of the six-day battle by Coast Guard units against the elements to save the tanker. Flying a Liberian flag, the tanker was bound for Salem, Mass. when it ran aground in international waters, causing a major oil spill.

of treatment fail to stop industrial chemical waste and plant nutrients from reaching waterways.

Occasionally waste water is further treated after the primary and secondary treatments have been performed. *Tertiary treatments* are performed to remove undesirable specific substances such as heavy metals, and phosphorus. Most tertiary treatments use chemical processes instead of relying on natural biological processes. In the tertiary treatment, water is produced that is fit to drink. Depending on the nature of the substances to be removed and the degree of purity desired, tertiary treatment can become very expensive. In spite of the cost, advanced waste water treatment programs have become a necessity in many industrialized urban communities.

16:9 The Oceans

Because of their huge and varied resources, we may expect that the oceans will become far more important in the future than they have been in the past. These resources include the vast quantities of seawater itself which can yield fresh water and many chemical substances. Almost all chemical elements have been detected in seawater. However, only common salt (sodium chloride), magnesium, and bromine are now being extracted from the sea in considerable amounts. As the demand for fresh water increases, desalination techniques will be used more often to obtain larger supplies. Offshore oil wells presently supply about one-fifth of the world's oil and gas, and it is believed that soon a third of the oil production will come from the ocean floor. The sea is also extremely important as a source of food. The annual catch is roughly 55 million tonnes.

Until recently, it was thought that we could use seawater as a dump for sewage and other effluents from cities and industries, because these wastes would rapidly be diluted and become harmless. This is no longer the case. In the last decade Jacques Cousteau has repeatedly sounded the alarm. He and the men of the exploring ship "Calypso" have shown that the oceans are vulnerable to rapid degradation.

If the resources of the oceans are going to be used more extensively, it is important that they be managed wisely. Coordinated action on an international scale must be taken to prevent pollution of the oceans, including the control of pesticides, radioactive substances, poisonous chemicals, and sewage coming from the land, ships, or sea-installations.

QUESTIONS

1. Write a brief account of the occurrence of water in Nature.

2. List five or more domestic uses of water not mentioned in this chapter.

3. List five or more industrial uses of water not mentioned in this chapter.

4. List five or more agricultural uses of water not mentioned in this chapter.

5. Explain why our civilization might face serious water shortages in the near future in spite of the fact that water is one of the most abundant substances on Earth?

6. Why is the expansion of water upon freezing important to Nature?

7. (i) Distinguish between natural and chemically pure water.
   (ii) Name some of the constituents of natural waters and suggest possible sources for these substances.

8. (i) Name five kinds of water pollutants and identify two sources for each.
   (ii) Give two possible effects on human beings, plants, or animals for each of the pollutants you have enumerated in 8 (i).

9. In many municipalities, the water supply undergoes successively sedimentation, coagulation, filtration and chlorination. Explain what the effects are of each of these treatments on raw water.

10. Describe five personal habits you could develop to help in the fight against water pollution.

11. Try to evaluate the water supply situation of your own community from the following aspects. You may have to obtain some of this information by contacting the proper municipal authorities on the matter.

    (i)   What source is used as the local water supply?
    (ii)   What is the condition of the "raw water" used?
    (iii) What treatment does this raw water receive?
    (iv)   What quantity of water is treated daily?
    (v)   Where is the treated water stored?
    (vi)   Is there a reserve water supply available for emergencies?
    (vii) How is the used water treated?

These young people are checking a river for pollution.

Berkey K & L Custom Services Inc.

3
BONDING

CHAPTER
17

IMPORTANT PERIODIC PROPERTIES

The elements have many physical and chemical properties. A few of these are density, melting point, boiling point, hardness, and chemical reactivity. Some of these properties permit quantitative measurements and from these, it can be seen that the properties tend to recur as suggested by the Periodic Law.

In this chapter, four properties that in some fundamental way underlie all the others will be presented: atomic size, ionization energy, electron affinity, and electronegativity.

17:1 Atomic and Ionic Size

From what is known about electronic motion in atoms, it is impossible to define exactly the size of a single isolated atom. Therefore, the radius cannot be measured in the usual way.

When two atoms of the same element are bonded, experimental evidence has shown that atomic radius may be defined as one half the distance between the two nuclei. Various experimental methods have been used to find such distances. The atomic radii derived from such findings generally agree. For example, the atomic

The elements of a family of the periodic table have similar properties because their atoms have similar electronic structures.

radius of carbon has been found to be 0.077 nm while that of chlorine is 0.099 nm. Carbon and chlorine, in turn, form a bond which, when measured, is found to be 0.177 nm. This is in good agreement with the sum of atomic radii of carbon and chlorine, 0.077 + 0.099 = 0.176 nm. An error of two per cent is not unreasonable in this type of work. Scientists have also measured the distance between atomic nuclei in crystals and in the molecules of gaseous elements and compounds.

If a bond has a length smaller than the sum of the atomic radii, it is caused by one of two factors: (1) The bond consists of two or three pairs of electrons instead of only one pair of electrons. Such are termed double or triple bonds. (2) The bond is ionic. Bonds are discussed in Chapter 18.

Four interesting points stand out when atomic and ionic radii are examined:
1. Atomic radii decrease in going from left to right across the periodic table. This is contrary to what one would expect. The regular addition of an electron to the successive atoms

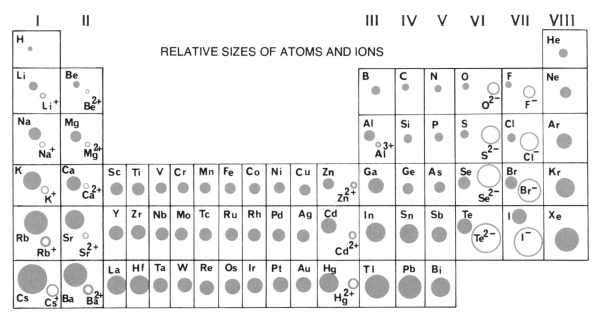

Fig. 17.1:
Atomic and ionic sizes

does not necessarily result in atoms of larger size. (See Fig. 17.1.)

2. Within a group of the periodic table, atoms increase in size with increasing electron shells. The changes in atomic size with the successive addition of electrons is shown in Fig. 17.2.

3. The size of a cation, or positive ion, is less than that of the corresponding neutral atom. This is explained by the extra positive charge on the nucleus attracting the electrons closer to itself.

4. The size of an anion, or negative ion, is greater than that of the neutral atom. This is explained by the increased repulsion of the electrons from one another in an electron shell carrying an extra negative charge.

17:2   Ionization Energy

As already mentioned, because of its energy, the electron does not fall into the nucleus. The addition of energy to the atom causes the electron to go into shells further removed from the nucleus. It is possible to add an amount of energy that would cause the electron to leave the atom entirely, thus forming an electrically charged particle called an ion. This process may be shown by an equation:

$$A + energy \rightarrow A^+ + e^-$$

where A is an atom losing one electron. The energy that can remove an electron from the atom to form the ion is termed the *ionization energy*.

Elements differ greatly in their ionization energies. This means that to remove one or more electrons from the atoms of certain elements is easy, but to remove them from others is difficult. The ease with which electrons may be removed is in accordance with the chemical properties of these elements. For this reason, the ionization energy is a valuable guide to the chemical properties of the elements.

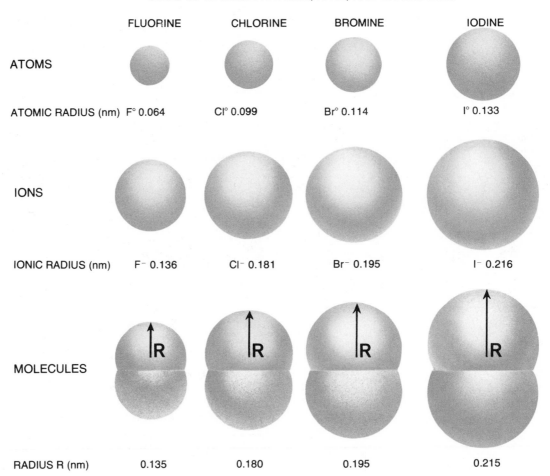

SIZES OF HALOGEN ATOMS, IONS, AND MOLECULES

	FLUORINE	CHLORINE	BROMINE	IODINE
ATOMS				
ATOMIC RADIUS (nm)	F° 0.064	Cl° 0.099	Br° 0.114	I° 0.133
IONS				
IONIC RADIUS (nm)	F⁻ 0.136	Cl⁻ 0.181	Br⁻ 0.195	I⁻ 0.216
MOLECULES	R	R	R	R
RADIUS R (nm)	0.135	0.180	0.195	0.215

Fig. 17.2:
Sizes of atoms, ions, and molecules of the halogens

Tables 17.1 and 17.2 show how the ionization energy changes within a group or a period. Obviously, as the atom increases in size, it becomes easier to remove an outermost electron. Going from left to right across a period, it becomes more difficult to remove such an electron.

Note the high values for the Noble Gases and the low values for the alkali metals. Fig. 17.3 shows the variations in the ionization energies needed to remove one electron from the atoms as the atomic number increases.

17:3   Electron Affinity

Atoms may gain electrons, and the energy released when this occurs is called *electron affinity*. The process may be shown by the equation on page 148:

TABLE 17.1

Ionization Energy of the Elements of Group 1

Elements	Electrons in Shells	Ionization Energy in kJ/mol
Lithium	2, 1	521
Sodium	2, 8, 1	486
Potassium	2, 8, 8, 1	410
Rubidium	2, 8, 18, 8, 1	401
Cesium	2, 8, 18, 18, 8, 1	372
Francium	2, 8, 18, 32, 18, 8,	?

TABLE 17.2

Ionization Energy of the Elements of Period 2

Elements	Numbers of Outermost Electrons	Ionization Energy in kJ/mol
Lithium	1	521
Beryllium	2	897
Boron	3	800
Carbon	4	1090
Nitrogen	5	1399
Oxygen	6	1312
Fluorine	7	1679
Neon	8	2084

Fig. 17.3:
How atomic size and ionization energies change period-ically with increasing atomic number of elements

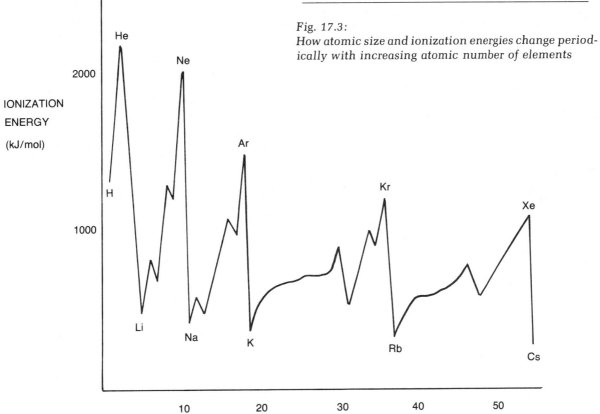

$$A + e^- \rightarrow A^- + energy$$

where A stands for the atom gaining an electron. The energy being liberated represents the electron affinity of the atom. Certain atoms show this property very readily, while others hardly show it at all. When an atom gains electrons, it becomes a negatively charged ion. The halogens of group VII are the best example of elements with high electron affinities because the addition of one electron to their atoms gives them a stable outer shell similar to the octet of a noble gas atom. The electron affinities of the atoms are rather difficult to determine and have been calculated for only a few elements.

17:4   Electronegativity

The *electronegativity* of an atom is a measure of its attraction for the electrons in the bond between itself and another atom. Atoms with a strong attraction for electrons have a high electronegativity. Fluorine, the smallest atom of group VII of the periodic table, has the highest electronegativity of all the elements; francium, the largest atom of

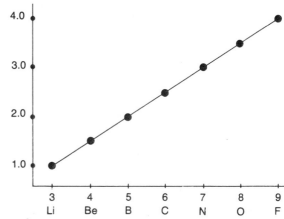

THE ELEMENTS OF THE SECOND PERIOD
AND THEIR ATOMIC NUMBERS

Fig. 17.4:
The electronegativities in the second period, Li to F

group I, has the lowest. Numerically, electronegativity values range from 4.0 for fluorine to below 1.0 for most of the alkali metals.

The electronegativity scale (Table 17.3) was derived by taking into account the energy required to

TABLE 17.3

THE ELECTRONEGATIVITIES OF ELEMENTS IN THE PERIODIC TABLE

2.1 H																	He
1.0 Li	1.5 Be											2.0 B	2.5 C	3.0 N	3.5 O	4.0 F	Ne
0.9 Na	1.2 Mg											1.5 Al	1.8 Si	2.1 P	2.5 S	3.0 Cl	Ar
0.8 K	1.0 Ca	1.3 Sc	1.5 Ti	1.6 V	1.6 Cr	1.5 Mn	1.8 Fe	1.8 Co	1.8 Ni	1.9 Cu	1.6 Zn	1.6 Ga	1.8 Ge	2.0 As	2.4 Se	2.8 Br	Kr
0.8 Rb	1.0 Sr	1.2 Y	1.4 Zr	1.6 Nb	1.8 Mo	1.9 Tc	2.2 Ru	2.2 Rh	2.2 Pd	1.9 Ag	1.7 Cd	1.7 In	1.8 Sn	1.9 Sb	2.1 Te	2.5 I	Xe
0.7 Cs	0.9 Ba	1.2 La	1.3 Hf	1.5 Ta	1.7 W	1.9 Re	2.2 Os	2.2 Ir	2.2 Pt	2.4 Au	1.9 Hg	1.8 Tl	1.8 Pb	1.9 Bi	2.0 Po	2.2 At	Rn
0.7 Fr	0.9 Ra																

remove an electron from an atom, the ionization energy, and the energy change when an electron is added to an atom, the electron affinity. The scale is used to predict and explain the type of bond that forms between a particular pair of atoms. If we examine Table 17.3 the following points are readily observed:

1. The highest electronegativities are shown by the most reactive non-metallic elements. These are the halogens of group VII of the periodic table.
2. The lowest electronegativities are shown by the most active metallic elements. These are the alkali metals of group I.
3. Within a period, electronegativities generally increase from left to right. In the first short periods, the values increase one-half unit with each group. For example, the electronegativities of Li, Be, B, C, N, O, F, and Ne are 1.0, 1.5, 2.0, 2.5, and so forth (Fig. 17.4).
4. Within a vertical column, electronegativity is usually greatest in the smallest atom and decreases with an increase in atomic size. Among the heavy metals, electronegativity values apparently do not follow this rule rigorously but are more or less constant.
5. Electronegativity values for the noble gases of group VIII are not readily available. For a long time it was believed that these elements formed no compounds; therefore, the concept of electronegativity did not apply to them. This belief will probably change now that xenon tetrafluoride and several other compounds have been synthesized.

17:5 Electronegativity Difference

When two atoms, A and B, combine, electrons may be shared between them or transferred from one to the other. If A and B have about equal affinity for

electrons, they will form a bond by sharing electrons more or less equally:

$$A^\cdot + {}_\circ B \;\rightarrow\; A \overset{\cdot}{:} B$$

Such a bond is referred to as a non-polar *covalent bond*. When the two atoms have sufficiently different electron-attracting power, the electrons they share are displaced toward the atom that draws them more strongly. This unequal sharing of electrons causes one atom to be slightly negatively charged and the other positively charged. When this occurs, the bond is termed *polar covalent*. If atom B has greater ability to attract electrons than A, the bond can be represented as follows:

$$A^\cdot + {}_\circ B \;\rightarrow\; A \overset{\cdot}{:} B \text{ or } \overset{* \; \delta^+ \qquad \delta^-}{A \overset{\cdot}{\frown}\, {}_\circ B}$$

If atoms have greater differences still in their electronegativity values, electrons may be transferred from one atom to the other. Such a transfer results in the formation of an *ionic bond*. For example, if B has a much stronger attraction for

TABLE 17.4

Effect of Electronegativity on the Nature of Bonds

Electronegativity Difference	Per Cent of Ionic Character	Type of Bond
0.2-0.7	1-9	Non-polar covalent ... Polarity, if present, is not significant
0.8-1.6	10-47	Polar covalent
1.7	50	50% ionic, 50% covalent
1.8-3.2	55-92	Ionic

* δ^+ and δ^- are Greek symbols that indicate slight charges are present.

electrons than A, electrons may be transferred from A to B, and two ions are thus formed:

$$A{\cdot} + {_\circ}B \rightarrow A^+ + {_\circ^{\cdot}}B^-$$

The electronegativity difference between two elements can thus help to describe the bonds formed between their atoms. Of course, since all gradations of polarity are possible, it is difficult in some cases to draw a clear distinction between ionic and covalent bonds. Table 17.4 was drawn up by chemists to express the nature of a chemical bond as "*percentage of ionic character*" based on electronegativity differences. In this tabulation,

we see that a difference of 1.7 in electronegativity is sufficient to cause an ionic bond to form between the atoms involved.

The value of 1.7 corresponds to about 50 per cent ionic character and 50 per cent covalent character. An electronegative difference greater than 1.7 means that the bond formed is more ionic than covalent while an electronegative difference smaller than 1.7 represents a bond more covalent than ionic. Many applications of electronegativity to bonding between atoms and to the chemical nature of compounds formed will be found in the study of the elements and their compounds.

QUESTIONS

1. Why may two combined atoms have a shorter bond length than the sum of the two atomic radii?

2. Offer an explanation as to why a cation is smaller and an anion is larger than the atom from which they are formed.

3. (i) Define the term *ionization energy*.
    (ii) Name two factors that determine the magnitude of the ionization energy of an element.

4. Suggest a reason why it becomes more difficult to remove one outer electron as one goes from left to right across a period.

5. Define the term *electron affinity*.

6. Write an ionic equation representing a fluorine atom becoming a fluoride ion.

7. How many nanometres are there in 1 cm?

8. Define *electronegativity*.

9. (i) Name the elements that have the highest electronegativity.
    (ii) Name the elements that have the lowest electronegativity.

10. Relate atomic size to electronegativity.

11. (i) What is meant by a non-polar covalent bond?
    (ii) When does a non-polar covalent bond form?

12. (i) What is a *polar covalent bond*?
    (ii) Under what conditions will a polar covalent bond form?

13. (i) What is an *ionic bond*?
    (ii) When does such a bond form?

14. Atom M whose electronegativity is 1.0 combines with atom N whose electronegativity is 3.5. Which of the following equations best represents this combination?

(i) $M^\bullet + {}_\circ N \rightarrow M {}_\circ^\bullet N$

(ii) $M^\bullet + {}_\circ N \rightarrow M^- {}_\circ^\bullet N^+$

(iii) $M^\bullet + {}_\circ N \rightarrow M^+ {}_\circ^\bullet N^-$

(iv) $M^\bullet + {}_\circ N \rightarrow M {}_\circ^= N^+$

15. Discuss what is meant by *percentage ionic character*.

16. Of what significance is an electronegativity difference of 1.7 between two atoms?

17. Account for the fact that the carbon-hydrogen bond is covalent while the fluorine-hydrogen bond is ionic.

18. List five covalent bonds formed with hydrogen.

19. List five covalent bonds formed with oxygen.

20. List five ionic bonds formed with oxygen.

21. Suggest a reason why hydrogen does not form a strong bond with many metals.

22. Re-arrange the following pairs of elements in the order of decreasing bond polarity: (a) hydrogen-bromine; (b) hydrogen-chlorine; (c) hydrogen-iodine; (d) hydrogen-fluorine.

23. Give the per cent ionic character and predict the type of bond formed between the following atoms:

(i) C—H	(vi) Mg—O	(xi) C—N
(ii) Cl—Cl	(vii) S—O	(xii) K—F
(iii) Fe—O	(viii) K—Cl	(xiii) H—O
(iv) N—H	(ix) I—O	(xiv) Li—Br
(v) Cl—O	(x) C—O	

CHAPTER
18

CHEMICAL BONDS

18:1   Chemical Bonds

Chemical change is the combining and the separating of atoms. But how do atoms combine, and what holds them together? Why is there a definite limit to the number of atoms that combine with each other in molecules or ions? The answers to these questions are given by the electronic structure of the atom. *Chemical combination is due to the attraction of atoms for the electrons of other atoms toward their unfilled shells.* If the attraction is great enough, the electrons leave their original atoms to fill the shells of another atom. If the attraction is not so great, the electrons may be shared by two atoms as a bond. The electronegativity of an element indicates the power of its atoms to attract electrons. Generally atoms gain, lose, or share electrons to assume the filled pattern of the atoms of the nearest noble gas in the periodic table.

18:2   Ionic Bonds

Ions form when only a small number of electrons need to be gained or lost by the atoms in order to form stable electronic patterns. *Positive ions* result from the loss of electrons, and *negative ions* result from the gain of electrons. An ionic bond results from the force of attraction between the positive and negative ions. Positive ions are called *cations*

Not only do electrons account for the structure of atoms, but they also proceed to join, or bond, atoms together. Bonding is achieved by giving, taking, and/or sharing electrons between atoms. There are even cases, however, where bonding is all but impossible—but always for good reason.

because they are attracted to the cathode during electrolysis; negative ions are called *anions*, because they move to the anode.

The atoms of metals may lose one, two, or three electrons, thus forming positively charged cations. The atoms of non-metals, either singly or in groups, may gain one, two, or three electrons, thus forming negatively charged anions. Sodium atoms have only one electron in the outer shells. This electron is easily removed as shown by its relatively low ionization energy. Chlorine atoms have seven electrons in their outer shells. Energy is released when an eighth electron is added as shown by the electron affinity of chlorine. When sodium and chlorine react, the sodium atom loses its single electron and the chlorine atom adds it to its outer shell. The reaction may be represented as follows:

$$Na° + .\overset{..}{\underset{..}{Cl}}: \rightarrow Na^+ \quad :\overset{..}{\underset{..}{Cl}}:^-$$

18:3 The Formation of an Ionic Compound

The formation of crystalline sodium chloride involves three steps. In the first, an electron is removed from the sodium atom. This requires an amount of energy called the ionization energy. Such a reaction is endothermic since it absorbs energy.

$$Na° + energy \rightarrow Na^+ + e^-$$

In the second step, this electron is added to the chlorine atom. This reaction releases an amount of energy called the electron affinity. Such a reaction is termed exothermic because it releases energy.

$$Cl° + e^- \rightarrow Cl^- + energy$$

In the third step, the positive sodium ions and the negative chloride ions attract each other and move toward one another. As they take positions next to each other, they form the sodium chloride crystal. This process also releases energy since particles with mutual attraction have come closer together. Thus, step three is exothermic.

The sum of the energy released in the second and third steps is greater than the energy required for the first. Hence, the formation of sodium chloride is exothermic. This is typical of the formation of all ionic compounds.

In the formation of an ionic compound, a significant change occurs in the sizes of the atoms involved. The metal atom becomes an ion of smaller size as its nucleus attracts the electrons closer, now that the positive charge on the nucleus ex-

ceeds the negative charge of the electrons. The non-metallic atom, in gaining electrons, becomes an ion of larger size as the electrons, now with an excessive negative charge, repel each other. This is shown with sodium and chlorine in Fig. 18.1.

18:4 Properties of Ionic Compounds

Ionic compounds are combinations of positive and negative ions. The forces of attraction between ions of opposite charge are strong, and, at ordinary temperatures, the ions are held in close contact in regular crystal patterns. Ionic substances are always solids at room temperature and usually have high melting points. NaCl melts at 800°C, LiF at 870°C, and MgF_2 at 1400°C. Many ionic salts dissolve in water because the polar water molecules (Chapter 21) form weak bonds with the cations and the anions. The formation of such bonds releases energy. Such energy can overcome the force of attraction between the ions of the solid salt, and also between the molecules of water. Solutions of ionic compounds display interesting electrical and chemical properties. These will be discussed in Chapter 24.

18:5 Covalence

Atoms of equal or slightly different electronegativity may form molecules by sharing one or more pairs of electrons. This is called *covalence*, and the bond formed is known as a *covalent bond*.

Some elements and compounds whose molecules are formed by covalent bonds between their atoms include H_2, Cl_2, O_2, HCl, H_2O, NH_3, and CH_4. Indeed, the majority of numerous compounds containing carbon are composed of covalent molecules.

Molecules which contain covalent bonds have definite structures. Some simple examples of such

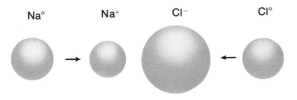

Fig. 18.1:
Changes of size when atoms form ions

structures will be discussed in the remainder of this chapter and in the next. Since the structure of molecules determines to a large extent the properties of their compounds, references to structure will be made frequently throughout the study of chemistry.

18:6 Covalence in H_2

In the molecule of hydrogen, H_2, a covalent bond is formed between the hydrogen atoms. Each atom has one electron which it shares

$$H° + .H \rightarrow H \overset{\circ}{:} H$$

with the other atom to form the covalent bond.

Let us attempt to picture how a covalent bond forms. The hydrogen atom has one electron in its outer shell. This electron has a certain spin in addition to its rapid motion about the nucleus. When two hydrogen atoms approach, their electrons pair up if they are spinning in opposite directions. A molecule of hydrogen is thus formed with a covalent bond between the hydrogen atoms (Fig. 18.2). Each hydrogen atom thus ends up with a stable electron structure similar to that found in helium.

18:7 The Chlorine Molecule

In the molecule of chlorine, Cl_2, a covalent bond is formed between the chlorine atoms. Each atom has seven electrons in the outer shell. Six are paired but the seventh electron is single or unpaired.

When two chlorine atoms approach with their unpaired electrons spinning in opposite directions, a covalent bond forms by the sharing of these two electrons between the chlorine atoms. Each chlorine atom thus ends up with the stable electron structure similar to that found in argon.

$$:\overset{..}{\underset{..}{Cl}}· + °\overset{\circ\circ}{\underset{\circ\circ}{Cl}}° \rightarrow :\overset{..}{\underset{..}{Cl}}:\overset{\circ\circ}{\underset{\circ\circ}{Cl}}°$$

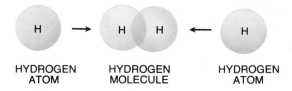

Fig. 18.2:
The formation of a molecule of hydrogen by electron sharing.

18:8 Covalence Between Unlike Atoms

In the molecule of hydrogen chloride, HCl, a bond has formed between an atom of hydrogen and one of chlorine. Hydrogen has one electron in its outer shell and chlorine has seven in its outer shell. The two atoms share a pair of electrons to form the bond between the H and Cl in HCl.

Here hydrogen and chlorine achieve stable electron structures:

$$H° + .\overset{..}{\underset{..}{Cl}}: \rightarrow H \: :\overset{..}{\underset{..}{Cl}}:$$

It should be remembered that the actual chemical formation of hydrogen chloride results from molecular hydrogen, H_2, reacting with molecular chlorine, Cl_2. The equation for this reaction is:

$$H_2 + Cl_2 \rightarrow 2HCl$$

18:9 Polar Covalent Bonds

Since the electronegativities of H and Cl are quite different, the electrons in the bonds are shared unequally, tending toward the more electronegative chlorine atom. However, no outright transfer of electrons occurs. The symbols $\delta+$ and $\delta-$ denote a small positive and negative charge respectively on the atoms they mark.

Thus, the bond in HCl is covalent, unlike that in ionic NaCl. Neither the hydrogen nor the chlorine atom can remove the electron completely from the other.

The electronegativity difference is great enough for the molecule of HCl to be polar with a positive pole near the hydrogen atom and a negative one near the chlorine (Fig. 18.3).

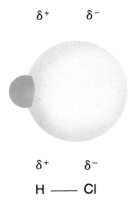

$$\delta^+ \qquad \delta^-$$
$$\text{H} \longrightarrow \text{Cl}$$

Fig. 18.3:
The polar covalent bond in HCl

Two other polar covalent boards of frequent occurrence are the OH and the NH, found most commonly in water and ammonia respectively. The oxygen and nitrogen atoms are more electronegative than the hydrogen. As a result the electrons in these bonds shift toward the oxygen and the nitrogen, and thus, polar bonds form:

$$\delta+ \quad \delta-$$
$$\text{H} - \text{N}$$

$$\delta+ \quad \delta-$$
$$\text{H} - \text{O}$$

18:10 Bond Energy

The formation of bonds liberates energy, while the breaking of bonds requires energy. The amount of energy needed to separate the atoms of a bond is called the *bond energy*.

When one Avogadro Number of hydrogen molecules is dissociated into H atoms, the energy required is 436.6 kilojoules called the bond energy of the H—H bond. The equation may be written as follows:

$$H_2 + 436.6 \text{ kJ} = 2H$$

Similar values for other pairs of atoms are known. (See Table 18.1).

In using bond energies, the assumption is made that each bond has a definite amount of energy associated with it, and this energy is not affected by neighboring atoms and bonds. This assumption is only approximately true, so that bond energies are merely the best average values obtainable for a large number of cases. They are not perfect and the error in their value is about five per cent.

Bond energies enable us to calculate the heat of a reaction. To do this, the energy needed to break the bonds in the reactants on the left-hand side of the

TABLE 18.1

Bond Energies

Bond	Kilojoules per mole
H—H	436.5
Cl—Cl	243.0
O=O	495.7
O—O	138.2
C—C	335.2
H—O	458.4
H—Cl	432.4
H—C	414.8
C—Cl	326.8
C—O	331.0
C=C	607.5

equation is computed, then the energy released is computed for the bonds formed in the products on the right-hand side of the equation. Finally, the difference is taken. Thus, the heat of reaction equals the energy of bonds formed in products minus the energy of bonds broken in reactants.

Example

What is the heat of reaction for

$CH_4 + Cl_2 \rightarrow CH_3Cl + HCl$?

Structurally,

$$\underset{\substack{| \\ H}}{\overset{\substack{H \\ |}}{H-C-H}} + Cl-Cl \rightarrow \underset{\substack{| \\ H}}{\overset{\substack{H \\ |}}{H-C-Cl}} + H-Cl$$

Bonds Broken

$4 \times C - H$	$= 4 \times 414.8$	$= 1659.2$
$1 \times Cl - Cl$	$= 1 \times 243.0$	$= 243.0$
		1902.2

Energy required: 1902.2 kJ

Bonds formed

$3 \times C - H = 3 \times 414.8$

$1 \times C - Cl = 1 \times 326.8$

$1 \times H - Cl = 1 \times 432.4$

Energy liberated: 2003.6 kJ

Heat of reaction: $2003.6 - 1902.2 = 101.4$ kJ

Since the energy liberated exceeds the energy absorbed, this reaction is exothermic.

QUESTIONS

1. (i) What is the origin of the charge on a negative ion?
   (ii) What is the origin of the charge on a positive ion?

2. Using the electronegativity concept, explain why sodium and chlorine combine so readily.

3. Potassium and chlorine combine together forming potassium chloride. Represent this reaction (i) by an ordinary balanced chemical equation; (ii) using the dot notation.

4. Repeat question 3 for the combination of magnesium and fluorine.

5. What common properties are shown by ionic compounds?

6. Explain covalence. Illustrate your answer by reference to the bond found in the molecule of hydrogen.

7. Why is the following reaction, $He + He \rightarrow He_2$, not likely to occur?

8. Using the electron dot notation show how: (i) 2 atoms of fluorine combine; (ii) 2 atoms of bromine combine; (iii) 2 atoms of oxygen combine; (iv) 2 atoms of nitrogen combine.

9. Explain how chlorine atoms form molecules.

10. Account for the fact that some covalent bonds are polar while others are non-polar.

11. Using Table 18.1 calculate the overall heat evolved or absorbed in the following reactions:

   (i) $H_{2(g)} + Cl_{2(g)} \rightarrow 2HCl_{(g)}$
   (ii) $2H_2O_{(g)} \rightarrow 2H_{2(g)} + O_{2(g)}$

MOLECULAR ARCHITECTURE

19:1 Introduction

As long as there are only two atoms in a molecule, the structure is that of a line joining two points. The presence of a third atom in the molecule poses the question of the shape or architecture of the molecule. Is the three-atom molecule still a straight line? or is it an angle or a triangle?

Early evidence about molecular architecture came from the chemical properties and the chemical reactions of the compounds. This is not surprising because the structure of a molecule has chemical significance. A chemical reaction involves the breaking and making of bonds between atoms. Since the structure of a molecule shows its bonds, it also suggests what reactions the compound would be expected to undergo. The structure of a molecule has physical significance as well. It will determine such physical properties as the melting and boiling points, density, conductivity, and solubility of the substance. It will also explain the radiation the compound will absorb or emit under suitable conditions.

Indeed, the most rapid and precise modern methods for finding molecular structures are based on observing how substances absorb or emit radiation. Such methods have enabled chemists to learn how the atoms of a molecule are linked together,

Buildings, cars, TV sets, animals and plants, all have structure, otherwise, they would not function as they do. Similarly molecules have structure which accounts for their properties.

how great the distance is between the atoms, and how large the angle is between the bonds. Scientists can also tell how strong the bonds are, how free the atoms are to vibrate, and other such fine detail. This chapter will be a brief introduction to this great field of study. Some of the ideas involved can be learned with the aid of the molecules of methane, water, and ammonia.

19:2 The Molecule of Methane, CH_4

In this molecule, one carbon atom is attached to four hydrogens. There are four C-H bonds.

$$\cdot \overset{\cdot}{\underset{\cdot}{C}} \cdot + 4H^\circ \longrightarrow H \overset{H}{\underset{H}{\overset{\cdot\circ}{\underset{\cdot\circ}{C}}}} H$$

Experiment shows that these bonds are at an angle of 109.5°, with respect to each other.

The four bonds are directed *symmetrically in space. It is as if the four electron pairs which make up the four bonds, repel one another to the utmost.* They are as far away from one another as they can possibly be, providing that they remain within the molecule. This is the reason the bonds orient themselves as they do. This is termed the *Valence Shell Electron Pair Repulsion Theory.*

To appreciate what the bonds have achieved through their mutual repulsion, think of a perfect cube in which diagonals are drawn (Fig. 19.1). The eight lines joining centre C to each of the eight corners are distributed symmetrically in space.

In the case of the carbon atom, there are only four bonds coming from the central point, and *they* are to be distributed symmetrically in space. Their

orientation must be toward every *second* corner of the cube (Fig. 19.2).

By measurement or calculation, we find that the angle between any pair of lines such as Cc and Ca is 109.5°. This is the very same angle as that found experimentally between any pair of bonds in the methane molecule. That molecule must have the structure shown in Fig. 19.2. This is a significant conclusion, and we now proceed to develop it further.

To obtain a simpler and clearer picture of what that structure must be, join every second corner of the cube. The structure that results is a *tetrahedron* (Fig. 19.3). This is a pyramid with four faces, each an equilateral triangle.

We have thus arrived at the conclusion that the

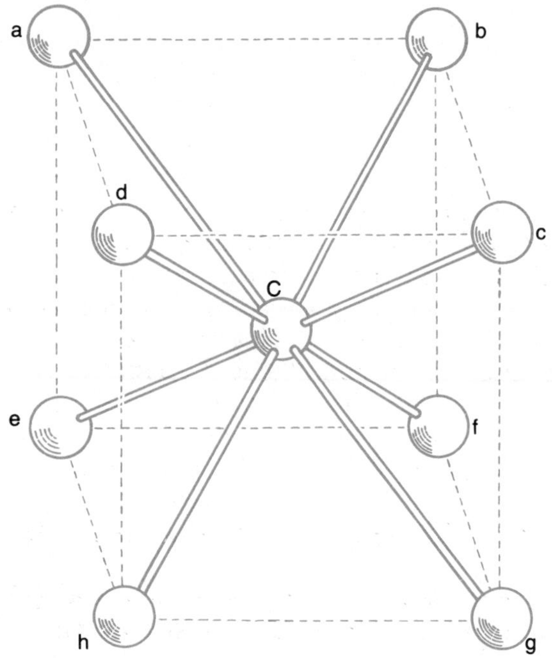

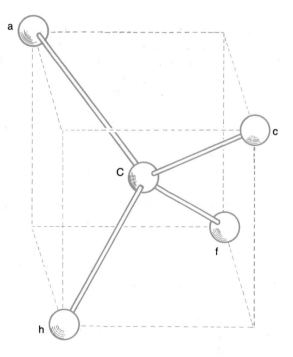

Fig. 19.1:
Symmetrical distribution in space for eight lines
Eight lines from the centre (C) of a cube are distributed symmetrically in space if they point to the eight corners of the cube.

Fig. 19.2:
Symmetrical distribution in space for four lines
Four lines from the centre of a cube are distributed symmetrically if they point to every second corner of the cube.

shape or architecture of the methane molecule is that of a tetrahedron. The carbon atom is at the centre and the hydrogen atoms are at the corners distributed symmetrically in the space around it.

In the vast majority of cases wherein one atom is joined to four others, the molecule assumes this shape. Some of the more familiar molecules and ions have this tetrahedral structure. (See Fig. 19.4)

19:3   The Molecule of Water, H₂O

This molecule consists of one oxygen and two hydrogen atoms. Each hydrogen is bonded to the oxygen atom and thus there are two O-H bonds in

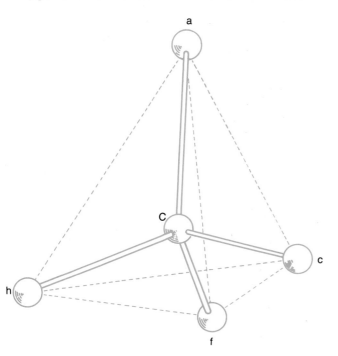

Fig. 19.3:
Four symmetrical lines in a tetrahedron
In the molecule of methane, four hydrogen atoms are arranged symmetrically about the carbon atom, as at the corners of a tetrahedron.

the molecule. Experiment shows that the angle between these bonds is 104.5°.

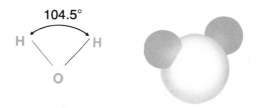

The atom of oxygen has two unpaired electrons in its outer shell. This enables it to combine with two atoms of hydrogen, forming the two polar covalent bonds of water molecule.

$$.\overset{..}{O}:+ 2H° \rightarrow H:\overset{..}{\underset{\overset{..}{H}}{O}}:$$

Electron pairs that exist as part of an atom (unshared electron pairs) occupy more space than those electron pairs that form as a result of sharing between two atoms. This happens because shared electron-pairs are attracted between two atoms and are pulled in more tightly than unshared pairs which tend to spread out around the nucleus. By spreading out in this way, the unshared pairs tend to push the shared pairs closer together and the angle is smaller than 109.5°. This is why water has an angle of 104.5° between its O-H bonds. The two unshared electron pairs around the oxygen atoms have pushed the two shared electron pairs in the O-H bonds closer together.

19:4   The Molecule of Ammonia, NH₃

This molecule consists of one nitrogen and three hydrogen atoms. Each hydrogen is bonded to the nitrogen atom and thus there are three N-H bonds in the molecule. Experiment shows that the angle between the bonds is 107.5°.

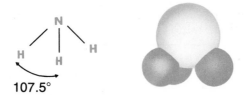

107.5°

The atom of nitrogen has three single electrons in its outer shell. Thus, it is able to combine with three hydrogen atoms to form the three polar covalent bonds of the molecule of ammonia.

$$\overset{\displaystyle\cdot}{\underset{\displaystyle\cdot\cdot}{N}}\cdot + 3H° \rightarrow H : \overset{\displaystyle\cdot\cdot}{\underset{\displaystyle\cdot\cdot}{N}} : H$$

Here, the one unshared pair of electrons on the nitrogen atom forces the three shared pairs slightly closer together, and the angle becomes 107.5°.

19:5   The Polarity of Molecules

Both the type of bonding between the atoms of a molecule and the shape of the molecule determine a very important property of a molecule known as its polarity.

In carbon tetrachloride for example, there are four C-Cl bonds arranged symmetrically about the central carbon atom. Each of these C-Cl bonds is very slightly polar covalent. There is a charge distribution about the molecule as shown in the following diagram.

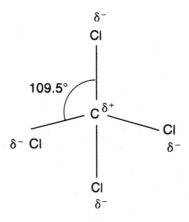

If the tendency for each chlorine atom to attract the bonding electron pair is indicated by means of a vector, then within the CCl_4 molecule there will be four vectors pointing as indicated:

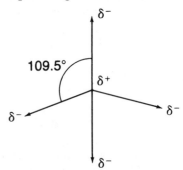

The net effect of adding these four vectors is zero. There is equal distribution of charge in all directions and the molecule, overall, is non-polar or is said to have no polarity even though each of its four bonds is slightly polar.

In the water molecule, with its bent shape and two polar covalent O-H bonds, there is a different result. When the vectors representing oxygen's tendency to attract the bonding electron pairs are considered with the shape, the following occurs:

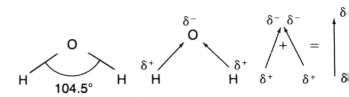

There is an accumulation of negative charge around the oxygen atom in all water molecules resulting in a positive "end" and a negative "end" on the molecule. Such molecules are polar overall and are said to have a *dipole* with two poles, one positive and one negative.

The polarity of a substance is very important. Knowledge of this property helps explain why various substances dissolve in some solvents and not in others. This property also helps explain many other physical properties of a substance such as its melting point and boiling point.

Three representations of the tetrahedron:

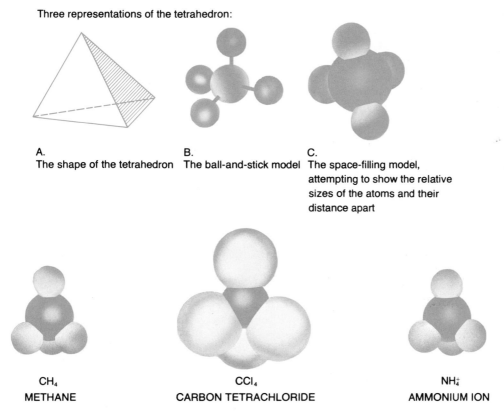

A.
The shape of the tetrahedron

B.
The ball-and-stick model

C.
The space-filling model,
attempting to show the relative
sizes of the atoms and their
distance apart

CH₄
METHANE

CCl₄
CARBON TETRACHLORIDE

NH₄⁺
AMMONIUM ION

Fig. 19.4:
Examples of tetrahedral structure

QUESTIONS

1. Draw a diagram to show the arrangement of electrons in the methane molecule.

2. Describe clearly the shape of a tetrahedron. Use a diagram to illustrate.

3. Using electron dot configurations, write equations representing the formation of hydrogen sulfide, H_2S, and phosphine, PH_3.

4. Which of the following molecules are likely to be polar? Why? H_2O, H_2S, NH_3, PH_3, CF_4, CO_2.

5. Two atoms of nitrogen combine together by sharing three pairs of electrons.
   (i)   Draw the electron dot structure of the resulting nitrogen molecule.
   (ii) Is this molecule polar or non-polar? Explain.

6. (i) Draw the electron dot representations for the following: $SiBr_4$; H_2Te; NH_4^+; HF; CH_3Cl.
   (ii) Indicate the general shape of each of the chemical species listed in (i).

CHAPTER
20

OXIDATION-REDUCTION

20:1 Some Examples of Oxidation-Reduction

These are chemical reactions in which electrons are transferred from one reactant to another.

When oxygen reacts with magnesium, magnesium oxide is the product.

$$2Mg + O_2 \rightarrow 2MgO$$

The original oxygen molecules and atoms are neutral. In the final product, the oxygen atoms have acquired a charge of 2– because two electrons have been transferred to each oxygen atom. The original magnesium atoms carry no charge, while the resulting magnesium ions in magnesium oxide have a charge of 2+. Therefore, in this reaction, oxygen attracts electrons from magnesium. Since oxygen has an electronegativity of 3.5 and magnesium of 1.2, it is not surprising that such an electron transfer occurs.

There are many reactions in which one substance attracts electrons from another. In some cases, the attraction leads to outright transfer of electrons from one atom to another and this results in the formation of ions. In other cases, the attraction leads only to a partial shift of electrons from one atom to another and this results in the forma-

tion of polar covalent bonds. In either case, the substance which attracts the electrons is called the *oxidizing agent*, and the substance which loses the electrons is called the *reducing agent*. Such substances may be atomic, molecular, or ionic. Examples of oxidizing agents and the reactions they undergo when they accept electrons are the following:

Oxygen	O_2	$+ 4e^- \rightarrow 2O^{2-}$
Chlorine	Cl_2	$+ 2e^- \rightarrow 2Cl^-$
Sulfur	S	$+ 2e^- \rightarrow S^{2-}$
Silver ion	Ag^+	$+ 1e^- \rightarrow Ag^0$
Copper (II) ion	Cu^{2+}	$+ 2e^- \rightarrow Cu^0$

Examples of reducing agents and the reactions they undergo when they donate electrons are the following:

Sodium	Na^0	$\rightarrow Na^+ + 1e^-$
Zinc	Zn^0	$\rightarrow Zn^{2+} + 2e^-$
Chloride ions	$2Cl^-$	$\rightarrow Cl_2 + 2e^-$

20:2   Some Terms

The processes of oxidation and reduction go on simultaneously. When electrons are transferred from reducing agents to oxidizing agents, the reducing agent is oxidized and the oxidizing agent is reduced. Thus, when Mg^0 loses electrons to oxygen and becomes Mg^{2+}, it is said to have been *oxidized*, or to have undergone *oxidation*.

In the same reaction, the oxygen has gained electrons and its electrical condition changed from 0 to 2−. It is said to have been *reduced* or to have undergone *reduction*.

An oxidizing agent oxidizes another substance, but is itself reduced.

A reducing agent reduces another substance, but is itself oxidized.

Thus oxidation and reduction are opposite reactions which take place simultaneously. The overall reaction involving both the loss and the gain of electrons is termed an *oxidation-reduction reaction*.

20:3   Oxidation-Reduction Reactions

If the oxidizing agent gains electrons and the reducing agent loses electrons, a chemical reaction might be expected when they are brought together. This does occur, provided the energy liberated when the oxidizing agent gains electrons is great enough to remove the electrons from the reducing agent. Systems in which such a chemical reaction proceeds are called electrical cells or batteries (Fig. 20.1). These are used to provide electrical energy in cars, airplanes, and in many other types of vehicles and devices.

How a Voltaic Cell Generates
Electrical Current

If a zinc strip is dipped into a copper sulfate solution, it becomes copper plated. In this reac-

tion, zinc atoms are *oxidized* to zinc ions by losing electrons. Copper ions are *reduced* to copper atoms by gaining those electrons:

$$Zn^0_{(s)} + Cu^{2+}_{(aq)} \rightarrow Zn^{2+}_{(aq)} + Cu^0_{(s)}$$

It is possible to use this oxidation-reduction reaction to generate an electric current. In a properly constructed cell, the two half-cells function in separate compartments so that electrons can flow from one to the other through an external wire.

In the cell shown in Fig. 20.1, the strips of copper and zinc are placed in solutions containing their respective ions. The two solutions are separated by a porous partition which permits the diffusion of ions. Zinc loses electrons more easily than does copper. This is in keeping with the statement that zinc is above copper in the electromotive series, or that the electronegativity of zinc is less than that of copper. When the two metals are connected externally a current flows through the wire at a certain voltage as shown by the voltmeter.

The cell operates as follows. At the zinc electrode, zinc atoms undergo oxidation by losing electrons and enter the solution as zinc ions:

$$Zn^0_{(s)} \rightarrow Zn^{2+}_{(aq)} + 2e^-$$

These electrons move through the wire to the copper electrode where reduction occurs. Copper ions from the solution gain the electrons and are deposited as atoms on the copper strip:

$$Cu^{2+}_{(aq)} + 2e^- \rightarrow Cu^0_{(s)}$$

The circuit is completed inside the solution by the movement of the positive ions towards the copper strip and the negative ions towards the zinc strip. The reaction goes on until either the zinc atoms or the copper ions are depleted.

It should be noted that an oxidation-reduction reaction is used to produce an electric current. This is exactly the opposite of what happens during electrolysis where an electric current is used to cause an oxidation-reduction reaction.

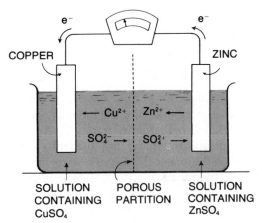

Fig. 20.1:
The Cu-Zn voltaic cell

20:4   The Car Battery

The car battery consists of plates of lead and lead dioxide, PbO_2. The lead acts as the reducing agent:

$$Pb \rightarrow Pb^{2+} + 2e^-$$

The lead dioxide acts as the oxidizing agent:

$$PbO_2 + 4H_3O^+ + 2e^- \rightarrow Pb^{2+} + 6H_2O$$

The chemical changes that the reducing agent and oxidizing agent undergo are shown separately. Each change is termed a *half-reaction* and both half-reactions constitute the overall reaction. Each electrode is termed a *half-cell* and both half-cells make up the complete cell (Fig. 20.2).

The reducing half-reaction shows electrons being given off. The oxidizing half-reaction shows them being taken on. The equations for both half-reactions are balanced for atoms and charges.

The H_3O^+ in the oxidizing equation shows that the reaction requires an acid medium. Sulfuric acid is used for this purpose. The overall chemical reaction is:

$$
\begin{array}{lll}
0 & 4+ & \text{discharge} \\
Pb & + \quad PbO_2 + 2H_2SO_4 & \rightleftharpoons \\
\downarrow & \uparrow & \text{charge} \\
2e^- & 2e^- & 2+ \\
 & & 2PbSO_4 + 2H_2O
\end{array}
$$

The reaction of the car battery, which is typical of oxidation-reduction reactions, proceeds in either direction — forward while it is delivering power to the ignition and other circuits in the car, and reverse as it is re-charged by the car generator.

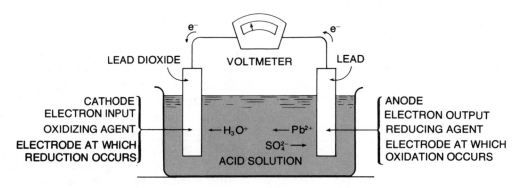

Fig. 20.2:
Oxidation and reduction in a car battery

20:5   Electrons in Electrolysis

The passage of a current through a solution can cause a chemical reaction. This process is termed *electrolysis*. We have already seen one such reaction, namely the electrolysis of water (Chapter 3).

Electroplating is an important application of electrolysis. Let us consider silver plating, a process used to cover the surface of a metallic article with a thin coat of silver. The article to be plated is connected to the negative terminal of the battery and a strip of metallic silver is connected to the positive terminal. These two electrodes (the article and the strip) are immersed into a silver salt solution (Fig. 20.3). When a current is passed through the solution, silver atoms from the silver strip give up electrons and enter the solution as silver ions:

$$Ag^0_{(s)} \rightarrow Ag^+_{(aq)} + 1e$$

These electrons are "pumped" by the battery through the external circuit to the spoon where they are taken up by the silver ions of the solution. Each silver ion gains one electron to become a neutral atom of silver:

$$Ag^+_{(aq)} + 1e \rightarrow Ag^0_{(s)}$$

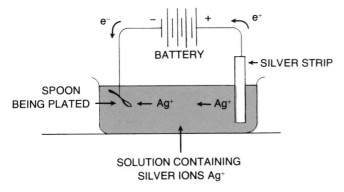

Fig. 20.3;
Silver plating

It is an experimental fact that to deposit 108 g of silver, the molar mass, or the mole of silver, requires 96 500 C*. Since the mole of silver is the Avogadro number of silver atoms or ions, and since each ion of silver requires one electron to be electrolyzed, therefore, one Avogadro number of electrons is required for the deposit of 108 g of silver atoms. Thus one Avogadro number of electrons is present in 96 500 C.

20:6   How the Avogadro Number Was First Found

To find the Avogadro number, we use the fact that one Avogadro number of electrons is 96 500 C. In addition, we also use the fact that the electrical charge on the electron is 1.6×10^{-19} C. This result was first obtained by Millikan in the oil drop experiment as described in Chapter 5. If N_A is the Avogadro number, we may write an equation:

$$N_A \times e = 96\,500$$

$$N_A = \frac{96\,500}{e^-}$$

Since $e = 1.60 \times 10^{-19}$

we have $N_A = \dfrac{96\,500}{1.60 \times 10^{-19}}$

$$= \frac{9.65 \times 10^4}{1.60 \times 10^{-19}}$$

$$= 6.02 \times 10^{23}$$

20:7   Oxidation Numbers

How can one recognize an oxidation-reduction reaction? As was discussed, such reactions can be used to generate the electric current in cells and batteries as the electrons pass from the atoms losing electrons (reducing agent) to the atoms gaining them (oxidizing agent).

*C is the SI symbol for coulomb.

Rules for Oxidation Numbers

For the purpose of writing, oxidation-reduction reactions can be recognized with the aid of *oxidation numbers. The oxidation number of an atom is the electrical charge it appears to have when calculated by arbitrary rules.* These rules make it possible to calculate the oxidation numbers for the reactants and products of a chemical change. If a substance has gained or lost electrons, this fact would be reflected in a change in the oxidation number.

Rule 1. The oxidation number of an atom of an uncombined element is zero. This is often shown by a zero written above the element to the right of its symbol:

$$Na^0, \ Cl_2^0, \ Mg^0, \ O_2^0, \ P_4^0$$

Rule 2. When a single atom becomes an ion by gaining or losing electrons, its oxidation number is the same as its charge. Thus, the oxidation numbers of Na^+, Mg^{2+}, Al^{3+}, Cl^-, are the same as the charges, namely $1+$, $2+$, $3+$, $1-$.

Rule 3. The algebraic sum of the oxidation numbers of all the atoms in the formula of a compound is zero. Thus for NaCl, the sum would be $1+$ for Na^+ and $1-$ for Cl^- or zero. For MgF_2, it would be $2+$ for Mg^{2+} and $2 \times 1-$ for the two fluoride ions. Again the sum is zero.

Rule 4. When electrons are shared in covalent bonds between two unlike atoms, they are counted as negative charges in the more electronegative of the atoms.

This would cause the charge on oxygen to be two minus $(2-)$ and that on the hydrogen one plus $(1+)$ in practically all of their compounds.*

Considering what was said about oxidation numbers, a practical definition of oxidation and reduction can now be given. An oxidation is a reaction in which the oxidation number of an atom is increased. Conversely, a reduction is a reaction in which the oxidation number of an atom is decreased:

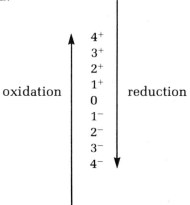

For example, in the reaction between magnesium and oxygen,

$$2Mg^0 + O_2^0 \ \rightarrow \ 2MgO,$$

the oxidation number of magnesium increases from 0 to $2+$; this is an oxidation. The oxidation number of oxygen decreases from 0 to $2-$; this is a reduction.

20:8   Examples

Calculate the oxidation numbers of sulfur in (a) H_2S, hydrogen sulfide; (b) SO_2, sulfur dioxide; (c) Na_2SO_4, sodium sulfate.

Solutions

(a) In hydrogen sulfide, one atom of sulfur is combined

---

* In peroxides such as H_2O_2, the oxidation number of oxygen is $1-$ instead of the usual $2-$. Bonding between the oxygen atoms permits the presence of two of them in the molecules of peroxides. The rules about oxidation numbers do not reflect all structural facts about molecules or ions.

In LiH, the oxidation number of hydrogen is $1-$ because its electronegativity is greater than that of lithium.

with two atoms of hydrogen whose oxidation number is $1+$. If the oxidation number of sulfur is x, we may write the equation:

$$2 \times (1+) + x = 0$$

since the sum of the oxidation numbers in a molecule is zero.

$$\therefore x = 2-$$

In H_2S, the oxidation number of sulfur is $2-$.

(b) In sulfur dioxide, one atom of sulfur is combined with two atoms of oxygen whose oxidation number is $2-$. If the oxidation number of sulfur is y, we may write the equation:

$$2 \times (2-) + y = 0$$
$$\therefore y = 4+$$

In SO_2, the oxidation number of sulfur is $4+$.

(c) In Na_2SO_4, two sodium atoms contribute two positive charges, since each has an oxidation number of $1+$. The four oxygen atoms contribute $8-$, since each has an oxidation number of $2-$. If the oxidation number of sulfur is z, then,

$$2 \times (1+) + 4(2-) + z = 0$$
$$\text{or} \quad z = 6+$$

We may interpret the results of these calculations as follows:

In H_2S, the sulfur atom is more electron attracting or more electronegative than the hydrogen. It forms polar covalent bonds with the hydrogen atoms in which the electrons are attracted to the sulfur.

In SO_2 and Na_2SO_4, the sulfur atom is less electron attracting than the oxygen. It forms polar covalent bonds with the oxygen atoms in which the electrons are attracted to the oxygen. Four electrons are thus attracted in the case of SO_2, 6 in the case of Na_2SO_4.

20:9 Balancing Oxidation-Reduction Equations

In some cases, oxidation-reduction reactions re-
quire equations with large coefficients. There is a need for a method that will help to balance such equations.

Essentially, to balance an oxidation-reduction equation, it is necessary to make sure that the number of electrons gained by the oxidizing agent is equal to the number lost by the reducing agent. How this can be achieved will be illustrated by the reaction commonly used to prepare chlorine gas.

Suppose it is necessary to balance

$$MnO_2 + HCl \rightarrow MnCl_2 + Cl_2\uparrow + H_2O$$

This is a reaction in which MnO_2 is the electron acceptor, gaining electrons from the chloride ions of hydrochloric acid. When the chloride ions lose electrons, they form chlorine atoms, which pair up to form molecules of chlorine gas.

Let us determine the oxidation numbers of the manganese and the chlorine in their compounds.

Originally, in MnO_2, the oxidation number of Mn is $4+$, being combined with two oxygen atoms, each $2-$. Finally, in $MnCl_2$, the oxidation number of Mn is $2+$, being combined with two chloride ions, each $1-$. Thus the oxidation number of the manganese changes from $4+$ to $2+$. Its oxidation number decreases, proving that Mn in MnO_2 accepts two electrons. This confirms its behaviour as the oxidizing agent.

Originally, in HCl, the oxidation number of Cl is $1-$, being combined with one hydrogen atom whose oxidation number is $1+$. Finally, some chlorine is given off as a gas, $Cl_2^0\uparrow$. For the chlorine thus evolved, the oxidation number is zero (Rule 1). Thus the oxidation number of the molecular chlorine has changed from $1-$ to 0 indicating the loss of one electron per ion thus transformed. This confirms the behaviour of the chloride ion as a reducing agent.

In the above reaction, each atom of Mn gains two electrons, while each molecule of chlorine forms through the loss of two electrons. Therefore, both Mn^{2+} and Cl_2^0 will have the same coefficient, thus ensuring that the number of electrons gained will equal the number lost. To each is assigned a coefficient of one (which is understood but not expressed).

$$\begin{array}{ccccc} 4+ & 1- & 2+ & 0 \\ MnO_2 & + HCl & \rightarrow MnCl_2 & + Cl_2^0\uparrow + H_2O \end{array}$$

$$1 \times 2e^- \quad = \quad 1 \times 2 \times 1e^-$$

With a coefficient of 1 for MnO_2, there will also be a coefficient of 1 for $MnCl_2$. Inspection now shows that 4 chlorine atoms are required by the right hand (or product) side; therefore, a coefficient of 4 is needed for HCl:

$$MnO_2 + 4HCl \rightarrow MnCl_2 + Cl_2^0\uparrow + H_2O$$

Four hydrogen atoms are now available, enough for 2 molecules of water. Hence, a coefficient of 2 is needed for H_2O:

$$MnO_2 + 4HCl \rightarrow MnCl_2 + Cl_2^0\uparrow + 2H_2O$$

With these coefficients, the oxygen atoms are also balanced and thus the entire equation is balanced.

In this reaction, some chloride ions, Cl^-, lost one electron to become Cl^0, others remained unchanged. In the above equation, Cl^0, the reducing agent, appears in HCl, $MnCl_2$, and Cl_2^0. The Cl's of $MnCl_2$ represent chloride ions, Cl^-, and thus they have not lost any electrons. It would be incorrect to place the arrow at this point to show electron loss.

The Cl's of HCl include those which *did* lose electrons to become Cl_2 as well as those which *did not*. It would be misleading to place the arrow at this point to show electron loss.

The Cl's of Cl_2^0 are indeed the result of electron loss. Therefore, this was the point at which the arrow was placed.

QUESTIONS

1. (i) Define in electronic terms: *oxidation, reduction, oxidizing agent, reducing agent.*
    (ii) Explain each of the above by reference to the reaction $2Mg + O_2 \rightarrow 2MgO$.

2. Give three examples of oxidizing agents and three examples of reducing agents. In each case, show the number of electrons gained or lost in a reaction you select.

3. What is an *oxidation number?*

4. What are the rules for calculating oxidation numbers?

5. Indicate the oxidation number of each element in the following compounds:

(i)	AgI	(v)	Na_2S	(ix)	$BiCl_3$
(ii)	NaBr	(vi)	Mg_3N_2	(x)	$ZnBr_2$
(iii)	$FeCl_2$	(vii)	CaF_2		
(iv)	$FeCl_3$	(viii)	Al_2O_3		

6. Indicate the oxidation number of each element in the following compounds:

   (i) H_2O
   (ii) K_2CO_3
   (iii) $KClO_3$
   (iv) CO
   (v) CO_2

   (vi) $KMnO_4$
   (vii) $BaSO_4$
   (viii) CuS
   (ix) NH_4OH
   (x) $CuCrO_4$

   (xi) H_2SO_4
   (xii) SO_3
   (xiii) CuO
   (xiv) $MnCl_2$
   (xv) MnO_2

7. Determine the oxidation number of chlorine in each of the following compounds:
   (a) NaCl (b) NaClO (c) $NaClO_2$ (d) $NaClO_3$ (e) $NaClO_4$

8. Explain how oxidation-reduction reactions might liberate electrical energy.

9. Write the overall reaction taking place in a car battery. Show clearly how this is an oxidation-reduction reaction.

10. Identify the following as oxidations or reductions:

    (i) $Cu^{2+} + 2e^- \rightarrow Cu^0$
    (ii) $Br_2^0 + 2e^- \rightarrow 2Br^-$
    (iii) $Mg^0 \rightarrow Mg^{2+} + 2e^-$
    (iv) $Zn^0 \rightarrow Zn^{2+} + 2e^-$
    (v) $Cl_2^0 + 2e^- \rightarrow 2Cl^-$

11. When the electrolysis of fused sodium chloride is carried out, chlorine gas forms at the positive electrode (anode) and metallic sodium forms at the negative electrode (cathode). Tell which of these reactions is an oxidation and which is a reduction. Represent the reactions separately by means of equations showing the electrons involved.

12. What is the significance of oxidation-reduction in terms of change in oxidation numbers?

13. Indicate which of the following are oxidation-reduction type reactions, and label the substances oxidized, the substances reduced, the oxidizing agents, and the reducing agents.

    (i) $Fe^0 + S^0 \rightarrow FeS$
    (ii) $NaOH + HCl \rightarrow NaCl + H_2O$
    (iii) $2FeCl_2 + Cl_2^0 \rightarrow 2FeCl_3$
    (iv) $CuO + H_2^0 \rightarrow H_2O + Cu^0$
    (v) $2Fe_2O_3 + 6H_2^0 \rightarrow 6H_2O + 4Fe^0$
    (vi) $Zn^0 + 2HCl \rightarrow ZnCl_2 + H_2^0$
    (vii) $2H_2^0 + O_2^0 \rightarrow 2H_2O$
    (viii) $NaCl + AgNO_3 \rightarrow AgCl + NaNO_3$
    (ix) $2Al^0 + 3H_2SO_4 \rightarrow Al_2(SO_4)_3 + 3H_2^0$
    (x) $2H_2S + SO_2 \rightarrow 2H_2O + 3S^0$

14. (i) What is the basic procedure in balancing oxidation-reduction equations?
    (ii) Balance the following equations using this method.

       (a) $Cu^0 + HNO_3 \rightarrow Cu(NO_3)_2 + NO_2 + H_2O$
       (b) $NH_3 + O_2^0 \rightarrow NO + H_2O$
       (c) $H_2S + SO_2 \rightarrow H_2O + S^0$
       (d) $KMnO_4 + H_2SO_3 \rightarrow K_2SO_4 + MnSO_4 + H_2SO_4 + H_2O$

15. Calculate the number of electrons released by a bar of silver, if 20.0 g of it go into solution during an electroplating process.

16. Consider the following diagram representing the set up of a voltaic cell:

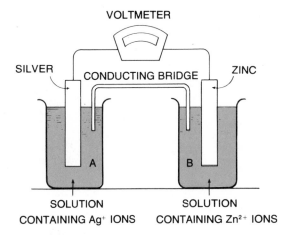

(i)   In which direction will the electrons flow?
(ii) Write the half-reaction taking place in beaker A.
(iii) Write the half-reaction taking place in beaker B.
(iv) Write the over-all reaction in ionic form.

17. How does a voltaic cell differ from an electrolytic cell?

18. When fused sodium chloride, NaCl, is electrolyzed, metallic sodium forms at the negative electrode and chlorine gas forms at the positive electrode. Draw a simplified diagram representing this electrolysis and write the ionic equations for the reactions that take place at the anode and at the cathode.

19. What mass of silver can be electroplated by a current of 3.0 A passing through a solution for one hour? (Remember that one ampere = one coulomb per second $(1A=1C/s)$).

20. (i)   How many electrons are needed for the electrolysis of one copper ion, Cu^{2+}?
    (ii) How many electrons are required for the electroysis of 1 mol of copper ions?
    (iii) Your answer in (ii) represents how many coulombs?

CHAPTER

21

LIQUIDS

21:1 Intermolecular Attraction

The model used to explain the behaviour of gases suggested that they consist of molecules in motion. The energy of motion of the molecules is their kinetic energy, and when heat energy is added, that kinetic energy increases. When heat is removed, the kinetic energy of the molecules decreases and the molecules move more slowly. Eventually as the gas is cooled, the speed is reduced more and more and the intermolecular attraction causes the molecules to condense to a liquid.

The intermolecular forces of attraction are called *van der Waals forces*, after the chemist who studied the behaviour of gases being cooled, compressed, and liquefied. Van der Waals forces result from attraction of the nuclei of one molecule for the electrons of another molecule. The attraction is significant only when the molecules are very close together. Although the van der Waals forces are powerful enough to hold the molecules together in the liquid state, they are not as strong as the chemical bonds that exist between atoms.

For chemically similar liquids, the greater the molar mass of a liquid, the larger the van der Waals forces they exert on one another. This fact is illustrated by the liquids listed in Table 21.1. Their boiling points increase with their molecular mass.

Water is an unusual liquid, and liquids are the least understood of the three states of matter.

TABLE 21.1

Boiling Points vs Molecular Masses

Liquid	Molecular Mass (u)	Boiling Point (°C)
Hexane, C_6H_{14}	86	69
Heptane, C_7H_{16}	100	98
Octane, C_8H_{18}	114	126

21:2 The Intermolecular Attraction in Water

In addition to van der Waals forces, which are present in all liquids, there are at least two other forces of attraction between the molecules of water. These cause water to be an unusual liquid in many respects. These forces arise because (a) water molecules are polar, and (b) the oxygen and hydrogen atoms in different water molecules exert a special attraction called hydrogen bonding, on one another (section 21.3).

Water molecules are polar for two reasons. First, the oxygen and hydrogen atoms differ in their ability to attract electrons, oxygen being the more electronegative of the two. Therefore, the bond between oxygen and hydrogen in the water molecule is a polar covalent bond. Second, the water molecule has a bent shape with an angle of about 105 degrees (Fig. 21.1).

Because the water molecule has this shape, the oxygen atom is a negative pole, while the region between the hydrogen atoms is a positive pole. Thus the water molecule consists of poles of positive and negative electricity, respectively. For this reason, it is termed a *dipole* (di-pole, two poles).

A liquid composed of polar molecules is called a *polar liquid*. In such a liquid, the molecules attract each other more strongly than in a non-polar liquid. The attraction between two dipoles takes place because the positive pole of one molecule attracts the negative pole of another.

21:3   Hydrogen Bonding

In the case of water, the polarity gives rise to an intermolecular force whose power is unique. The oxygen atom in a water molecule is not only bonded to two hydrogen atoms, but it is attracted to hydrogen atoms belonging to other molecules as well (Fig. 21.2). As a result, the force of intermolecular attraction is unusually powerful in water.

Hydrogen bonding is a powerful intermolecular force present in compounds containing —OH and —NH groups, as well as in hydrogen fluoride, HF.

What evidence is there for hydrogen bonding? The simplest and most convincing proof for hydrogen bonding is found by comparing the boiling points of water and the compounds resembling water. Two ideas, illustrated in Table 21.1, are essential to the proof. First, the higher the boiling point of a compound, the greater is the force of attraction between the molecules. Second, large molecules attract each other more strongly than small molecules, other things being equal. With these thoughts in mind, compare the boiling points of water H_2O, hydrogen sulfide H_2S, hydrogen selenide H_2Se, and hydrogen telluride H_2Te. These compounds resemble water in the sense that

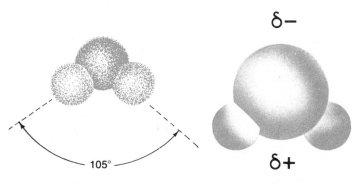

a. The bent shape of
   the water molecule

b. The dipolar nature of
   the water molecule

Fig. 21.1: The water molecule

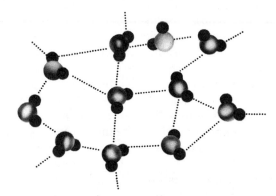

Fig. 21.2:
Hydrogen bonds between water molecules are shown by dotted lines.

oxygen, sulfur, selenium, and tellurium are elements of group VI of the periodic table. Since they are compounds of hydrogen with another element, they are called *hydrides*. Their boiling points and molecular masses are given in Table 21.2 and shown graphically in Fig. 21.3.

Note that the boiling point of water is much higher than that of even hydrogen telluride. This is true despite the fact that the molecule of water is the smallest and lightest of the four. True to form, the boiling points of the three other compounds decrease as the molecules become smaller (Fig. 21.3).

What explanation can be offered for hydrogen bonding? Let us refer to water molecules as an example of how hydrogen bonds might be pictured. Recall that the oxygen atom is highly electronegative and so attracts the electrons of the OH bond.

$$O: \quad H$$

Under these conditions, the H is attracted to the unshared pairs of electrons in an oxygen atom of another water molecule. Thus H serves as a bridge linking two oxygen atoms from two water molecules. This bridge, called a *hydrogen bond*, causes the water molecules to be rather strongly attracted to one another (Fig. 21.3). Thus the high boiling point of water is said to be due to the large amount of energy needed to break the hydrogen bonds

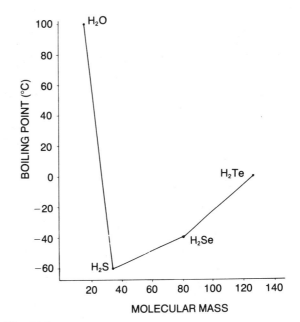

Fig. 21.3:
Evidence for hydrogen bonding
The unusually high boiling point of water is due to hydrogen bonding between its molecules.

between the water molecules. Other properties of water, including some of utmost ecological importance, can be accounted for in the same way (Sections 21.4, 5, 6, 7, 8, 9).

Nitrogen and fluorine are also highly electronegative, as is oxygen. Their atoms also have unshared pairs of electrons. Thus hydrogen bonding between molecules containing N-H and F-H can be similarly explained.

21:4 Liquids Have a Definite Volume

Because of the intermolecular forces of attraction, liquids retain their own volume and do not distribute themselves throughout the whole space of the containing vessel, as gases do. Since the molecules of a liquid still have the freedom to glide past each other, the liquid takes the shape of the vessel it occupies.

TABLE 21.2

The Boiling Points of the Hydrides of Group VI

Elements of Group VI and their Atomic Mass		Their Hydrides and Molar Mass		Boiling Points °C
Oxygen	(16)	H_2O	(18)	+100
Sulfur	(32)	H_2S	(34)	−60
Selenium	(79)	H_2Se	(81)	−40
Tellurium	(128)	H_2Te	(130)	0

21:5   The Vapour Pressure of Liquids

A liquid gradually evaporates if it is left in an open vessel. In *evaporation*, the molecules of the liquid pass into the air in the form of a gas or vapour. In order to be able to do so, the molecules must have enough energy to overcome the intermolecular attractive forces. The molecules gain this energy after colliding with their neighbours.

At any one time, only a relatively small fraction of all the molecules have this amount of energy. These molecules escape into the air and do not return to the liquid, thus causing evaporation.

If the liquid is in a closed vessel, the process of evaporation still goes on, since the molecules escape from the liquid as before. Now the molecules have only a limited space in which to fly about. Soon they must fall back into the liquid. This is called *condensation*. Two processes are now going on in the closed vessel, evaporation and condensation. These processes go on at equal rates, thus establishing a *dynamic equilibrium* (Fig. 21.4).

In such a condition, no change appears to be taking place, but in reality two opposite changes are going on at equal rates. Some molecules leave the liquid to enter the vapour, while others leave the vapour to return to the liquid.

The pressure that the molecules in the vapour above the liquid exert is called the *vapour pressure*, and it depends on the temperature only. The size, shape, or fullness of the vessel do not alter the vapour pressure of a liquid.

Since the vapour pressure depends on the escape of the molecules from a liquid, the more powerful the force of intermolecular attraction, the smaller the vapour pressure of the liquid will be. The vapour pressure of water is less than that of a non-polar liquid of the same molar mass.

21:6   Boiling Point

When a liquid is heated, the heat energy makes the molecules move more rapidly as their energy in-

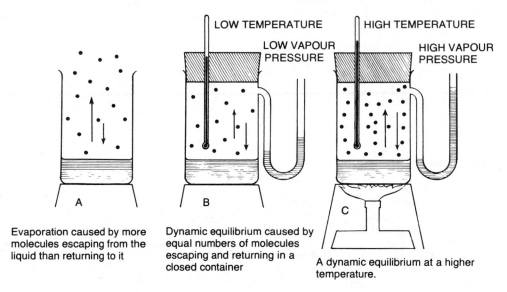

LOW TEMPERATURE

LOW VAPOUR PRESSURE

HIGH TEMPERATURE

HIGH VAPOUR PRESSURE

A
Evaporation caused by more molecules escaping from the liquid than returning to it

B
Dynamic equilibrium caused by equal numbers of molecules escaping and returning in a closed container

C
A dynamic equilibrium at a higher temperature.

Fig. 21.4:
Evaporation of a liquid in an open vessel and dynamic equilibrium in a closed vessel

creases. This causes more molecules to overcome the molecular attraction and escape from the liquid as a vapour. Thus the vapour pressure of a liquid increases rapidly as its temperature is raised (Fig. 21.5). A point is reached where the vapour pressure becomes as great as the atmospheric pressure. It is then that the liquid begins to boil. The temperature at which the vapour pressure of a liquid becomes 101.3 kPa, the standard pressure of the atmosphere, is called the normal boiling point of the liquid. The greater the molecular attractive forces in a liquid, the higher will be its boiling point (Fig. 21.5).

21:7   Heat of Vaporization

When a liquid changes to its vapour, the molecules need to be separated from one another. To do this, the forces of intermolecular attraction must be overcome, and this requires work. The energy for this work is called the *heat of vaporization*. When a liquid changes to a vapour, the heat of vaporization must be supplied to the liquid, and when the vapour condenses to the liquid state, the same amount of energy is liberated. As a general rule, *heat is required when matter passes from a state where the particles are closer, or are held more rigidly together, to a state where they are further apart, or are held less rigidly.* Such is the case in vaporization and melting. When the opposite occurs, that is, when matter passes from a state where the particles are held loosely to a state where they are held more firmly, heat is given out. Such is the case in condensation and freezing. (See Table 21.3.)

As would be expected, in liquids of stronger intermolecular forces the heat of vaporization is greater than in liquids of weaker forces. Thus the heat of vaporization of water is 2263 joules per gram (J/g) while the heat of vaporization of octane is about 587 J/g. The heat of vaporization may be represented by Q_r, measured in joules per gram (J/g), or by ΔH_r, measured in joules per mole (J/mol). The energy of condensation is similarly expressed as the heat of condensation, Q_c, in J/g, and the molar heat of condensation, ΔH_c, in J/mol.

21:8   Freezing Point

If a liquid is cooled, the loss of heat means a lowering of molecular energy and molecular motion. Upon continued cooling, a point is reached where the molecules move so slowly that the intermolecular forces cause the molecules to assume certain positions in a geometrical pattern called a *crystal*. The substance is thus *solidified* or *frozen*. The solid is usually in the form of rigid crystals, and any molecular motion that does remain is limited to vibration only.

As in the case of boiling and condensation, freezing is a reversible process which occurs at a definite temperature. The reverse process is called *melting* or *fusion*. (See Table 21.3.)

A definite amount of heat is needed to overcome the intermolecular forces in the solid and to permit the molecular motion needed for melting. This is called the *heat of fusion*. When the liquid freezes the heat of fusion is liberated. The symbol for the heat of fusion may be represented by Q_f, measured in joules per gram (J/g), or by ΔH_f (J/mol). The heat of solidification is similarly expressed as Q_s, in J/g, and the molar heat of solidification, ΔH_s, in J/mol.

The following equations show *phase* changes and the molar heat associated with each change.

$$H_2O_{(s)} \;+\; 6.0 \text{ kJ} \;\rightarrow\; H_2O_{(l)}$$
$$H_2O_{(l)} \;\rightarrow\; H_2O_{(s)} \;+\; 6.0 \text{ kJ}$$
$$H_2O_{(l)} \;+\; 40.5 \text{ kJ} \;\rightarrow\; H_2O_{(g)}$$
$$H_2O_{(g)} \;\rightarrow\; H_2O_{(l)} \;+\; 40.5 \text{ kJ}$$
$$Na_{(s)} \;+\; 2.6 \text{ kJ} \;\rightarrow\; Na_{(l)}$$

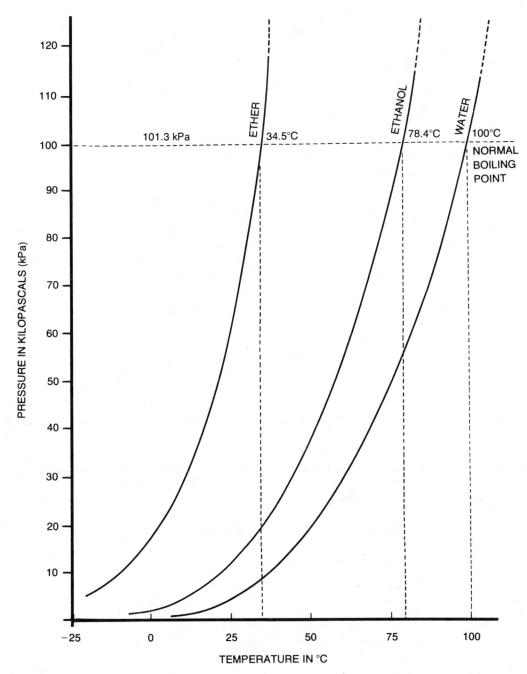

Fig. 21.5:
Graph showing how the vapour pressure of a liquid changes with temperature

Table 21.3

Molar Heat of Vaporization and Molar Heat of Fusion

Substance	Melting Point °C	Boiling Point °C	ΔH_f kJ/mol	ΔH_v kJ/mol
Ammonia	−78	−33	8	23
Argon	−189	−186	1	6
Copper	1083	2595	13	304
Mercury	−38	357	2	58
Sodium	98	892	3	101
Sodium chloride	800	1465	28	171
Water	0	100	6	40

21:9 Thermal Properties of Substances

When a solid, a liquid, or a gas is heated at a temperature other than the melting or boiling point, the temperature of the substance increases. The number of joules required to raise the temperature of one gram of the substance one degree Celsius is called the *specific heat capacity* of that substance (Table 21.4). The specific heat capacity of a substance is represented by the symbol c.

Table 21.4

Specific Heat Capacities of Some Common Substances (J/g °C)

Aluminum	0.895	Lead	0.130
Copper	0.385	Sodium chloride	0.773
Gold	0.130	Steam	2.00
Ice	2.13	Sulfur	0.573
Iron	0.451	Water	4.19

The specific heat capacity of water, $c = 4.19$ J/g °C, means that 4.19 J are absorbed by one gram of water when its temperature rises by one degree Celsius.

Therefore, the quantity of heat absorbed by 10.0 g of water when the temperature rises from 20.0°C to 75.0°C could be calculated by the following equation: $Q = m \times \Delta t \times c$

where
Q = quantity of heat
m = mass
Δt = change in temperature
c = specific heat capacity

In our problem, the heat absorbed is

$$Q = m \times \Delta t \times c$$
$$= 10.0 \text{ g} \times 55.0°C \times 4.19 \text{ J/g °C}$$
$$= 2\ 300 \text{ J}$$

21:10 The Unusual Behaviour of Water at Its Freezing Point

The density of water is greater than that of ice. There is greater mass per unit volume in the liquid than in the solid. This means that there must be more molecules per unit volume after the crystal of ice is broken down by melting than while it was still intact. How can this be explained?

The water molecules exert a special attraction on each other by hydrogen bonding. In the liquid state, the molecules are free to glide past each other. In the solid state, free molecular motion from point to point is eliminated. The hydrogen bonds become the cohesive force that helps to form the crystal of ice. Each oxygen atom is now attached, not merely attracted, to four hydrogen atoms — two combined chemically, two held by hydrogen bonding. The resulting ice structure is relatively uncrowded; that is, there is much space between the molecules, owing to the rigidity of the hydrogen bonds (Fig. 21.6).

When ice melts, some of the hydrogen bonds break and the molecules of water crowd together as the ice structure collapses. As a result, the molecules take up less space and the liquid has a greater density than the ice (Fig. 21.7).

From 0°C to 4°C, the volume continues to decrease as more hydrogen bonds break. Meanwhile, thermal agitation drives the molecules further apart. Above 4°C, the expanding effect of thermal agitation exceeds the crowding effect caused by the continuing breakage of hydrogen bonds. This explains why 4°C is the temperature of maximum density. In ice, the hydrogen bonds hold the molecules in an "open" crystal lattice. Freezing causes expansion of volume. In water, the hydrogen bonds are not rigid, and the molecules come closer together. Melting causes contraction in volume.

It should be noted that hydrogen bonds remain an attractive force between water molecules in the liquid state, and even to a certain extent, in the gaseous state.

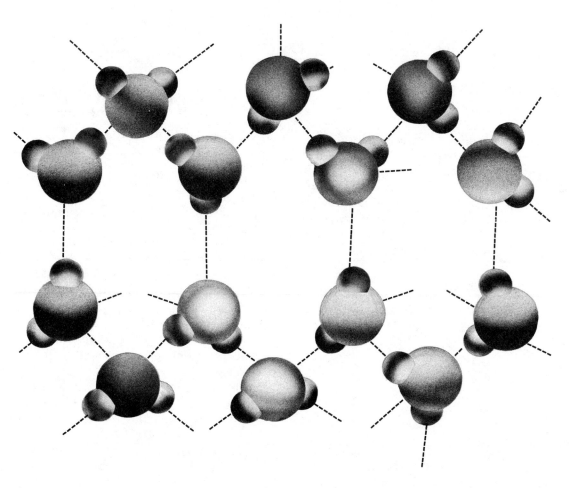

Fig. 21.6:
The crystal structure of ice, showing molecules of water held rigidly by hydrogen bonds

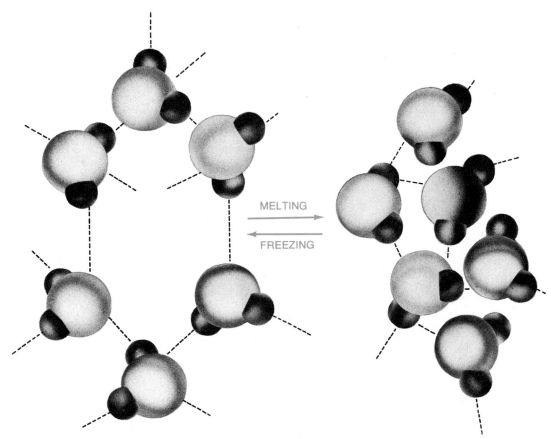

Fig. 21.7:
Expansion and contraction of water on freezing and melting

QUESTIONS

1. Why does lowering the temperature of a gas cause it to condense to a liquid?

2. What are van der Waals forces?

3. Why is the water molecule polar? Draw a diagram to illustrate your answer.

4. Draw a graph similar to that shown in Fig. 21.3. Plot on the graph the normal boiling points of hydrogen iodide, HI (−35°C), hydrogen bromide, HBr (−67°C), hydrogen chloride, HCl (−84°C), and hydrogen fluoride, HF (19°C). Label and join the four points obtained by straight lines. Draw conclusions concerning intermolecular forces of attraction present in these compounds.

5. Octane, C_8H_{18}, is said to be a non-polar liquid. Explain clearly what is meant by this statement.

6. Explain why the density of water (18 g/mol) is greater than that of octane (114 g/mol) in spite of the fact that octane has a greater molar mass.

7. Explain dynamic equilibrium by reference to an evaporating liquid in a closed container.

8. What is meant by the term *vapour pressure*?

9. How is vapour pressure related to the force of intermolecular attraction?

10. Consider Fig. 21.4 b and c in which dynamic equilibrium exists between the liquid phase and the vapour phase. Compare these from the point of view of the number of molecules leaving the liquid and returning to it.

11. Relate boiling point to atmospheric pressure.

12. How is boiling point related to the forces of intermolecular attraction in a liquid?

13. Referring to Fig. 21.5, determine the temperature at which water boils under the following pressures: (i) 40 kPa   (ii) 20 kPa   (iii) 10 kPa   (iv) 50 kPa.

14. What is *heat of vaporization*?

15. Why is the heat of vaporization of octane less than that of water?

16. Why is heat absorbed when the particles of matter making up a substance are forced further apart?

17. Why is energy given up when a liquid changes to a solid?

18. (a) What is *heat of fusion*?
    (b) The heat of fusion of water is 335.2 J/g. What does this mean?

19. How many joules are required to convert 10 g of water at 100°C to steam at 100°C?

20. Describe the structure of ice.

21. Why does water expand upon freezing?

22. Explain carefully why the maximum density of water is at 4°C.

23. Calculate the heat of fusion, Q_f, in J/g of the following substances:
    (i) ammonia; (ii) copper; (iii) sodium chloride; (iv) water.

24. Calculate the heat of vaporization, Q_v, in J/g, of the following substances: (i) argon; (ii) mercury; (iii) sodium; (iv) water.

25. How many kilojoules would be required to convert 5.00 mol of water at 100°C into steam at 100°C?

26. How much heat must be supplied to a 9.00 g piece of ice to melt it completely? Give your answer in joules.

27. How many kilojoules are liberated when 3 mol of steam at 100°C condenses to water at 100°C?

28. How much heat is absorbed by each of the following solid substances when it is converted to a liquid? Assume that each solid substance is already at its melting point temperature.
    (i)   5.0 g of ammonia;   (iii)   100 g of sodium chloride;
    (ii)   30.0 g of copper;   (iv)   150 g of ice.

29. How many kilojoules would be required to change 25.0 g of ice at −10.0°C to steam at 110°C, given that the specific heat of ice is 2.13 J/g and that of steam is 2.00 J/g?

CHAPTER

22

SOLIDS

22:1 The Kinetic Molecular Theory Applied to Solids

A solid is rigid; it has a definite shape with enough mechanical strength to resist changes in its shape. An examination of many solids shows that their structure has a definite geometrical form. They are said to be *crystalline*. Although the particles of a solid do not wander freely, they vibrate back and forth about their fixed positions. When the solid is heated sufficiently, the vibrations of its atoms, molecules, or ions, become great enough to break the bonds that hold them in the crystal and the solid melts.

22:2 The External Structure of Crystals

A crystal is always bounded by flat surfaces or planes which meet at right angles or at some other characteristic angles. Crystals can be classified according to their geometrical forms. The structures of crystals are best described in terms of imaginary axes drawn through their centres and parallel to the planes. All crystals that have been studied belong to one or other of six fundamental arrangements of axes. These six *crystallographic systems* are illustrated in Fig. 22.1. The study of the structure of crystals is called *crystallography*.

To some, the term "solid" means lifeless and uninteresting. Haven't they heard of solid state stereo?

22:3 The Internal Structure of Crystals

The external shape of a crystal is the result of the spatial arrangement of the particles that make up the crystal. This three-dimensional, ordered array of particles is called the *crystal lattice*. The lattice may be considered to be made up of *unit cells* which are each the smallest portion of the crystal lattice.

To get an idea of how the unit cell recurs throughout a crystal, think of displays of spherically shaped fruit in a food store. Oranges and grapefruit are often arranged carefully in rows forming a layer; other rows are then fitted into the shapes formed by the spheres of the level shown in Fig. 22.2.

The shape of the unit cell, and therefore of the whole crystal, depends on the force of attraction between the particles, on whether the particles are the same or different, and, if they are different, on their relative sizes.

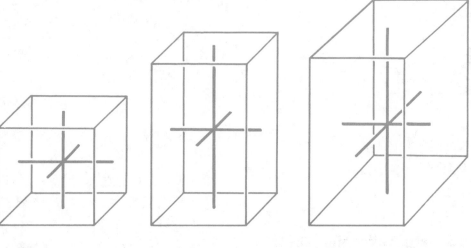

a. CUBIC

3 equal axes all at right angles to one another

b. TETRAGONAL

2 equal axes and 1 axis of different length; all at right angles to one another

c. ORTHORHOMBIC

3 unequal axes all at right angles to one another

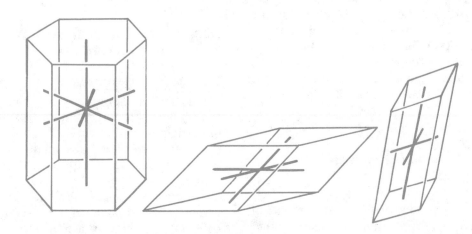

d. HEXAGONAL

3 equal axes and a 4th of different length; 3 at 60° to one another and the 4th at right angles to the other 3

e. MONOCLINIC

3 unequal axes, 2 at right angles to each other; the 3rd is at right angles to one but not to the other

f. TRICLINIC

3 unequal axes, no two at right angles to the others

Fig. 22.1:
The six crystallographic systems

Fig. 22.2:
The regular spacing of ions or atoms in a crystal

The unit cell of a given crystallographic system may be one of a few types with the same shape. For example, in the cubic system alone, there are three common types. The lattice may be made up of *simple cubic*, *face-centred cubic*, or *body-centred cubic* cells (Fig. 22.3).

22:4   Types of Solids

Knowledge about crystal structure makes it possible to relate important physical properties of solids to their crystalline structure. In addition to the above classification, crystals can be classified also according to the chemical nature of their particles. This yields four types of solids: covalent, ionic, molecular, and metallic. Table 22.1 lists for each type, the nature of the particles occupying the lattice points, the nature of the bonds involved, a few characteristic properties, and some examples.

Covalent Atomic Solids
In *covalent solids* the points of the crystal lattice are occupied by atoms which share electrons with their neighbours. These covalent bonds extend in fixed directions and bind the crystal in a giant interlocking structure. The covalent bonds are quite strong and as a result the solids are quite hard, have a high melting point, and are poor conductors of electricity.

The classic example of this type of solid is diamond, in which all the carbon atoms are held together in a lattice by covalent bonds. Each atom is joined to four others at exactly the same distance from one another. Any atom may be considered to be at the centre of a tetrahedron with four atoms at the corners. This pattern repeats itself throughout the entire crystal which becomes a giant molecule (Fig. 22.4).

In graphite, on the other hand, each atom is joined to only three others by covalent bonds. The three covalent bonds lie in the same plane with an angle of 120 degrees between them. In this way, the carbon atoms arrange themselves at the corners of adjacent hexagons, forming planes. The atoms in a given plane are held together by strong covalent linkages, but the forces between the planes are weak. As a result, the planes can glide readily past one another. This causes graphite to be soft and flake-like. Furthermore, this structure requires only three of the electrons of the carbon atoms to form strong covalent bonds. One electron is relatively free to move, giving graphite its power to conduct electric current, a property that diamond does not have.

Ionic Solids
The particles that occupy the lattice points in an *ionic solid* are positive and negative ions. The binding forces that hold the crystal together are the fairly strong electrostatic attractions between the ions of opposite charge. Therefore, these solids have rather high melting points, are hard and brittle, and are poor conductors of electricity. Examples of ionic solids include sodium chloride, $NaCl$, potassium nitrate, KNO_3, and sodium sulfate, Na_2SO_4.

Fig. 3.2 shows the lattice of sodium chloride, which, like all ionic salts, exists only in the ionic, not in the molecular condition. In the lattice, every sodium ion has six chloride ions as nearest neighbours; one to the right and one to the left, one above and one below, one in front and one behind. Similarly, every chloride ion has six sodium ions as immediate neighbours.

Molecular Solids

In *molecular solids* the lattice points are occupied by molecules. The forces of attraction between the molecules of such solids can be of two kinds. The relatively weak van der Waals attractions are present in all molecular solids. If the molecules of the solid are polar, additional forces act between the poles of opposite charges. However, these forces are not very strong when compared to covalent or ionic bonds. Thus, molecular crystals have low melting points, are usually quite soft and do not conduct the electric current. Iodine crystals, I_2, dry ice, CO_2, and ordinary ice, H_2O, are examples of molecular solids.

TABLE 22.1

Types of Solids

Types	Covalent	Ionic	Molecular	Metallic
Particles occupying lattice points	atoms	positive and negative ions	molecules	positive ions
Binding force between particles	shared electrons	electrostatic attraction	van der Waals and dipole-dipole intermolecular attraction	electrical attraction between positive ions and negative electrons
Strength of binding force	very strong	fairly strong	weak	dependant on the number of mobile electrons
Properties	hard, high melting point, non-conductors	hard, brittle medium melting point, non-conductors	soft, low melting point, non-conductors	wide range of hardness and melting point, good conductors
Examples	diamond, C; quartz, SiO_2; carborundum or silicon carbide, SiC	sodium chloride, NaCl; potassium nitrate, KNO_3	iodine, I_2; ice, H_2O; dry ice, CO_2	sodium aluminum iron
Pictorial representation				

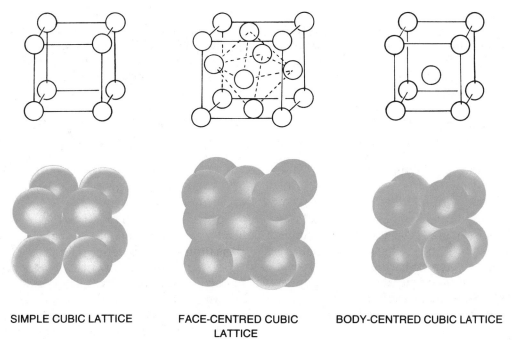

SIMPLE CUBIC LATTICE   FACE-CENTRED CUBIC LATTICE   BODY-CENTRED CUBIC LATTICE

Fig. 22.3:
Unit cells of the cubic system

DIAMOND: TETRAHEDRAL STRUCTURE   GRAPHITE: HEXAGONAL STRUCTURE

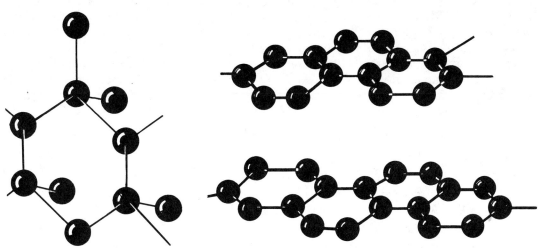

Fig. 22.4:
Crystal structure of diamond and graphite

Metallic Solids

The crystal lattice of *metallic solids* consists of atoms in which the outer electrons are free to move from atom to atom under the slightest electrical stimulus. In reality, because their outer electrons are free to move about in the metal lattice, the particles that make up the metallic crystal are positively charged ions, rather than atoms. The mobile electrons belong to the crystal as a whole and are the cohesive force in the metal. This mobility of electrons gives the metals their high electrical conductivity. The number of free electrons available for bonding varies from group to group in the periodic table. This partly explains why the properties of metals vary as they do. Some are better conductors than others; their melting points and their degree of hardness vary over a wide range. Potassium melts at 62°C while iron melts at 1535°C. Sodium is so soft that it can be cut with a knife. Tungsten is a hard metal used to make alloys that can cut steel.

22:5   Efflorescence and Deliquescence

Theoretically, molecules might escape from solids as they do from liquids. If this occurred, the solid would then have a vapour pressure. Thus molecules of carbon dioxide escape readily from dry ice, solid carbon dioxide. Most solids, however have only a negligible vapour pressure.

A certain class of salts, containing *water of hydration*, have a definite vapour pressure at any particular temperature due to the evaporation of some of the molecules of water of hydration. If these salts are placed in an area where the humidity is so high that the water vapour pressure in the air is greater than that of salt, then some water might condense on the salt. This phenomenon, called *deliquescence*, continues until the rate of condensation on the salt and evaporation from the salt become equal.

If, on the other hand, the humidity is so low that the vapour pressure of the salt is greater than that of the environment, then the water of hydration evaporates. This phenomenon, called *efflorescence*, also continues until evaporation and condensation go on at equal rates.

Sodium sulfate is an example of a salt with ten molecules of water of hydration per formula unit of salt. In this form, the hydrate would be represented by $Na_2SO_4 \cdot 10H_2O$. The loss of water, and the condensation of water may be represented by the equation:

$$\overset{\text{efflorescence}}{\underset{\text{deliquescence}}{Na_2SO_4 \cdot 10H_2O \rightleftharpoons Na_2SO_4 + 10H_2O}}$$

(solid)   (solid)   (vapour)

If the hydrated salt is placed in an environment where the vapour pressure of water is less than that of salt, the latter steadily loses its water of hydration, thus becoming a lower hydrate, or completely anhydrous. The reverse occurs if the vapour pressure of the environment is greater than that of the anhydrous salt or of the lower hydrate.

QUESTIONS

1. What is a *crystalline solid*?

2. In terms of the kinetic molecular theory, explain why: (i) solids are practically incompressible; (ii) solids expand when heated; (iii) solids have a definite shape.

3. Why must a solid absorb heat in order to melt?

4. What is meant by the following terms: (i) crystallographic systems; (ii) crystal lattice; (iii) unit cell?

5. What types of cubic cells occur? Illustrate your answer with diagrams.

6. List the six main crystalline systems and give the distinguishing characteristics of each.

7. What explanation can be given for the hardness of diamond?

8. Why is graphite so much softer than diamond?

9. Account for the fact that graphite will conduct an electric current while diamond will not.

10. Describe the crystalline structure of sodium chloride.

11. Account for the fact that ionic solids do not conduct the electric current even though they are made of positive and negative ions.

12. Atom A belongs to group I of the periodic table and atom B belongs to group VII. What type of solid results when the two atoms combine to form compound AB? Predict the general properties of compound AB with regard to hardness, melting point, conductivity in the solid state, and conductivity in the liquid state.

13. Describe the crystalline structure of metals.

14. Why are metals good conductors of electricity?

15. What is the main cohesive force in metals?

16. What is a *hydrate*?

17. What is the percentage of water of hydration in sodium sulfate decahydrate, $Na_2SO_4 \cdot 10H_2O$?

18. How many kilograms of anhydrous copper (II) sulfate can be obtained from 100 kg of copper (II) sulfate pentahydrate $CuSO_4 \cdot 5H_2O$?

4

SOLUTIONS AND REACTIONS

Noranda Mines Limited

CHAPTER

23

SOLUTIONS

23:1 Nature of Solutions

Solutions have been defined in section 3:6 as homogeneous mixtures. Because solutions are of widespread importance in chemistry, they are discussed more intensively in this chapter. Their importance is apparent when it is realized that the majority of chemical reactions that occur in nature as well as in the chemical industries take place in solution. For example, unless food is in solution, it cannot be absorbed by the blood.

A solution is usually formed when a gas, a liquid, or a solid is dissolved in a liquid, called the *solvent*; but gases and even solids may act as solvents (Table 23.1). The substance dissolved is called the *solute*. A *solution* may be redefined as a homogeneous mixture of solute and solvent.

23:2 Solubility

Ethanol and water mix with one another in all proportions to form a solution. Such liquids are said to be perfectly *miscible*. On the other hand, oil and water are *immiscible*; they do not mix with one another.

In many cases, there is a limit to the amount of solute A that will dissolve in a given amount of solvent B under specified conditions. When this amount, called the *solubility* of A in B, is exceeded,

Where chemistry overlaps with biology and industry — and the tap water we drink, and the food we eat.

the excess remains undissolved. For example, 36 g of sodium chloride dissolve in 100 g of water at 20°C. When the solubility of a solute is determined at various temperatures, the results can be shown as a *solubility curve* (Fig. 23.1).

When enough solute is added to a solvent so that the limit of solubility is reached, the solution is said to be *saturated*. If more solute is added, it

TABLE 23.1

Types of Solutions

Solute	Solvent	Examples
solid	liquid	brine (sodium chloride in water)
liquid	liquid	antifreeze (alcohol in water)
gas	liquid	soda water (carbon dioxide in water)
solid	gas	naphthalene in air (sublimation of moth balls)
liquid	gas	humid air (water vapour in air)
gas	gas	air (oxygen in nitrogen)
solid	solid	brass (zinc in copper)
liquid	solid	amalgams (mercury in gold)
gas	solid	hydrogen in platinum

remains undissolved. The saturated solution will be in equilibrium with the undissolved solute. In this condition, the solute enters and leaves the solution at the same rate. If the solution contains less solute than it is capable of dissolving at a given temperature, it is *unsaturated*.

With certain solutes such as sodium thiosulfate, $Na_2S_2O_3$, and sodium acetate, CH_3COONa, it is possible to prepare solutions which contain more of the dissolved solute than the normal saturation quantity. Such solutions are *supersaturated* and can be prepared by cooling saturated solutions or by evaporation. These solutions are unstable and crystallize easily when jarred or when a crystal of the solute is added to them.

Factors Affecting Rate of Solution of Solids in Liquids
The solubility curve for potassium nitrate indi-

cates that about 30 g dissolve in 100 g of water at room temperature, about 20°C. If this amount is simply added to the water, considerable time may be required for it to dissolve completely. The process of dissolving may be speeded up by agitation or stirring, by reducing the size of the crystals, and by heating the solution. These three methods increase the rate of dissolving by increasing the contact between solute and solvent.

23:3   The Process of Dissolving

As is well known, certain solvents readily dissolve certain solutes, but not others. While we are still unable to predict perfectly what solute will dissolve in what solvent or the extent of any given solubility, nevertheless, we may learn a great deal

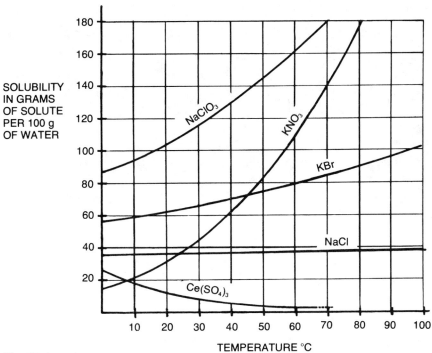

Fig. 23.1:
Solubility curves

about the process of dissolving by considering the intermolecular or interionic forces that come into play.

When solute A dissolves in solvent B, the intermolecular or interionic forces of A and of B both have to be overcome. The solute must be broken down to its molecules or ions, and even the solvent molecules need to be separated somewhat to make room for the molecules or ions of the solute. To separate the particles of solute requires energy, as does the separation of a solid in melting or of a liquid in vaporizing. Such energy might be provided by the formation of bonds between the solute and the solvent.

When salt dissolves in water, the powerful interionic forces between the sodium and chloride ions, as well as the hydrogen bonds between the water molecules, both have to be overcome. The energy needed to break these bonds is supplied by the new bonds formed between the ions and the water molecules. Such bonds are referred to as *ion-dipole bonds*, the ions being Na^+ and Cl^-, while the dipoles are the water molecules.

When an ionic compound, such as sodium chloride, is placed in water, the partly positive hydrogen atoms of the water molecules surround the negative chloride ions, while the partly negative oxygen surrounds the sodium ions (Fig. 23.2).

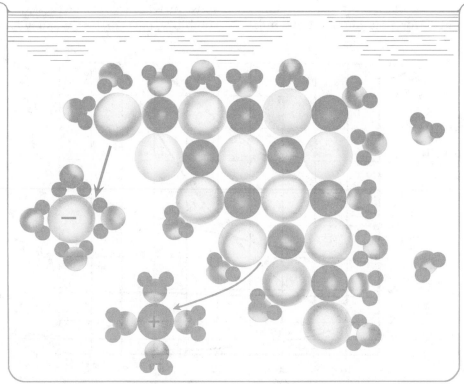

Fig. 23.2:
Polar water molecules are attracted to ions in the process of dissolving salts

The formation of these ion-dipole bonds releases enough energy to separate the ions of the solid salt and the molecules of the water (Fig. 23.3).

Experiments have shown that when surrounded by water, the force of attraction between electrically charged bodies is reduced to 1/80 of its normal strength. This property is described by saying that water has a *dielectric constant* of 80. Water is also able to dissolve organic compounds containing hydroxide groups (—OH) in their molecules by forming hydrogen bonds with these groups. Such organic compounds include alcohol and sugar.

When, by contrast, oil is added to water, no bonds form between the non-polar molecules of oil and the polar molecules of water; therefore, no energy is released for breaking the powerful hydrogen bonds of the water. As a result, oil cannot dissolve in water; nor can water dissolve in oil. Similarly, when salt is added to an oil, there is no possibility of bonds forming between the ions of the salt and the molecules of oil. Thus, no energy is provided for breaking the interionic bonds of the salt, and, as a result, salt cannot dissolve in oil.

Again, the intermolecular forces in non-polar liquids are not very strong. When, therefore, one non-polar compound is added to another, it is easy for the solute and solvent molecules to be separated. For this reason non-polar substances readily dissolve in one another.

23:4   Factors Affecting Solubility

The concentration of a given saturated solution depends on the nature of the solvent, the nature of the solute, the temperature, and the pressure.

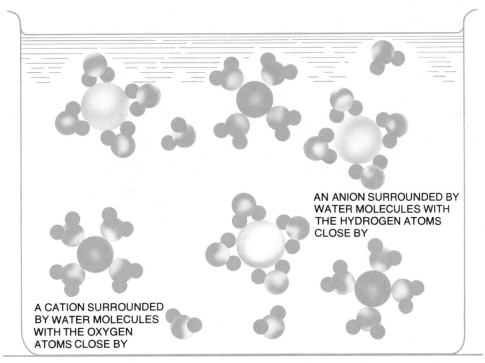

AN ANION SURROUNDED BY WATER MOLECULES WITH THE HYDROGEN ATOMS CLOSE BY

A CATION SURROUNDED BY WATER MOLECULES WITH THE OXYGEN ATOMS CLOSE BY

Fig. 23.3:
Hydrated ions in a solution

The Nature of Solvent and Solute

As was pointed out in the previous section, sodium chloride dissolves in water but does not dissolve in oil. Some gases are extremely soluble in water while other gases are only slightly soluble. The dissolving mechanism of sodium chloride in water revealed that the formation of new bonds between solvent and solute made the reaction possible. No doubt, as knowledge about the structure of matter improves, better explanations of solubility will be possible.

Effect of Temperature

As a general rule, gases dissolve in liquids to a larger extent at low temperatures than at high temperatures, while liquids and solids show the opposite behaviour. This may be explained by considering the effect of temperature on the solute and solvent in each case. The addition of heat increases the kinetic energy of all the particles of the solution. Such increased motion results in a greater tendency of gas molecules to escape from the solution; hence, the lower solubility of gases. The increased motion of the molecules of liquids and the particles of solids helps to break the bonds between them. This explains the higher solubility of liquids and solids.

Effect of Pressure

Changes in pressure have practically no effect on the solubility of solids and liquids. However, gases are more soluble in liquids as pressure is raised. A familiar example is furnished by carbonated beverages. The gaseous solution is bottled under pressure. When the cap is removed, the pressure on the solution is reduced and the carbon dioxide gas escapes, causing the observed effervescence.

23:5   General Solubility Rules

Chemists often consider a substance to be soluble when more than 0.1 mol can be dissolved in 1 L of solution (0.1 mol/L). Certain generalizations can be made concerning the solubility of common substances in water based on this general principle. Apart from a few unimportant exceptions, the following statements hold true.

1. All alkali (Li^+, Na^+, K^+, Rb^+, Cs^+, Fr^+) and ammonium (NH_4^+) compounds are soluble.
2. All acetates (CH_3COO^-), chlorates (ClO_3^-), and nitrates (NO_3^-) are soluble.
3. All chlorides (Cl^-), bromides (Br^-), and iodides (I^-) are soluble except those of copper (I) (Cu^+), lead (II) (Pb^{2+}), mercury (I) (Hg_2^{2+}), and silver (Ag^+).
4. All sulfates (SO_4^{2-}) are soluble except those of calcium (Ca^{2+}), strontium (Sr^{2+}), barium (Ba^{2+}), radium (Ra^{2+}), and lead (Pb^{2+}).
5. All normal carbonates (CO_3^{2-}), phosphates (PO_4^{3-}), and sulfites (SO_3^{2-}) are insoluble, with the exceptions of the alkali (Li^+, Na^+, K^+, Rb^+ Cs^+ Fr^+) and ammonium (NH_4^+) compounds.
6. All sulfides (S^{2-}) are insoluble, except those of alkali (Li^+, Na^+, K^+, Rb^+, Cs^+, Fr^+), alkaline earth (Be^{2+}, Mg^{2+}, Ca^{2+}, Sr^{2+}, Ba^{2+}, Ra^{2+}), and ammonium (NH_4^+) compounds.
7. All hydroxides are insoluble except those of the alkali (Li^+, Na^+, K^+, Rb^+, Fr^+), strontium (Sr^{2+}), barium (Ba^{2+}), radium (Ra^{2+}), and ammonium (NH_4^+) compounds.
8. All negative ions form soluble compounds with the hydrogen ion, H^+.

One practical use of these solubility rules is that we can predict qualitatively whether an insoluble solid will form when solutions containing different ions are mixed. A solid that forms when two solutions are mixed is known as a *precipitate*. For example, if a solution of sodium chloride, NaCl, is mixed with a solution of silver nitrate, $AgNO_3$, a precipitate will form because silver chloride is insoluble in water:

$$Ag^+_{(aq)} + Cl^-_{(aq)} \rightarrow AgCl_{(s)} \uparrow$$

However, if the sodium chloride solution is mixed with a solution of calcium nitrate, $Ca(NO_3)_2$, no precipitate results because the two possible compounds that could form ($CaCl_2$ and $NaNO_3$) are soluble.

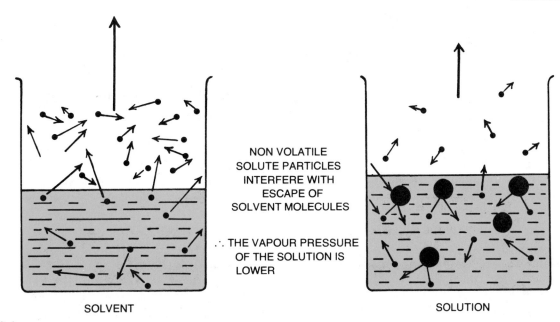

NON VOLATILE
SOLUTE PARTICLES
INTERFERE WITH
ESCAPE OF
SOLVENT MOLECULES

∴ THE VAPOUR PRESSURE
OF THE SOLUTION IS
LOWER

SOLVENT

SOLUTION

Fig. 23.4:
Lower vapour pressure of a solution compared to a pure solvent

23:6   Concentration of Solutions

A solution containing a large amount of solute is termed *concentrated* whereas one containing a small amount is called *dilute*. These terms do not give information about the exact amounts of solute present in a solution. Knowing the amount of solute is important to the chemist. The concentration of a solution may be expressed in a number of ways.

The concentration is sometimes reported on a percentage basis. This could be a percentage by *mass* or a percentage by *volume*. *Percentage by mass* represents the number of grams of solute present in 100 g of solution. Thus a 5% solution of sugar in water contains 5 g of sugar in 100 g of solution. *Percentage by volume* shows how many millilitres of solute are present in 100 mL of solution. For instance, a 3% solution of hydrogen peroxide contains 3 mL of H_2O_2 per 100 mL of solution.

Molarity

Units of concentration that indicate the relative number of solute molecules or ions present in a solution are called *chemical units*. In chemistry, the unit for molar concentration is stated in moles per cubic metre (mol/m^3) or in moles per litre* (mol/L). The number of moles of a solute dissolved in a litre of solution is known as the molarity. The number of moles of a substance may be found by dividing its mass by its atomic or formula mass.

The reason for using molarity is to indicate how many particles of solute are present in the sample of the solution. Such information is more important than merely the mass or volume of solute because chemical reactions occur among the molecules or ions of the dissolved reactants.

The symbol for molarity is c, expressed in units of mol/L.

* $1 \ mol/m^3$ is equivalent to $0.001 \ mol/L$.

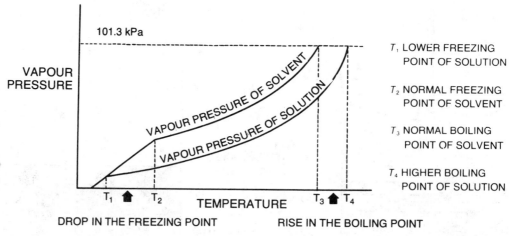

101.3 kPa

VAPOUR PRESSURE

VAPOUR PRESSURE OF SOLVENT

VAPOUR PRESSURE OF SOLUTION

T_1 LOWER FREEZING POINT OF SOLUTION

T_2 NORMAL FREEZING POINT OF SOLVENT

T_3 NORMAL BOILING POINT OF SOLVENT

T_4 HIGHER BOILING POINT OF SOLUTION

T_1 T_2 TEMPERATURE T_3 T_4

DROP IN THE FREEZING POINT   RISE IN THE BOILING POINT

Fig. 23.5:
Vapour pressure, boiling and freezing points of a solvent and a solution

Example

What is the molarity of a solution of hydrochloric acid, HCl, (molar mass 36.5 g/mol) containing 20.0 g of HCl in 500 mL of solution?

Solution

Since molarity is the number of moles of solute per litre of solution, molarity may be found by dividing the number of moles of solute (n) by the volume in litres (v) of the solution.

Mathematically,

$$\text{Molarity} = c = \frac{\text{moles of solute}}{\text{litres of solution}} = \frac{n}{v}$$

where n, the number of moles of HCl in 20.0 g, is

$$\frac{20.0 \text{ g}}{36.5 \text{ g/mol}} \quad \text{or} \quad \frac{20.0}{36.5} \text{ mol}$$

and v, the number of litres of solution, is 0.50 L

$$\therefore \text{Molarity} = \frac{n}{v} = \frac{20.0 \text{ mol}}{36.5 \times 0.50 \text{ L}}$$

$$= 1.10 \frac{\text{mol}}{\text{L}}$$

This 1.10 mol/L solution contains 1.10 mol of solute per litre of solution.

23:7   Physical Properties of Solutions

When a non-volatile solute is dissolved in a liquid, the vapour pressure of the liquid is lowered because some of the solvent molecules collide with the solute particles near the surface of the liquid, thus preventing their escape. Since the vapour pressure of a liquid is due to the number of molecules escaping, the vapour pressure is lowered (Fig. 23.4).

The more solute particles there are, the greater is the number of interfering collisions and the greater is the drop in vapour pressure. Attraction between solute and solvent particles also makes it more difficult for solvent to escape. These considerations explain what is actually observed experimentally, namely, that the drop in the vapour pressure depends on the number of solute particles present in unit mass of solvent.

The lowering of the vapour pressure of a solution automatically causes its boiling point to be higher than that of the solvent. A liquid normally boils at the temperature at which its vapour pressure is equal to 101.3 kPa or one atmosphere. The addition of a non-volatile solute lowers the vapour pressure of the solution below that of the solvent. Therefore, at the normal boiling temperature, the vapour pressure of the pure solvent is 101.3 kPa but that of the solution is less. The solution is not yet at its boiling point. To cause the solution to boil, it must be heated until its vapour pressure will also be equal to 101.3 kPa. The additional temperature to which it must be heated for this reason is called the *rise in the boiling point* (Fig. 23.5). By similar reasoning, the solution freezes below the normal freezing temperature of the solvent.

QUESTIONS

1. Define *solution*, *solute*, and *solvent*. Give an example of each.

2. What is the importance of solutions?

3. What is meant by *miscible liquids*? Give an example.

4. Define *solubility* and *precipitate*.

5. Using the data available in Fig. 23.1, give the approximate solubility for the following salts at the given temperatures: (i) sodium chlorate at 20°C; (ii) potassium nitrate at 10°C; (iii) potassium bromide at 90°C; (iv) sodium chloride at 90°C; (v) potassium bromide at 100°C.

6. The solubility of silver nitrate at various temperatures was determined in the laboratory. Graph the solubility curve of silver nitrate using the data obtained and shown below.

Temperature (°C)	0	10	20	30	40	50	60	70	80	90	100
Solubility (g of $AgNO_3$ per 100 g water)	115	160	215	270	335	400	470	550	650	760	910

7. Explain what happens when a crystal of the solute is dropped into: (i) an unsaturated solution; (ii) a saturated solution; (iii) a supersaturated solution.

8. How can the dissolving of sugar in water be speeded up?

9. Describe what forces need to be overcome in forming a solution.

10. Why does the formation of a solution require energy?

11. What are *ion-dipole bonds*?

12. Describe how water dissolves a salt like sodium chloride.

13. What is meant by the statement, "The dielectric constant of water is 80"?

14. How does water dissolve compounds containing hydroxide groups?

15. Why does water not dissolve oil?

16. Why does oil not dissolve salt?

17. What mass of sodium chloride would be required for 150 g of solution 5% by mass NaCl?

18. Why do two oil-like substances usually mix?

19. What factors affect solubility?

20. Why does a rise in temperature decrease the solubility of a gas but usually increase the solubility of a solid?

21. When a glass of cold water is left standing in a warm room, bubbles of gas appear on the inside walls of the glass. Explain why.

22. Is a saturated solution necessarily a concentrated solution? Explain.

23. In what ways may the concentration of a solution be expressed?

24. Describe how a 1.0 mol/L solution of sodium chloride would be prepared.

25. What mass of nitric acid, HNO_3, is present in 1 L of 0.1 mol/L solution?

26. Calculate the number of grams of each of the following compounds required to prepare 1 L of solution: (i) 1.0 mol/L KNO_3; (ii) 2.0 mol/L H_2SO_4; (iii) 0.5 mol/L $KClO_3$; (iv) 0.1 mol/L $C_{12}H_{22}O_{11}$; (v) 3.0 mol/L HNO_3.

27. Calculate the number of grams of solute needed to make the solutions listed below:
     (i) 1000 mL of 0.5 mol/L NaCl;   (iv) 2000 mL of 0.09 mol/L $AgNO_3$;
     (ii) 200 mL of 1.5 mol/L KCl;   (v) 250 mL of 3.1 mol/L $BaCl_2$.
     (iii) 100 mL of 0.3 mol/L HCl;

28. Give two reasons why the addition of a non-volatile solute to a liquid lowers the vapour pressure.

29. How does the non-volatile solute raise the boiling point?

30. Using the general solubility rules given in this chapter, decide which of the following substances are likely to be soluble in water.
     (i) NaOH   (v) NH_4Cl (ix) $Ca_3(PO_4)_2$
     (ii) $PbCl_2$ (vi) HCl   (x) LiBr
     (iii) CuS   (vii) $MgCO_3$ (xi) CH_3COONa
     (iv) $CuSO_4$ (viii) K_2SO_3 (xii) $Mg(OH)_2$

31. Indicate in which cases a precipitate is likely to appear when equal volumes of concentrated solutions of the following pairs of substances are mixed.
     (i) Na_2SO_4 and NH_4Br (vi) $CuSO_4$ and Li_2SO_3
     (ii) MgS and KOH   (vii) $BeBr_2$ and K_2S
     (iii) $AgNO_3$ and KI   (viii) LiOH and CH_3COOH
     (iv) $ZnCl_2$ and $NaClO_3$ (ix) $CaCl_2$ and $Al_2(SO_4)_3$
     (v) Na_2CO_3 and $FeCl_2$ (x) K_2SO_4 and $SrCl_2$

32. A solution of hydrochloric acid has an initial concentration of 6.0 mol/L. What will be the final concentration of the solution by diluting 200 mL of this acid to one litre volume?

33. One litre of a solution of $CuSO_4$, 2 mol/L, is diluted to 10 L. What is the concentration of the diluted solution?

34. To what volume must 100 mL of a 6.0 mol/L HCl solution be diluted in order that the resulting solution be 1.0 mol/L?

35. What will be the concentration of a solution prepared by mixing 400 mL of a 2.0 mol/L HCl solution with 600 mL of a 3.0 mol/L HCl solution?

36. Calculate the concentration (in mol/L) of a solution containing 10g of each of the following in 1L of solution: (i) H_2SO_4 (ii) HCl (iii) $Ca(OH)_2$ (iv) NaOH (v) $CaCl_2$

CHAPTER

24

ELECTROLYTES AND NON-ELECTROLYTES

Some solutions can conduct the electric current. They and their solutes are called electrolytes.

24:1 Conductance

Salt and sugar, two familiar compounds that look alike, are both soluble in water; but close examination reveals that their solutions behave quite differently. Each is typical of a class of solutions of different electrical, physical, and chemical properties. The two classes of solutions are termed electrolytes and non-electrolytes respectively.

Fig. 24.1 shows an electric bulb connected in series with two electrodes that dip into a solution. A switch enables a current to be turned on or off. If the liquid in the beaker conducts an electric current, the bulb will glow; otherwise it will not. By means of this apparatus, it can be shown that water solutions of such substances as sugar, methanol, and glycerol are non-conductors and, hence, *non-electrolytes*.

Similarly, water solutions of other substances such as sodium chloride, sodium hydroxide, and hydrochloric acid are good conductors. These are typical *electrolyte* solutions. Also, different elec-

trolytes of the same concentration conduct current to a different extent. Consequently, electrolytes are further classified as *strong* and *weak*, depending on their ability to conduct an electric current.

The passage of direct current through electrolyte solutions may decompose them. Such decomposition, termed *electrolysis* (section 20:5) results in the liberation of hydrogen or a metallic element at the cathode and oxygen or other gases at the anode. In some cases the metallic anode may disintegrate during electrolysis.

Electrolyte solutions may also be used to generate electric voltage, thus acting as an electric cell or battery. Electricity is generated when two different metals are placed in an electrolyte solution and connected externally (section 20:4).

24:2 Physical Properties of Electrolytes

When a solid is dissolved in a liquid, it causes the vapour pressure of the liquid to decrease. This, in turn, raises the boiling point of the solution above that of the solvent and lowers the freezing point of the solution below that of the solvent (section 23:7).

Experiment shows that in the case of non-electrolytes, one mole of solute dissolved in one kilogram of water causes the boiling point to become 0.52°C higher and the freezing point 1.86°C lower than the normal values for pure water. The interesting point is that the same changes in the boiling and freezing point of water are produced by one mole of any non-volatile dissolved compound, provided the resulting solution is a non-electrolyte. Since one mole of any non-electrolyte compound always represents the same number of particles, it may be stated that the rise in the boiling point and the drop in the freezing point of a solution depend only on the number of particles of solute present in the solution per unit mass of solvent.

For electrolytes, on the other hand, the rise in the boiling point or drop in the freezing point is greater than for non-electrolyte solutions of the same concentration. Many electrolytes raise the boiling point and lower the freezing point almost twice as much as non-electrolytes do for the same concentration. An aqueous solution of sodium chloride behaves in this way. Other electrolytes raise the boiling point and lower the freezing point to a greater or lesser extent than does sodium chloride.

24:3 Chemical Properties of Electrolytes

The properties of an aqueous electrolyte solution consist of the properties of its cations, its anions, and the solvent — water. Thus, every electrolyte has two sets of chemical properties due to its solute, and still another due to its solvent. These properties are independent of one another. All electrolytes with common ions have similar properties. Thus, all solutions which contain the hydronium ion, H_3O^+, have a set of properties in common; they are called by a common name — *acids*. Similarly, all the solutions with at least moderate amounts of hydroxide ions, OH^-, have properties in common, and are called *bases*. In the same way, all electrolytes containing other ions in common, such as the sodium ion, would show the properties typical of that ion. The chemical properties of electrolytes and their solutions make it easy to classify them as acids, bases, and salts.

Electrolytes are chemically active, reacting more

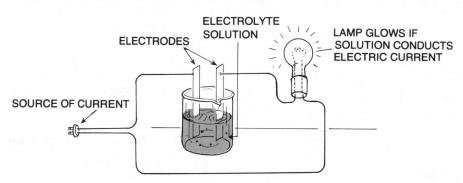

Fig. 24.1:
Conductivity of electrolytes

rapidly than non-electrolytes. For example, when an acid is added to a base, the neutralization reaction occurs readily. When silver nitrate is added to sodium chloride, both in solution, precipitation of silver chloride occurs immediately. Acetic acid reacts instantly with sodium hydroxide, NaOH, but very slowly with ethanol, C_2H_5OH. Both sodium hydroxide and ethanol have the OH group; but sodium hydroxide is an electrolyte while ethanol is not.

24:4   The Electrolytic Dissociation of Substances in Solution

Among the several theories advanced to explain the properties of electrolyte solutions, one proposed by a Swedish chemist, Arrhenius, in 1885, was fairly successful. His theory, known as the *Theory of Electrolytic Dissociation*, has evolved as more knowledge about the structure of the atom has accumulated. Consequently, modern theories about electrolytes are refinements of the older ones.

The following is a summary of the modern ideas about electrolytes and ions.

1. Ionic solids, such as salts and strong bases, consist of ions. When these compounds dissolve, the molecules of water weaken the attraction between their cations and anions, and soon these ions are free and separate.

2. Some covalent compounds furnish ions by reacting chemically with water or other solvents. Such reactions cause the formation of hydronium ions, H_3O^+, and other ions. Acids and weak bases behave in this way. For example, the reaction between hydrogen chloride and water and that between ammonia and water can be represented, using electron-dot formulas, as follows:

3. The number of positive charges equals the number of negative charges in an electrolyte solution.

4. The ionization of weak electrolytes is a reversible reaction. A dynamic equilibrium exists between the process of molecules dissociating into ions and that of the reassociation of the ions into molecules. If the number of ions present at any time is relatively small in this reversible reaction, the electrolyte is termed *weak*. For example, when a 0.1 mol/L acetic acid solution, CH_3COOH, is prepared, about 1% of the molecules react with the water to form acetate and hydronium ions:

In some electrolyte solutions, on the other hand, practically all the solute particles in solution exist as ions. Solutes of this type are the *strong* electrolytes. The terms strong and weak electrolytes refer to the *degree of ionization* these substances undergo when dissolved in water.

24:5   Explanation of Conductance and Electrolysis

To explain conductance and electrolysis, a simple case will now be discussed, namely, the electrolysis of a concentrated copper (II) chloride solution.

Copper (II) chloride consists of copper (II) ions, Cu^{2+}, and chloride ions, Cl^-. When water comes in contact with copper (II) chloride, the small polar water molecules surround the copper (II) and the chloride ions, thereby dissolving the salt and liberating its ions from the crystal lattice:

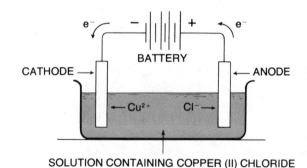

Fig. 24.2:
Electrolysis of copper (II) chloride

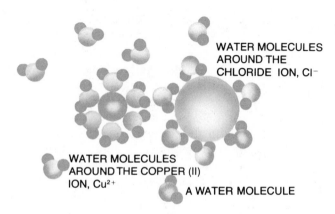

WATER MOLECULES
AROUND THE
CHLORIDE ION, Cl⁻

WATER MOLECULES
AROUND THE COPPER (II)
ION, Cu²⁺

A WATER MOLECULE

If two inert electrodes (carbon or platinum) are introduced into a concentrated solution and a voltage is applied to them, the positive copper (II) ions migrate to the negative cathode while the negative chloride ions migrate to the anode (Fig. 24.2). At the cathode, each copper (II) ion gains two electrons and is reduced to an atom of copper:

$$Cu^{2+} + 2e^- \rightarrow Cu^0$$

Thus, copper metal is deposited on the cathode. Similarly, at the anode, each chloride ion gives up one electron and is oxidized to an atom of chlorine. Two such atoms form a molecule of chlorine and, in this way, chlorine gas is liberated at the anode:

$$Cl^- \rightarrow Cl^0 + 1e^-$$
$$2Cl^0 \rightarrow Cl_2^0\uparrow$$

The reactions taking place at the electrodes are referred to as *half-reactions* because they take place simultaneously and can be combined into a single over-all reaction:

cathode half-reaction: $Cu^{2+} + 2e^- \rightarrow Cu$

anode half-reaction: $2Cl^- \rightarrow Cl_2^0 + 2e^-$

over-all reaction: $Cu^{2+}_{(aq)} + 2Cl^-_{(aq)} \rightarrow$
$$Cu_{(s)} + Cl_2^0\uparrow_{(g)}$$

During electrolysis, electrons have been removed from the cathode and returned to the anode. Thereby, the solution has effectively transferred electrons from cathode to anode. In this manner the solution acts as a conductor of the electric current.

Notice the difference in the way the electrolyte solutions on the one hand, and metal conductors on the other, conduct the electric current. In ionic or electrolytic conduction, it is the *motion of the ions* to the electrodes, and their *reactions* at the electrodes, which result in the conductance of the current. In electronic or metallic conduction, the *electrons themselves move* from one electrode to the other.

24:6 Explanation of the Abnormal Freezing and Boiling Points of Electrolyte Solutions

As noted earlier, the change in the boiling and freezing point produced by adding solute to solvent depends only on the number of solute particles, and not on their kind. One mole of any non-electrolyte furnishes 6.02×10^{23} solute particles in solution. When electrolytes are dissolved in water, they furnish ions to the solution in one way or another. Such ions are more numerous than the undissociated molecules would be. For example, one mole of sugar dissolved in 1000 g of water furnishes one mole of molecules of sugar, but one mole of sodium chloride supplies two moles of ions, that is, one mole of Na^+ ions and one mole of Cl^- ions. The excessive number of ions is responsible for the excessive rise in the boiling point or drop in the freezing point.

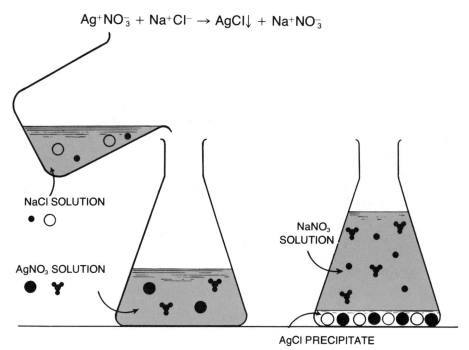

$$Ag^+NO_3^- + Na^+Cl^- \rightarrow AgCl\downarrow + Na^+NO_3^-$$

NaCl SOLUTION

● ○

AgNO₃ SOLUTION

● Y

NaNO₃ SOLUTION

AgCl PRECIPITATE

Fig. 24.3:
Reaction between Na^+Cl^- and $Ag^+NO_3^-$

24:7   Explanation of the Chemical Activity of Electrolytes

Since ions have an electrical charge, it may be assumed that oppositely charged ions attract each other and collide much more quickly and directly than in reactions involving non-electrolytes.

The reactions that ions undergo in solution are best studied by noting only the ions involved in the chemical change. For this reason, their equations are often written in the ionic form. For example, in the reaction between solutions of sodium chloride and silver nitrate (Fig. 24.3) only the chloride ions and the silver ions come together to form an almost insoluble precipitate. The sodium ions and the nitrate ions take no part in the reaction and remain in the solution as free ions; they are merely spectator ions. The *net ionic equation* representing this reaction is:

$$Cl^-_{(aq)} + Ag^+_{(aq)} \rightarrow AgCl_{(s)}\downarrow$$

This equation represents the reaction between any solution containing chloride ions with any solution containing silver ions. For example, in the reaction between solutions of sodium chloride and silver nitrate the complete ionic equation is

$$Ag^+ + NO_3^- + Na^+ + Cl^- \rightarrow AgCl\downarrow + Na^+ + NO_3^-$$

QUESTIONS

1. Define *electrolyte, non-electrolyte, anion,* and *cation.* Give three examples of each.

2. When the two electrodes of an apparatus used for testing the conductivity of a substance are placed in granular sodium chloride, the bulb does not glow, but if the salt is heated until it melts, then the light shines. Explain these observations.

3. Compare electrolytes and non-electrolytes from the point of view of the following general properties: (i) electrical conductance; (ii) effect on the boiling point of water; (iii) effect on the freezing point of water; (iv) speed of reaction.

4. Copper (II) sulfate, $CuSO_4$; copper (II) nitrate, $Cu(NO_3)_2$; and copper (II) chloride, $CuCl_2$; all produce blue solutions when dissolved in water. Suggest a reason for this phenomenon.

5. Into what classes of compounds may electrolytes be divided?

6. How do water molecules cause ionic substances to dissociate during the solution process?

7. How do water molecules cause some covalent substances to form ions during the solution process?

8. Why is an electrolyte solution electrically neutral?

9. Why is there a marked difference between the conduction of an electric current in a solution of sodium chloride and in a solution of acetic acid of the same molar concentration?

10. Pure hydrogen chloride in the liquid state is considered to be a non-electrolyte. However, HCl is a strong electrolyte in aqueous solution. Why?

11. Why would it be better to write the formula of sodium chloride as Na^+Cl^- rather than NaCl?

12. Explain the electrolysis of a concentrated solution of hydrochloric acid, considered to be hydronium ions, H_3O^+ and chloride ions, Cl^-. Give equations representing the reactions taking place at the anode and at the cathode.

13. Distinguish between the terms *metallic conduction* and *electrolytic conduction*.

14. Calculate the number of electrons needed to liberate 10.0 g of copper metal from copper (II) chloride by electrolysis.

15. (i) What mass of hydrogen and oxygen would be obtained by the electrolysis of 10.0 g of water?
    (ii) What volume would this hydrogen occupy at $-10°C$ and 100 kPa of pressure?

16. What mass of water would be decomposed by electrolysis to yield 10.0 L of oxygen recovered at 20°C and 104 kPa pressure?

17. Why are electrolytes generally more active chemically than non-electrolytes?

18. Which aqueous solution has the lower vapour pressure, a 1.0 mol/L solution of sugar, $C_{12}H_{22}O_{11}$, or a 1.0 mol/L solution of sodium chloride, NaCl? Explain.

19. Solution X contains 100 g of sugar, $C_{12}H_{22}O_{11}$, dissolved in 1000 g of water and solution Y contains 100 g of ethyl alcohol, C_2H_5OH, dissolved in 1000 g of water. Which solution has the lower freezing point? Why?

20. Which of the following substances is likely to cause the greatest lowering of the freezing point of water when a mole of it is dissolved in 1 kg of water?
    (i) $C_{12}H_{22}O_{11}$ (iii) NaCl
    (ii) $CuCl_2$ (iv) CH_3COOH

21. Re-write the following equations in their net ionic form:

(i) $Zn_{(s)}$ + $CuSO_{4(aq)}$ → $ZnSO_{4(aq)}$ + $Cu_{(s)}$
(ii) $NaOH_{(aq)}$ + $HCl_{(aq)}$ → $H_2O_{(l)}$ + $NaCl_{(aq)}$
(iii) $KCl_{(aq)}$ + $AgNO_{3(aq)}$ → $KNO_{3(aq)}$ + $AgCl{\downarrow}_{(s)}$
(iv) $Fe_{(s)}$ + $CuSO_{4(aq)}$ → $FeSO_{4(aq)}$ + $Cu_{(s)}$
(v) $BaCl_{2(aq)}$ + $H_2SO_{4(aq)}$ → $BaSO_4{\downarrow}_{(s)}$ + $2HCl_{(aq)}$

CHAPTER
25

ACIDS AND BASES

25:1 Acid-Base Phenomena

Long before chemistry had become a quantitative science, it had been observed that many substances had certain properties in common. Those with a sour taste were called *acids* (Latin acidus — sour). When chemists studied acids and their solutions, they found that the substances showed other common properties as well. Litmus, a vegetable dye, turns a pinkish red when it comes in contact with an acid. When acids react with certain metals, hydrogen is liberated.

Another group of compounds, also found to have common properties, taste bitter; their solutions feel slippery; they reverse the colour effect that the acids produce on dyes. They are called *bases*.

The most interesting property of acids is their reaction with bases and, conversely, that of bases is their reaction with acids, in the course of which the properties of both the acids and the bases disappear. Hence the reaction is termed *neutralization* (Latin neuter — neither). The products of this reaction are water and a salt.

Since phenomena like the above were observed relatively early in chemical history, it is not surprising that the theories offered to explain them have grown in depth with the passing of time. Lavoisier (1770) believed that acid properties were

These are substances with distinctive properties that can interact chemically to form a neutral product.

caused by the presence of oxygen. Indeed, the name oxygen means "the producer of acids," but substances were soon found which had acid properties even though they did not contain oxygen. One such compound is hydrogen chloride, HCl, which forms hydrochloric acid when dissolved in water.

25:2 Arrhenius Theory of Acids and Bases: The Water Definitions

In 1885, Arrhenius proposed the idea that an acid was a substance that liberated "hydrogen ions" to its water solution, while a base furnished hydroxide ions. This theory was successful in explaining many important facts. Any substance that could furnish hydrogen ions or hydroxide ions to its water solution would show the properties of acids or bases respectively. Furthermore, the removal of the H^+ and OH^- by their formation of water would explain how acids and bases neutralize one another:

$$H^+ + OH^- \rightarrow HOH$$

So successful was Arrhenius in explaining acid-base behaviour that we still often use his definitions of acids and bases, although they have certain shortcomings.

With the establishment of the modern knowledge of the structure of the atom, it became apparent that the hydrogen ion was the proton. In essence then, the Arrhenius theory suggested that there were free protons in aqueous solutions. There is no evidence for the presence of free protons in solutions, just as there is no evidence for the presence of free electrons in any solution. Therefore, a modified theory of acid-base behaviour was needed.

25:3 The Bronsted-Lowry Theory of Acids and Bases

An *acid* is a substance whose molecules or ions can donate protons in a chemical reaction, while a *base* is a substance whose molecules or ions can accept protons in a chemical reaction. An acid is a *proton donor*; a base is a *proton acceptor*.

Since HCl is a proton donor, it is an acid according to this theory. Under certain conditions, the ammonium ion, NH_4^+ is a proton donor, as in the following reaction:

$$NH_4^+ + OH^- \rightarrow NH_3 + HOH$$

According to the Bronsted-Lowry theory, NH_4^+ is also an acid in such reactions. The older theory did not apply the term acid to such ions. Similarly, OH^- is a proton acceptor, but so too is ammonia, NH_3, when the above reaction is reversed. The latter also would be called a base by the Bronsted-Lowry theory.

When an acid donates its proton, the remainder of the acid can act as a base, and it is called the *conjugate base* of the original acid. Under suitable conditions, the base may recombine with a proton to re-form the acid.

Examples are:

Acid	= Proton	+ Conjugate base
HCl	= H^+	+ Cl^-
NH_4^+	= H^+	+ NH_3
HOH	= H^+	+ OH^-

The ionization of an acid or a base is itself a chemical reaction between the acid or the base and the solvent. For example, the ionization of hydrochloric acid is a reaction between hydrogen chloride and water:

$$HCl + H_2O \rightarrow H_3O^+ + Cl^-$$

The hydrogen chloride donates a proton to the water. Therefore, the hydrogen chloride acts as acid, or proton donor, while the water acts as base, or proton acceptor. When hydrogen chloride donates its proton, the chloride ion is left. Therefore, the chloride ion is the conjugate base of hydrogen chloride.

Similarly, the hydronium ion may lose its proton under certain conditions. It then becomes the water molecule. Thus the water molecule is the conjugate base of the hydronium ion.

The Arrhenius theory presented the ionization of HCl as:

$$HCl \rightarrow H^+ + Cl^-$$

The Bronsted-Lowry theory presents the ionization of HCl as a reaction between an acid and a base, producing another acid and base:

Acid 1	+ Base 2	$\rightarrow$	Acid 2	+ Base 1
HCl	+ H_2O	$\rightarrow$	H_3O^+	+ Cl^-

In the reaction between ammonia and water, we have a similar acid-base exchange:

Acid 1	+ Base 2	$\rightarrow$	Acid 2	+ Base 1
H_2O	+ NH_3	$\rightarrow$	NH_4^+	+ OH^-

In this last reaction, water acts as a proton donor while ammonia acts as a proton acceptor. Therefore, water is the acid in the reaction, while ammonia is the base.

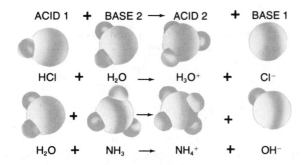

Fig. 25.1:
Bronsted-Lowry theory of acids and bases

When the water molecule loses its proton, the hydroxide ion remains. Therefore, the hydroxide ion, OH^-, is the conjugate base of the water molecule, H_2O.

In some reactions, the ammonium ion donates protons and thus acts as an acid. Upon donation of the proton, the ammonia molecule remains. Therefore, the ammonia molecule is the conjugate base of the ammonium ion, NH_4^+. The equation may be written as:

$$\text{Acid 1} + \text{Base 2} \rightarrow \text{Base 1} + \text{Acid 2}$$
$$NH_4^+ + OH^- \rightarrow NH_3 + HOH$$

In the reaction with hydrogen chloride, HCl, water acts as a base, or proton acceptor. In the reaction with ammonia, NH_3, water acts as an acid, or proton donor. A substance that can act as either an acid or a base is called *amphoteric*.

25:4   Neutralization

Neutralization is the reaction between acid and base. A common example is the reaction between hydrochloric acid and sodium hydroxide:

$$HCl + NaOH \rightarrow NaCl + HOH$$

This neutralization goes practically to completion because the hydrochloric acid and sodium hydroxide are a strong acid and base respectively and the water hardly ionizes at all. Neutralization may be used to find the concentration of acids and bases. The procedures of making such measurements are called *acidimetry* (measurement of acid), and *alkalimetry* (measurement of base). These are carried out by *titration*, a process of reacting volumes of solutions until a colour change occurs in an added indicator. Titration is a *volumetric method of anlaysis* and is both convenient and rapid.

The apparatus used in titration consists of a *burette* and a *pipette*. The burette is a straight tube graduated in tenths of millilitres, with a stopcock or pinch clamp at the bottom through which the solution is run out drop by drop. The pipette is a straight tube used for drawing a definite volume of solution.

A *standard solution*, one whose concentration is known accurately, must be used. Both acidic and alkaline standard solutions are prepared by the analytical chemist. The standard acid is used for titrating the unknown base, and vice versa. A measured volume of the acid is added by means of the pipette into a beaker or flask.

A few drops of an indicator such as phenolphthalein are added. (This indicator is colourless in acid and pink in base). Alkaline solution is then added from the burette, and the mixture is stirred continuously. As the *end point* approaches, a pink colour appears briefly. This is a signal for the solution to be added drop by drop, a procedure which is continued until the first permanent colour appears. The reaction has then reached its end point. The volume of solution run out of the burette is observed and the data are ready to be used in titration calculations.

25:5   Examples

Example 1
What mass of aluminum hydroxide, $Al(OH)_3$, will supply one mole of OH^-?

Solution
Since aluminum hydroxide furnishes three OH^- ions per molecule, the molar mass furnishes three Avogadro numbers of hydroxide ions per mole. Therefore, the mass of $Al(OH)_3$ that will supply one mole of OH^- ions is one third of the molar mass of $Al(OH)_3$,

$$= \frac{Al(OH)_3}{3} \text{ g}$$

$$= \frac{78.0}{3} \text{ g}$$

$$= 26.0 \text{ g}$$

Example 2
What is the concentration, expressed in moles per litre, of a solution containing 6.5 g of H_2SO_4 in 500 mL of solution?

Solution

$$\text{Concentration} = \frac{\text{moles of solute}}{\text{litres of solution}}$$

For H_2SO_4, the molar mass is $2.0 + 32.0 + 64.0 = 98.0$ g and the number of moles (n) of H_2SO_4 in 6.5 g is $\frac{6.5 \text{ g}}{98.0 \text{ g/mol}}$ Therefore, the concentration (c) in units of mol/L is:

$$c = \frac{n}{V} = \frac{\dfrac{6.5 \text{ g}}{98.0 \text{ g/mol}}}{\dfrac{500 \text{ mL}}{1000 \text{ mL/L}}}$$

$$= 0.13 \text{ mol/L}$$

Example 3
What is the concentration of hydrogen ions in the above solution? Assume complete ionization.

Solution
Since by assumption, each molecule of H_2SO_4 provides two hydrogen ions, the number of moles of hydrogen ions is double the number of moles of H_2SO_4. As a result, the concentration of hydrogen ions will be double the molar concentration of H_2SO_4. The concentration of

$$H^+ = 2 \times 0.13$$
$$= 0.26 \text{ mol/L}$$

Example 4
What is the concentration of a sample of HCl solution if a volume of 25.0 mL of 0.10 mol/L NaOH is required for the neutralization of 20.0 mL of the acid?

Solution
Since HCl and NaOH react in the molar ratio of 1 to 1, the number of moles of HCl will be equal to the number of moles of NaOH in the completed neutralization. The number of moles, n may be found from the equation

$$\text{Concentration } c = \frac{n}{V}$$

$$\text{therefore } n = cV$$

At the end point,
the number of moles of A = the number of moles of B; that is,
$$n_A = n_B$$
or,
$$c_A V_A = c_B V_B$$

where subscripts A and B refer to acid and base respectively. We have these values:

$$c_A = \text{unknown}$$
$$V_A = 20.0 \text{ mL}$$
$$c_B = 0.10 \frac{\text{mol}}{\text{L}}$$
$$V_B = 25.0 \text{ mL}$$

Substituting,

$$c_A = \frac{c_B V_B}{V_A}$$

$$= \frac{0.10 \dfrac{\text{mol}}{\text{L}} \times 25.0 \text{ mL}}{20.0 \text{ mL}}$$

$$= 0.13 \text{ mol/L}$$

Since both c_A and c_B are expressed in millilitres, it is unnecessary to change them to litres.

25:6   Free Hydronium Ions

An important property of any water solution is the number of free hydronium ions it contains. In pure water, as well as in all water solutions, both hydronium and hydroxide ions are present.

In pure water, the number of hydronium ions and hydroxide ions is equal. This is easily explained by the way these ions form. Since water is both proton donor and proton acceptor, at any time there will be a few water molecules which have donated protons to others:

As a result of this reaction, one litre of pure neutral water contains one ten-millionth of an Avogadro number of hydronium ions and hydroxide ions. To simplify, one ten-millionth is expressed as 10^{-7}, and the symbol [   ] is used to express the concentration of the ions in the solution. This symbol stands for the number of moles of solute per litre of solution. Thus, $[H_3O^+]$ stands for the moles of hydronium ions per litre of solution. We may report the above experimental fact about pure water by writing:

$$[H_3O^+] = 10^{-7}$$

The number of hydroxide ions is exactly the same as that of hydronium ions since they originate from the same dissociated molecules in the ratio of one to one. With an equal number of hydronium and hydroxide ions, pure water is neither acidic nor basic; it is termed *neutral*.

25:7   The Ion Product of Water

In neutral water, $[H_3O^+]$ and $[OH^-]$ both have a value of 10^{-7}. Their product $[H_3O^+] \times [OH^-]$ is equal to $10^{-7} \times 10^{-7}$ or 10^{-14}.

It can be shown experimentally that in all water solutions the product of the concentrations of the hydronium and hydroxide ions is 10^{-14}. This value is an important constant, termed the *ion product of water*.

In acid solutions, the hydronium ion concentration is larger than that of the hydroxide ion. In akaline solutions the reverse is true. Nevertheless, in all cases

$$[H_3O^+]\,[OH^-] = 10^{-14}$$

25:8   The pH Scale

The pH *scale* is used to simplify further the way of expressing the hydronium ion concentration. On this scale, a liquid would be described as having a pH of 7 when the concentration of the hydronium ion is 10^{-7}. The pH represents the *negative logarithm* * *of the hydronium ion concentration of water, or of any aqueous medium.* In pure and neutral water, the pH is 7 and the pOH, similarly defined, is also 7.

Suppose a solute is introduced which increases the number of hydronium ions to a value ten times as great as in neutral water; this means that the number of hydroxide ions declines automatically to one-tenth the value in neutral water.

Ten times as great as 10^{-7} is
$$10^{-7} \times 10^1$$
$$= 10^{-7+1}$$
$$= 10^{-6}$$

Therefore, in this solution $[H_3O^+] = 10^{-6}$ and pH = 6.

Also $[OH^-] = 10^{-8}$ and pOH = 8.

* Recall that 10^5 has a logarithm of 5.

Note that the product of $[H_3O^+]$ and $[OH^-]$ equals 10^{-14} in both solutions. The sum of pH and pOH is 14 in both cases.

The solution whose pH is 6 contains 10 times as many hydronium ions per litre as one of pH 7. Such a solution, which contains more hydronium ions than neutral water, is called an *acidic solution*. *Acid solutions have a pH smaller than 7.*

By contrast, suppose that a solute that is added to water causes the hydronium ions to become one-tenth of their former number in neutral water. This results in a tenfold increase in the number of hydroxide ions over their number in neutral water. In order to describe this solution, we may write that:

$$[H_3O^+] = 1/10 \text{ of } 10^{-7}$$
$$\text{or } 10^{-7} \times 10^{-1}$$
$$= 10^{-1-7}$$
$$= 10^{-8}$$
$$\text{While } [OH^-] = 10^1 \times 10^{-7}$$
$$= 10^{-6}$$
$$\text{Again } [H_3O^+][OH^-] = 10^{-14}$$

According to the definitions of these terms, the pH

of this solution is 8 and the pOH is 6.

Such a solution containing fewer hydronium ions and more hydroxide ions than neutral water is called an *alkaline solution. Alkaline solutions have a pH greater than 7.*

25:9   The Measurement of pH

The pH of a solution may be determined by using dyes that change colour with a change in pH. Such dyes have a definite colour at a definite pH. The dyes may be placed in solution or on strips of paper similar to litmus papers. A solution of dyes used for this purpose is called a *Universal Indicator*, and the strips of paper are called pH *papers*.

The fundamental method for measuring the pH of a solution is to measure the voltage between the solution and a standard one, by means of a suitable electrical circuit. The instrument which is employed for this purpose is called a pH *meter*. The other methods mentioned before are calibrated by reference to the values found by the pH meter.

QUESTIONS

1. List the main general properties of acids and of bases.

2. What is the Arrhenius theory of acids and bases? Why is it called "the water theory of acids and bases"?

3. Why is the Arrhenius theory not satisfactory for acids?

4. What is the Bronsted-Lowry, or proton, theory of acids and bases?

5. Show by equations how the Arrhenius and the Bronsted-Lowry theories would represent the ionization of HCl in water.

6. Define the term *amphoteric*. Give an example.

7. Describe clearly how covalent bonds are formed when ammonia reacts with water, when hydrogen chloride reacts with ammonia, and when hydrogen chloride reacts with water.

8. Define the terms *neutralization, acidimetry, alkalimetry, titration, indicator,* and *end point*.

9. Describe clearly how a solution of hydrogen chloride could be titrated with a solution of sodium hydroxide.

10. What is the purpose of titration?

11. Define molarity. What are the units of molarity?

12. (i) What is the molarity of a hydrochloric acid solution containing 10 g HCl/L?
    (ii) What would be its molarity if it contained 10 g HCl per 100 mL?

13. Find the molarity of a sulfuric acid solution containing 9.8 g H_2SO_4 per 500 mL.

14. What mass of each of the following would be necessary to prepare one litre of a 0.1 mol/L solution of: (i) HCl; (ii) HBr; (iii) H_2SO_4; (iv) H_3PO_4; (v) NaOH; (vi) $Ca(OH)_2$?

15. Find the molarity of the following solutions: (i) 10 g of HCl in 1 L; (ii) 100 g of H_2SO_4 in 500 mL; (iii) 80 g of NaOH in 2 L; (iv) 30 g of $Ca(OH)_2$ in 10 L?

16. Calculate the molarity of a HCl solution if a volume of 10 mL of it is neutralized by 25 mL of 1.0 mol/L NaOH.

17. Find the grams of NaOH per litre of solution, if 15 mL of the solution are neutralized by 8.0 mL of a 0.1 mol/L HCl solution.

18. What would be the molarity of a solution prepared by mixing 400 mL of 0.5 mol/L HCl with 100 mL of 0.75. mol/L H_2SO_4? What would be the concentration of H_3O^+ ions in this mixture?

19. Give an equation to show the dissociation of water.

20. What is the concentration of hydronium ions in pure water?

21. Why is pure water neither acidic nor basic?

22. What is meant by the term "the ion product of water"?

23. Define pH.

24. Explain why a neutral solution is said to have a pH of seven.

25. Explain how the pH scale expresses the acidity or alkalinity of a solution.

26. What is a "Universal Indicator solution"?

27. What mass of hydronium ion would be found in 3 L of a completely dissociated 0.1 mol/L solution of hydrochloric acid?

28. What is the pH of a water solution containing 1.0×10^{-6} mol/L of H^+ ions?

29. The OH^- ion concentration of a water solution is 1.0×10^{-9} mol/L. What is the pH of this solution?

30. Calculate the per cent of ionization of a 0.05 mol/L acetic acid solution knowing that this solution contains only 1.0×10^{-3} mol/L of H^+.

31. Calculate the pH value of a 0.050 mol/L H_2SO_4 aqueous solution assuming complete ionization.

32. What is the OH^- ion concentration of a solution whose pH is 8?

33. What is the pH of a 1.0×10^{-3} mol/L NaOH solution assuming complete ionization?

CHAPTER

26

CHEMICAL KINETICS AND REACTION RATES

Chemical kinetics deal with the details of how chemical reactions take place. The subject tries to answer such questions as "What actually takes place between the molecules, ions or atoms of the reactants? How do they collide? With what energy do they collide? Do they form products directly? Do they form intermediate substances which may then change into products? How is the reaction affected by temperature, light, surface, catalysis, concentration, and other effects?" These are important questions which need to be answered for a better control over chemical change.

26:1 Heat of Reaction and Heat Content

Because of its structure and its physical state, every substance has a characteristic internal energy known as the *heat content*. Each mole of a substance has a characteristic heat content just as it has a characteristic mass. As reactants change to products in a chemical change, heat is evolved or absorbed because the heat contents of these respective substances are different. This heat exchange which accompanies a chemical reaction

Some chemical reactions are as slow as the corrosion of copper which may go on for centuries. Others are as rapid as the explosion of dynamite. Chemical kinetics studies reaction rates to find out why they differ.

is termed the *heat of reaction*, and is measured experimentally. Heat is released during an exothermic change and absorbed during an endothermic reaction.

To illustrate the ideas of the heat content and the heat of reaction, consider the synthesis of water represented by

$$2H_2 + O_2 \rightarrow 2H_2O + 572.5 \text{ kJ}$$

For one mole of water, the thermochemical equation would be

$$H_{2(g)} + \tfrac{1}{2}O_{2(g)} \rightarrow H_2O_{(l)} + 286.3 \text{ kJ}$$

The equation tells us that (a) the product water has a heat content lower by 286.3 kJ/mol than the elements composing it and (b) the heat of reaction is 286.3 kJ in this case.

If one mole of water is decomposed to produce hydrogen and oxygen, this much energy must be supplied to the reaction. In the electrolysis of water, an endothermic reaction, it is supplied as electric energy. The equation is

$$H_2O_{(l)} + 286.3 \text{ kJ} \rightarrow H_{2\,(g)} + \frac{1}{2}O_{2\,(g)}$$

Here the products, 1 mol of hydrogen plus $\frac{1}{2}$ mol of oxygen, have a heat content higher by 286.3 kJ than the original mol of water. The two reactions may be shown by a reversible equation:

$$H_{2\,(g)} + \frac{1}{2}O_{2\,(g)} \rightleftharpoons H_2O_{(l)} + 286.3 \text{ kJ}$$

26:2   The Change in Heat Content

Chemists symbolize the heat content of a substance by the letter H. The *change in heat content* during a reaction, the heat of reaction, is the difference between the heat content of the products and the heat content of the reactants. The heat of reaction then becomes ΔH, the Greek letter Δ (delta) signifying "change in."

$$\Delta H = \frac{\text{heat content}}{\text{of products}} - \frac{\text{heat content}}{\text{of reactants}}$$

In this notation, the ΔH for an exothermic reaction has a negative sign. Thus, in the synthesis of water,

$$\Delta H = -286.3 \text{ kJ}$$

and the thermochemical equation

$$H_{2(g)} + \frac{1}{2}O_{2(g)} \rightarrow H_2O_{(l)} \quad \Delta H = -286.3 \text{ kJ}$$

has the same meaning as

$$H_{2\,(g)} + \frac{1}{2}O_{2\,(g)} \rightarrow H_2O_{(l)} + 286.3 \text{ kJ}$$

According to this sign convention the heat of reaction is said to be negative when the heat content of the system is decreasing (exothermic reaction). It is said to be positive when the heat content of the system is increasing (endothermic reaction).

26:3   Heat of Formation and Heat of Combustion

The *heat of formation* of a compound refers to the heat exchange during the synthesis of one mole of that compound from its elements in a specified state. Generally, such reactions are exothermic, and thus are written with a negative sign. The heat of formation of water is -286.3 kJ/mol.

Fuels, whether for the furnace, automobile, or rocket, are energy-rich substances and the products of their combustion are energy-poor substances. In these combustion reactions the energy yield may be very high and the products of the chemical action may be of little interest compared to the quantity of heat energy evolved.

The combustion of one mole of pure carbon (graphite) yields 393.9 kJ of heat energy:

$$C_{(s)} + O_{2\,(g)} \rightarrow CO_{2\,(g)} \quad \Delta H = -393.9 \text{ kJ}$$

The heat of reaction evolved by the complete combustion of one mole of a substance is called *the heat of combustion* of the substance.

26:4   The Conservation of Energy in Chemical Change

The heat absorbed in decomposing a compound is equal to the heat evolved in its formation under the same conditions. At constant pressure the total heat of reaction of a system is the same regardless of the intermediate steps involved.

This is in accord with the Law of Conservation of Energy. Let us apply these principles to the thermochemical equation for the combustion of carbon monoxide:

$$C_{(s)} + \frac{1}{2}O_{2\,(g)} \rightarrow CO_{(g)} \quad \Delta H = -110.6 \text{ kJ}$$
$$CO_{(g)} + \frac{1}{2}O_{2\,(g)} \rightarrow CO_{2\,(g)} \quad \Delta H = -283.3 \text{ kJ}$$

Adding

$$C_{(s)} + O_{2(g)} \rightarrow CO_{2(g)} \quad \Delta H = -393.9 \text{ kJ}$$

If carbon were burned so as to combine completely with oxygen to form carbon dioxide in one direct step, the heat evolved would also be 393.9 kJ/mol.

$$C_{(s)} + O_{2(g)} \rightarrow CO_{2(g)} \quad \Delta H = -393.9 \text{ kJ}$$

The above illustrates that thermochemical equations may be combined by addition. They may also be combined by subtraction, in which case, their heat change is reversed. Their coefficients may be multiplied or divided. By such combinations, chemists are able to calculate heat effects for chemical operations.

Exothermic and Endothermic Reactions explained in terms of heat content

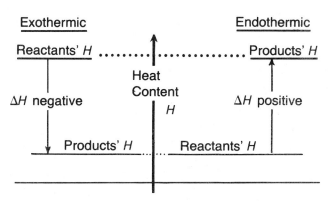

Example: Hydrogen + Oxygen $\rightleftharpoons$ Water

Heat Content: Higher $\rightleftharpoons$ Lower

Reaction: Exothermic
                    $\longrightarrow$
                  Endothermic
                    $\longleftarrow$

Thermochemical Equations:

$$2H_{2(g)} + O_{2(g)} \rightarrow 2H_2O_{(l)} \longrightarrow \Delta H = -572.5 \text{ kJ}$$

$$2H_2O_{(l)} \rightarrow 2H_{2(g)} + O_{2(g)} \longrightarrow \Delta H = +572. \text{ kJ}$$

Different pathways for a chemical reaction show the same energy change:

Illustrated by 2 pathways for $C + O_2 \rightarrow CO_2$, $\Delta H = -393.9$ kJ

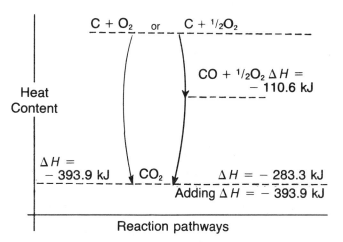

Reaction pathways

26:5   The Activation Energy

When hydrogen and oxygen are mixed at room temperature, why do they not combine spontaneously to form water?

Hydrogen and oxygen gases exist as diatomic molecules. The bonds of these molecules must be broken before the new bonds of the molecules of product can form. Bond breaking requires energy and thus an initial energy input is needed to "activate" the molecules of the reactants. Once the reaction begins, the energy released is enough to activate other molecules. The energy needed to activate the reactants is the *activation energy* of this reaction. In this case the energy may be supplied by an electric spark, a flash of light, or a flame from a burner. Figure 26.1 shows graphically the course of a reaction and the part played by the activation energy.

26:6   Molecular Collisions in Gas Reactions

Consider what happens in a reaction in which reactants and products are all gaseous. The formation of hydrogen iodide from hydrogen and iodine is such a gaseous reaction:

$$H_{2\,(g)} + I_{2\,(g)} \rightleftharpoons 2HI_{\,(g)}$$

For hydrogen to react with iodine vapour, their molecules must collide. If they do so with enough energy to disrupt their bonds, new bonds leading to the formation of the new molecules of the product may form.

The minimum energy required for this is termed the activation energy of the $H_2 + I_2$ reaction. It is not surprising that the rate of the reaction depends on the number of molecules travelling at such high speeds that their collisions can furnish the activation energy. This is discussed more fully in section 26:11.

26:7   The Activated Complex

When molecules with enough activation energy collide, their present bonds break and new ones form. For a brief instant of time a transition state with weak bonds may exist, and this is termed the *activated complex*.

The activated complex may then change in one of two ways:

1. It may form new bonds and thus new product molecules.
2. It may change back to the original reactants by reforming the original bonds.

THE ROLE OF THE ACTIVATION ENERGY IN A CHEMICAL REACTION

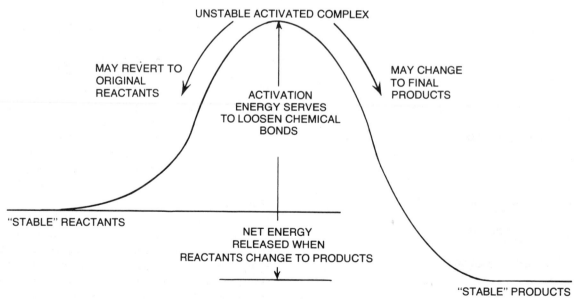

Fig. 26.1:
The role of the activation energy in a chemical reaction

Let us now return to the $H_2 + I_2$ reaction. In the pathway for this reaction, the two reactant molecules are believed to form an activated complex having the intermediate configuration $H_2I_2\ddagger$ shown in Fig. 26.2. (The symbol $\ddagger$ is commonly used to designate the activated complex.)

Starting with hydrogen and iodine, the bonds of their molecules must be weakened by collision to form the activated complex $H_2I_2\ddagger$. The activation energy absorbed for this is 180.2 kJ/mol.

If the complex then goes on to separate into two molecules of HI, 190.17 kJ of energy are evolved. As a result, the net heat evolved is 10.5 kJ and the reaction is slightly exothermic:

$$H_{2(g)} + I_{2(g)} \rightarrow 2HI_{(g)} + 10.5 \text{ kJ}$$

The reverse reaction goes back along the same reaction pathway forming the same activated complex. Now the bonds between hydrogen and iodine atoms in the molecules of HI need to be weakened by collision, and this requires 190.7 kJ/mol. If the complex then decomposes into molecules of H_2 and I_2, only 180.2 kJ/mol is liberated. As a result, the net energy change is the absorption of 10.5 kJ/mol.

$$2HI_{(g)} + 10.5 \text{ kJ} \rightarrow H_{2(g)} + I_{2(g)}$$

The energy profile for this reversible reaction is shown in Fig. 26.3.

26:8 Factors Affecting the Speed of a Reaction

The speeds of reactions differ greatly. For example, the explosion of dynamite is a chemical reaction that happens at great speed. Other reactions, however, are extremely slow. The question whether the speed of a reaction could be controlled is often important in industry; it might be the deciding factor that determines whether a certain chemical reaction may be used economically or not.

The speed of a chemical reaction may be defined as the number of moles reacting or produced per unit time per unit volume. Five important factors influence the rate of a reaction: (a) the nature of the reactants; (b) the temperature; (c) the amount of exposed surface of the reactants; (d) catalysts; (e) the concentration of the reactants. In some reactions, light and pressure are important deciding factors.

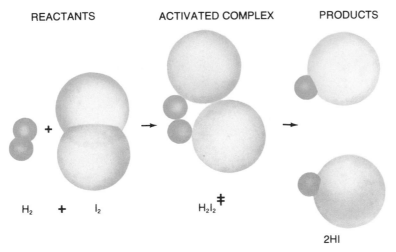

REACTANTS   ACTIVATED COMPLEX   PRODUCTS

H_2 + I_2 $H_2I_2\ddagger$ 2HI

Fig. 26.2:
The activated complex

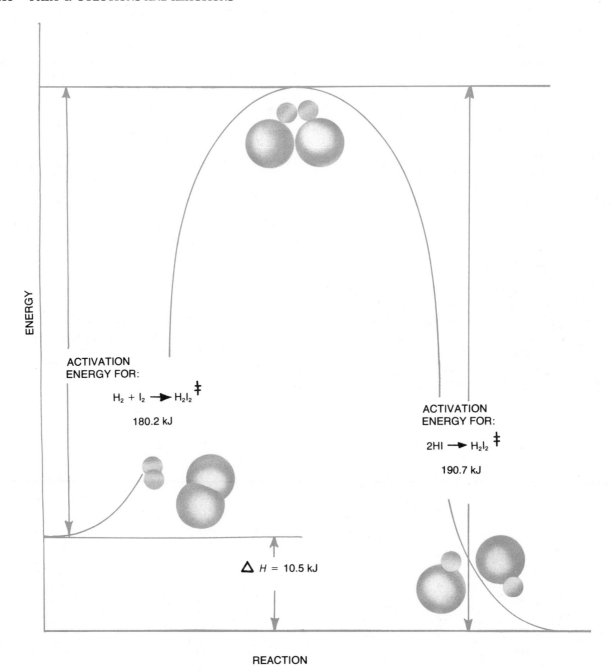

ENERGY

ACTIVATION
ENERGY FOR:

$H_2 + I_2 \longrightarrow H_2I_2{}^{\ddagger}$

180.2 kJ

ACTIVATION
ENERGY FOR:

$2HI \longrightarrow H_2I_2{}^{\ddagger}$

190.7 kJ

$\Delta H = 10.5$ kJ

REACTION

Fig. 26.3:
The energy profile of the hydrogen-iodine reaction

26:9   The Nature of the Reactants

Some substances are extremely reactive and others are less so; the difference is often ascribed to the very nature of the material. No doubt as knowledge about the structure of matter improves, better explanations will be offered for differences in reaction rates. Sodium is a very reactive metal, while silver is inert; hydrochloric acid ionizes to a large extent, while acetic acid ionizes only to a slight extent; oxygen is a reactive gas, while nitrogen is not.

26:10   The Effect of Temperature on Reaction Rates

Reactions are always faster at high temperatures and slower at low temperatures. An application of this principle is a refrigerator, which lowers temperatures and thereby slows down the chemical reactions that spoil foods. For most reactions the speed approximately doubles with each rise of 10°C.

In order to react chemically, molecules must have at least enough energy to decompose or to rearrange themselves when they collide. Such molecules are *activated* (section 26:5) and the energy responsible for this condition is called the *energy of activation.* At any temperature only a certain fraction of all the molecules have energies equal to the energy of activation. When the temperature is raised about 10°C, the number of molecules in this class is doubled, and the rate of reaction is doubled also.

26:11   The Distribution of Energy Among Molecules

To explain the effect of temperature on the rate of reaction, it must be understood that the molecules of a given system do not all have exactly the same energy. Their average kinetic energy is determined by the temperature; but some molecules have energies greater than the average, while others have less. The reason for this uneven distribution of energy is molecular collision, for as the molecules collide some are speeded up and others are slowed down. The kinetic energy of some molecules increases, while that of others diminishes, even though the average remains the same at any particular temperature.

The energy distribution among the molecules may be illustrated by a graph (Fig. 26.4). The vertical axis of the graph refers to the percentage of the molecules, while the horizontal axis refers to the energy per mole.

Thus the point A refers to a low value of the energy possessed by a small percentage of the molecules; point C refers to a high value of energy also possessed by a small percentage of the molecules; and point B refers to the average energy possessed by the largest percentage of the molecules. The graph line ABC describes the distribution of the energy at a temperature T.

Suppose that for a certain reaction, the energy of activation is E. The number of molecules having at least this amount of energy is shown by the area under the curve to the right of E.

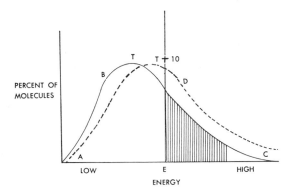

Fig. 26.4:
Energy distribution curve

If the temperature is raised 10°C, all the molecules will have a higher kinetic energy. A new graph along the dotted line shows the distribution of energy at the higher temperature.

The average increase in the kinetic energy of the molecules has been relatively small. Thus, if the temperature is about 300 K, then a 10 degree rise is only about a three per cent increase in the absolute temperature which is not enough to explain the doubling of the rate of reaction, an increase of 100 per cent. An examination of the area under the curve beyond the point E shows that the area has doubled. In other words, the number of molecules having the energy of activation has become twice as great.

26:12   The Amount of Exposed Surface of the Reactants

Chemical reaction occurs at the surfaces of the reacting substances. For example, when zinc is placed in dilute hydrochloric acid, the acid comes in contact with the zinc at the surface of the metal, and that is where reaction occurs. By reducing the size of the pieces of zinc, the exposed surface is increased. Any increase in surface area increases the rate of reaction (Fig. 26.5).

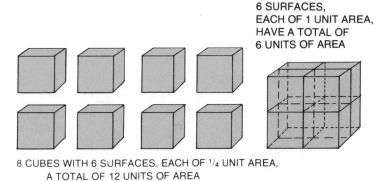

1 CUBE WITH
6 SURFACES,
EACH OF 1 UNIT AREA,
HAVE A TOTAL OF
6 UNITS OF AREA

8 CUBES WITH 6 SURFACES, EACH OF ¼ UNIT AREA,
A TOTAL OF 12 UNITS OF AREA

Fig. 26.5:
Increased surface with subdivision

26:13   Catalysts

Catalysts are substances that affect the rate of reaction. Generally, they speed up certain chemical changes, although some are known to slow them down. The catalyst itself is not altered by the reaction and may be recovered afterwards weighing as much as it did originally.

Of all the factors, perhaps the action of a catalyst is the most dramatic. This may be seen in the laboratory preparation of oxygen by heating potassium chlorate. In the presence of the catalyst, manganese dioxide, only moderate heat is needed to decompose potassium chlorate. In the absence of the catalyst, potassium chlorate must be heated to a much higher temperature and for a much longer period of time in order to obtain similar results.

Catalysts are used in industry in the making of ammonia, nitric acid, sulfuric acid, rubber, plastics, textiles, and many other substances. Nature uses catalysts for all the chemical reactions that occur in living organisms. Such catalysts are called *enzymes* and are produced chemically by the body, being distributed by the bloodstream to the points where they function.

To explain how catalysts work, it is supposed that reactant molecules collect on the surface of the catalyst where it is easier for other molecules to collide with them or react with them. Collection of one substance on the surface of another is termed *adsorption*. Some catalysts have the ability to adsorb certain reactants, and this may partly account for their effectiveness.

Some catalysts form unstable compounds or radicals with the reactants. Such are termed *intermediate products* since they decompose to form the final products of the reaction. When the final product is formed, the catalyst is restored to its original state. The catalyst may now repeat its performance by combining with another molecule of reactant, and so on. This would explain why the catalyst does not become depleted or altered.

It may happen that the catalyst has the ability to

activate the molecules of reactants adsorbed on its surface. They might become strained or their bonds might be weakened. This would render the molecule unstable, or activated. Another possible explanation of how a catalyst works is that it provides another pathway along which the reaction can proceed. This alternate pathway might require a lower activation energy (Fig. 26.6)

Although the catalysts may speed up chemical reactions, there are two important limitations on their behaviour. First, they cannot cause a reaction; they can only speed up reactions that proceed more slowly without them. Second, the catalyst speeds up the establishment of equilibrium (section 26:15) by accelerating the forward and reverse reactions to the same extent. It does not influence the position of the equilibrium by producing any

more of a desired product than would have been formed without the catalyst.

26:14 The Effect of Concentration

A splint that only glows in air bursts into flame when put into pure oxygen. The air is only about 20 per cent oxygen, so that only one-fifth of all the molecules coming in contact with the splint can react with it to cause combustion. The result is a feeble glow. In pure oxygen, the oxygen molecules are five times as numerous as in air. Therefore the reaction is more rapid, and the splint bursts into flame.

Careful experiment shows that when two sub-

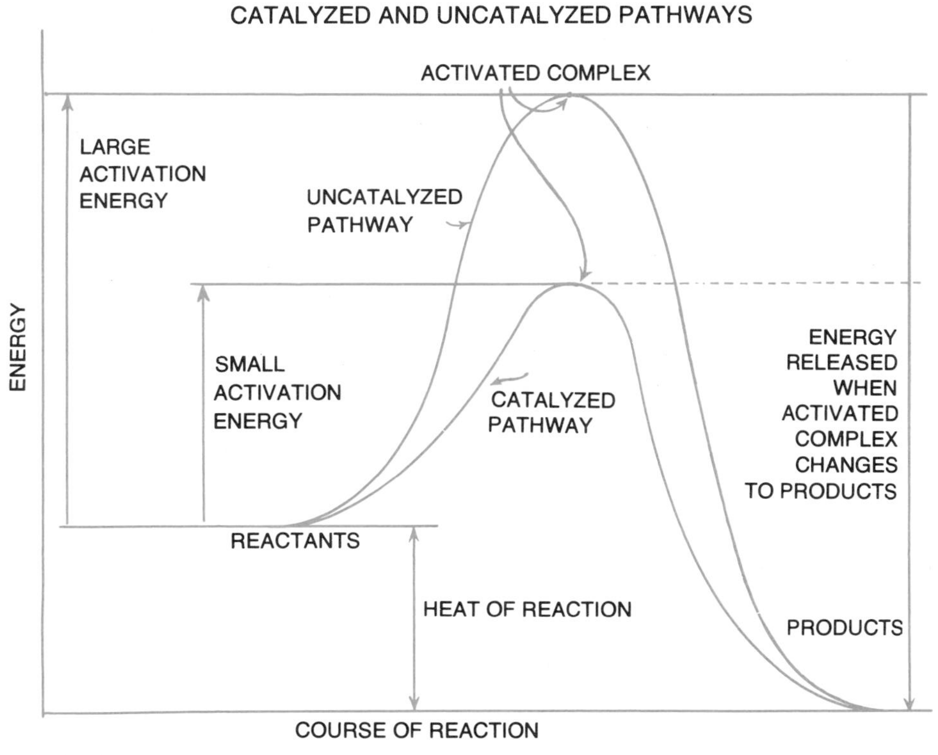

Fig. 26.6:
How a catalyst might work in certain reactions

stances react, the speed of the reaction is proportional to the relative number of the reacting molecules or ions.

The *Law of Mass Action*

The conclusion just reached is named the *Law of Mass Action*. Suppose that A and B are the reactants of a chemical change:

$$A + B \rightarrow \text{Products}$$

When the concentration of A and B are each one mole per litre, there is a certain number of collisions between their particles and the rate r of the reaction is k_1 moles per litre per second. This may be represented by

$$\vec{r} = k_1$$

If, now, the concentration of A is made two moles per litre, there will be twice as many collisions between particles of A and particles of B since the particles of A are twice as many. Therefore, the rate of the reaction becomes twice as great as it was formerly. Now it is

$$k_1 \times 2$$

Similarly if the concentration of B is made three moles per litre, the collisions between particles of B and those of A become three times as numerous and the rate of the reaction also becomes three times as great.

Therefore, when the concentration of A is two moles per litre, and that of B is three moles per litre, the rate is six times as great as when the concentration of either was only one mole per litre.

Generally, if the concentration of A is represented by [A] and that of B by [B], then the rate of reaction would be expressed as follows:

$$\vec{r} = k_1 [A] [B]$$

This is the mathematical expression of the Law of Mass Action.

For a reaction in a solution, the rate depends on the molar concentration of the reactants. For gas reactions, the rate depends on the pressures of the reacting gases, since pressure depends on the number of molecules present.

26:15   Reversible Reactions

In many chemical changes, the products formed react among themselves to form the original materials. Such are called *reversible reactions*. To represent these, two arrows pointing in opposite directions are used; that is, from the reactants to the products and from the products back to the reactants. To show this, suppose A and B represent reactants that form products C and D. Then, the reversible reaction would be:

$$A + B \rightleftharpoons C + D$$

When A and B are first mixed, their concentration is relatively high and, therefore, the number of collisions between their molecules is large. As a result, the reaction between A and B (the "forward reaction") will be rapid. Gradually, the concentrations of A and B decrease, and the reaction between them slows down. Meanwhile, products C and D have been forming in ever increasing amounts as a result of the reaction between A and B. The "reverse reaction" between C and D starts, slowly at first and more rapidly as more of C and D accumulate. Eventually the forward and the reverse reactions will be going on at equal rates. Such a condition is called *chemical equilibrium*.

Law of Chemical Equilibrium

According to the Law of Mass Action, the rate of the reaction between A and B is given by

$$\vec{r} = k_1 [A] [B]$$

and that between C and D is given by

$$\overleftarrow{r} = k_2 [C] [D]$$

As stated above, at chemical equilibrium the

rates of the forward and the reverse reactions are equal,

$$\vec{r} = \overset{\leftarrow}{r}$$

therefore, $\quad k_1 [A] [B] = k_2 [C] [D]$

or $\quad \dfrac{[C] [D]}{[A] [B]} = \dfrac{k_1}{k_2} = K_c$ (since k_2 and k_1 are constants).

This is the mathematical expression of the *Law of Chemical Equilibrium*. In its simplest form, the law states that *when a reversible reaction reaches equilibrium, the products and the reactants bear a constant ratio to one another.* That constant ratio is called the *equilibrium constant, K_c.*

When reactions are more complex than the above illustrations, the mathematical expression of the Law of Mass Action and the Law of Chemical Equilibrium become more complex too. The ideas employed in more complex cases are extensions of those discussed in the present case.

26:16   Principle of Le Chatelier

Every reversible reaction reaches its own specific equilibrium. This state depends on the pressure and temperature. Once these are given, the concentrations of the reactants and products will be in a definite ratio. It is even possible to calculate the amounts of reactants and products at the equilibrium.

To obtain an idea of how to predict what occurs in a system in equilibrium, imagine a reversible reaction such as $A + B \rightleftharpoons C + heat$, where A and B are reactants. If more A is added, collisions between molecules of A and B increase, and chances of a reaction between them improve; and the amount of C increases. Similarly, if some A is removed, collisions between molecules of A and B become fewer, and the rate of the forward reaction $A + B \rightarrow C$ is diminished. However, the reverse reaction $C \rightarrow A + B$ will go on at the same rate as before, and as a result there will be less C at the new equilibrium.

To summarize, *if a system in chemical equilibrium is subjected to a change or stress, the reaction that relieves the stress will be favoured.* This is called the *Principle of Le Chatelier.* If this principle is applied to the example $A + B \rightleftharpoons C + heat$, the following events may be predicted:

1. When the temperature of the system at equilibrium is raised, the added heat is used to decompose C. Less C will be present in the new equilibrium at the higher temperature.
2. When the temperature is lowered, less heat is present in the system. This causes the decomposition reaction of C to be slowed down since heat is required for this as seen by the equation. Thus less of A and B would be present at the new equilibrium.
3. If A and B are gases, their combination into product C is a reaction in which the number of gas molecules is diminished. Upon subjecting the mixture to higher pressure, the number of molecules of A and B per unit volume will be greater. Therefore, the collisions between them will increase and the chance of chemical reaction will be better, which will cause more of C to form through reaction of A with B. The removal of some of A and B will mean a reduction of the pressure. The stress to which the system was subjected has been partly removed.

26:17   Predicting Results

A good illustration of the ideas about equilibrium is provided by an important reaction, the exothermic formation of ammonia from hydrogen and nitrogen in which four gas molecules change into two:

$$3H_2 + N_2 \rightleftharpoons 2NH_3 + heat$$

The following results may be predicted for this reaction:

1. An increase in pressure will favour the production of ammonia.
2. An increase in temperature will favour the breakdown of ammonia.
3. The removal of ammonia will favour the production of more from the union of hydrogen and nitrogen.

In practice, all of these predictions are confirmed.

Another illustration of the effect of concentration changes on equilibrium is demonstrated by the following reaction:

$FeCl_3$ +   3KCNS $\rightleftharpoons$
Iron   +   potassium
(III)   thiocyanate
chloride   (colourless)

Fe $(CNS)_3$ +   3KCl
Iron   +   potassium
(III)   chloride
thicoyanate
(red)

If more of either of the reactants is added to this equilibrium, the mixture becomes darker red because the equilibrium shifts to the right. If potassium chloride is added, the red colour fades because the reaction is reversed.

26:18   "Irreversible" Reactions

Most reactions are reversible to some extent. If, however, one or more of the products are removed, the reverse reaction cannot take place. When this occurs, the forward reaction is said to go to completion. The reaction is termed *irreversible* for practical purposes. No reaction is completely irreversible.

The three most common examples of removal of a product are by the escape of gas, the precipitation of an insoluble product, and the formation of a non-ionized (or poorly ionized) compound.

When sodium chloride, NaCl, and silver nitrate, $AgNO_3$, are reacted in solution, the reaction goes to completion because of the formation of the almost insoluble silver chloride:

$$Na^+_{(aq)} + Cl^-_{(aq)} + Ag^+_{(aq)} + NO^-_{3(aq)} \rightarrow$$
$$AgCl\downarrow_{(s)} + Na^+_{(aq)} + NO^-_{3(aq)}$$

or as a net ionic equation:

$$Cl^-_{(aq)} + Ag^+_{(aq)} \rightarrow AgCl\downarrow_{(s)}$$

When zinc is treated with hydrochloric acid, hydrogen gas is liberated. This causes the reaction to go to completion, since the hydrogen is collected *outside* the reaction flask:

$$Zn_{(s)} + 2HCl_{(aq)} \rightarrow ZnCl_2_{(aq)} + H_2\uparrow_{(g)}$$

or as a net ionic equation:

$$Zn_{(s)} + 2H_3O^+_{(aq)} \rightarrow Zn^{2+}_{(aq)} + 2H_2O_{(l)} + H_2\uparrow_{(g)}$$

When hydrochloric acid neutralizes sodium hydroxide, water forms. Since the ionization of water is exceedingly small, the removal of the hydronium and hydroxide ions is complete, and the reaction is termed irreversible:

$$H_3O^+ + OH^- \rightarrow 2H_2O$$

26:19   Spontaneous and Forced Reactions — The Free Energy

Chemical reactions involve energy. Exothermic reactions release heat, and endothermic reactions require heat, as was discussed earlier. Similarly, some chemical reactions can do work as they proceed while others require that work be done upon them to make them go.

A familiar reaction which performs work as it proceeds is that which takes place in a voltaic cell or battery delivering electricity which can be put to many uses. An electrolytic cell is an illustration of a system where electrical work from the outside causes electrolysis, a chemical reaction, to proceed in the cell.

When a chemical reaction does work, the maximum amount of work performed at constant temperature and pressure can be measured, and is called the *free energy of the reaction*. This is an appropriate name because the system performs this work freely and spontaneously, and it is up to us to take advantage of it, as we do in placing an appliance in the circuit of a voltaic cell.

Work is defined as the product of force and distance. Therefore in a system which does work, there must be some unbalanced or unchecked force, and this is the cause of the work done. An example of an unbalanced force would be the greater tendency for one electrode of a cell to attract electrons than for the other electrode to do so. This greater attraction causes the electrons to move in one direction, thereby giving them kinetic energy which can operate an appliance. When the force is spent, the system is in equilibrium and no more work can be done. A system in equilibrium has no capacity for giving free energy to any appliance or to the surroundings. An example is a "dead" battery. The "dead" battery may, however, be recharged by applying an external voltage to it. This in effect, is doing work on the battery to force

the necessary chemical reaction to take place by electrolysis.

Chemical systems may therefore be classified as:

1. Those in which reactions go spontaneously and are able to give or lose free energy to the outside. Example: the discharging of a battery.
2. Those in chemical equilibrium, which are unable to give free energy to the outside. Example: the dead battery.
3. Those in which reactions are forced to take place by doing work upon them, or giving them free energy from the outside. Example: recharging a battery.

The idea of the free energy is a most useful one in biology. Many chemical reactions go on in living organisms, and it appears as if their objective is to place stores of free energy at the disposal of the animal or plant.

Finally, even if a chemical reaction can give free energy, it might not go automatically if the reactants are not activated. For this, *the energy of activation* needs to be supplied. The materials in the head of a match burn spontaneously, once the energy of activation is supplied by friction.

QUESTIONS

1. Define *rate of reaction*.

2. List the factors that affect the rate of a reaction.

3. Explain carefully what is meant by *energy of activation*.

4. Why does a rise of ten Celsius degrees usually double the speed of a reaction? Draw a graph to make your explanation clear.

5. Give an example of the effect of surface on the rate of reaction.

6. What is meant by *adsorption*?

7. Describe three ways by which catalysts may affect the speed of a reaction.

8. What are two important limitations on the behaviour of catalysts in chemical reactions?

9. Explain why a glowing splint bursts into flame in oxygen but not in air.

10. State the Law of Mass Action.

11. What is a reversible reaction?

12. Explain what is meant by chemical equilibrium.

13. (i) State the principle of Le Chatelier.
    (ii) Explain this principle by making clear what would happen in an exothermic reaction, A + B $\rightleftharpoons$ C + heat, where equilibrium has been established (i) if the temperature is raised, and (ii) if the temperature is lowered.

14. In the reaction $3H_2 + N_2 \rightleftharpoons 2NH_3$ + heat, describe three ways by which the equilibrium could be shifted.

15. In the reaction $FeCl_3 + 3KCNS \rightleftharpoons Fe(CNS)_3 + 3KCl$, how could the equilibrium be shifted to form more $Fe(CNS)_3$? How could it be shifted to form less?

16. What are the three types of irreversible reactions? Give an example of each type.

17. A student prepares hydrogen gas in the laboratory by the reaction of zinc with a 3 mol/L hydrochloric acid solution. What would be the effect on the speed of the reaction if a 6 mol/L solution of HCl were used?

18. Hydrogen and iodine combine together to form hydrogen iodide. Fig. 26.3 represents the potential energy curve for this reaction.
    (i)   Is this reaction exothermic or endothermic?
    (ii) How much energy would have to be supplied to the reactants if ten moles of HI is to be produced?
    (iii) What would be the effect of a catalyst on (i) the activated energy and (ii) on the ΔH of this reaction?

CHAPTER

27

THE HALOGENS

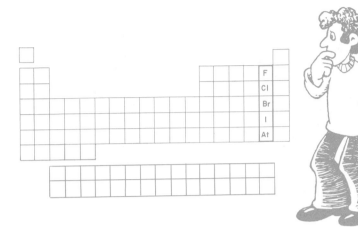

27:1 The Halogen Elements

The five elements fluorine, chlorine, bromine, iodine, and astatine of group VII in the periodic table are called the *halogens*. The word halogen means *salt former*, and these five elements occur in nature as salts rather than as free elements.

The halogens have many common characteristics, because in the outermost shell they each have seven electrons. Six are paired and the seventh is unpaired. In chemical combination the halogens normally gain one electron to pair with this seventh electron when they share electrons in covalent bonds. They are usually the more electronegative of the pair of atoms bonded and, for these reasons, are said to be strong oxidizing agents. Electronegativity among the halogens decreases with increase in atomic size; consequently

A family of salt-forming elements.

fluorine is the most electronegative. The smaller, lighter halogens are able to replace the larger, heavier ones from their compounds.

The distribution of electrons in the atoms of these elements is given in Table 27:1.

27:2 Chlorine

Discovery and Occurrence

The story of chlorine began in the year 1774, when a Swedish pharmacist by the name of Scheele dis-

Table 27.1

Electrons in the Halogen Atoms

| Element | Atomic Number | Shell Numbers | | | | | |
		1	2	3	4	5	6
Fluorine	9	2	7				
Chlorine	17	2	8	7			
Bromine	35	2	8	18	7		
Iodine	53	2	8	18	18	7	
Astatine	85	2	8	18	32	18	7

covered that the mineral called pyrolusite (crude manganese dioxide) gave off a greenish-yellow gas on exposure to hydrochloric acid. He found that this gas stung his nose and throat and nearly blinded him. He also noted that it had an acid taste in water and that it bleached flowers and attacked metals. In 1810, Sir Humphry Davy showed, by failing to decompose it, that the gas was an element. He called it chlorine from the Greek words meaning *greenish-yellow*.

Chlorine is not found free in nature because it is a very active element. Its most important compound is sodium chloride, which is found in sea water and in salt deposits in the Earth. Other chlorides, such as those of potassium, calcium, and magnesium, are also present in these salt deposits which were formed by the evaporation of inland seas many centuries ago. This process may be seen taking place today in such areas as the Dead Sea and the Great Salt Lake.

Preparation

A common method of preparing chlorine is to cause removal of one electron from chloride ions. This may be done by treating hydrochloric acid with manganese dioxide.

In this reaction, manganese dioxide removes the electron from the chloride ions. The manganese dioxide is thus an oxidizing agent while the chloride ion is a reducing agent. The reaction is as follows:

$$MnO_2 + 4HCl \rightarrow MnCl_2 + Cl_2\uparrow + 2H_2O$$

The half-reaction of the reducing agent is:

$$2Cl^- - 2e \rightarrow 2Cl^0$$
$$2Cl^0 \rightarrow Cl_2\uparrow$$

The half-reaction of the oxidizing agent:

$$MnO_2 + 4H_3O^+ + 2e \rightarrow Mn^{2+} + 6H_2O$$

The chlorine is collected by the upward displacement of air because it is heavier than air and is moderately soluble in water. The apparatus used is

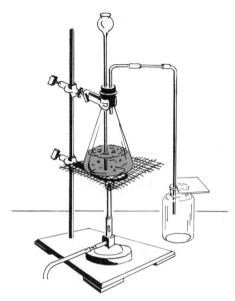

Fig. 27.1:
Laboratory preparation of chlorine

illustrated in Fig. 27.1. The greenish-yellow colour of the gas determines when the bottles are full.

An alternate source of chloride ions is sodium chloride, which, when treated with MnO_2 and sulphuric acid, produces chlorine.

$$2NaCl + MnO_2 + 2H_2SO_4 \rightarrow$$
$$Na_2SO_4 + MnSO_4 + Cl_2\uparrow + 2H_2O$$

Note that the ionic equations for this reaction are exactly the same as those in the previous reaction, because the same ions are involved.

Commercial Preparation

Chlorine, hydrogen, and sodium hydroxide are all produced when brine is electrolyzed. The process is carried out industrially in specially designed cells such as the one shown in Fig. 27.2

Sodium hydroxide drips through the cathode and collects at the bottom of the cell. Chlorine is discharged at the anode, and hydrogen gas is discharged at the cathode. The reason for the dis-

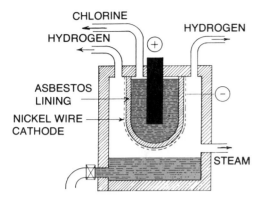

Fig. 27.2:
Electrolysis of brine in the Nelson cell

TABLE 27.2

Physical Properties of Fluorine, Chlorine, Bromine, and Iodine

Element	Melting Point (°C)	Boiling Point (°C)	Colour and State at Ordinary Conditions
Fluorine	−223	−187	pale yellow gas
Chlorine	−102	−35	greenish-yellow gas
Bromine	− 7.2	59	deep red liquid
Iodine	113.5	184	steel-gray solid

TABLE 27.3

Main Oxidation Numbers of Chlorine

Oxidation Numbers	Examples
1 −	NaCl, sodium chloride
	HCl, hydrogen chloride
0	Cl_2, molecular chlorine
1 +	NaClO, sodium hypochlorite
	HClO, hypochlorous acid
3 +	$NaClO_2$, sodium chlorite
	$HClO_2$, chlorous acid
5 +	$NaClO_3$, sodium chlorate
	$HClO_3$, chloric acid
7 +	$NaClO_4$, sodium perchlorate
	$HClO_4$, perchloric acid

charge of hydrogen gas instead of metallic sodium is that less energy is required to convert hydronium ions to hydrogen atoms and molecules than to convert sodium ions to sodium atoms. Sodium hydroxide collects in the solution as electrolysis proceeds:

$$2NaCl + 2H_2O \rightarrow Cl_2\uparrow + H_2\uparrow + 2NaOH$$

To prevent the chlorine from reacting with the sodium hydroxide in these cells, the anode is usually covered with an asbestos diaphragm.

Chlorine can also be prepared commercially along with metallic sodium by the electrolysis of fused sodium chloride.

Physical Properties

Some physical properties of the elements are given in Table 27.2

Chlorine is $2\frac{1}{2}$ times as heavy as air. It is moderately soluble; one volume of water dissolves about two volumes of the gas at 20°C and 101.3 kPa pressure. Chlorine has a penetrating odour, and it causes pain when inhaled. Alcohol or ammonia fumes help to ease the irritation. It forms a golden, coloured liquid at about −35°C and 101.3 kPa. It is transported as a liquid in steel cylinders.

Chemical Properties

With seven electrons in its outer shell, chlorine can assume several positive oxidation numbers as well as one negative oxidation number as Table 27.3 shows.

In accordance with its electronic structure, the following are some chemical properties of chlorine:

1. Chlorine reacts with most metals to form chlorides. The presence of a trace of moisture speeds up the reaction between chlorine and the less reactive metals. Some examples are:

$$2Fe + 3Cl_2 \rightarrow 2FeCl_3$$
$$Cu + Cl_2 \rightarrow CuCl_2$$

2. Chlorine reacts with hydrogen; a mixture of chlorine and hydrogen reacts vigorously when ignited or exposed to a strong light source:

$$H_2 + Cl_2 \rightarrow 2HCl$$

If a hydrogen generator is set up and allowed to run until all the air is expelled, the hydrogen may be ignited safely at the end of the delivery tube. If lowered into a jar of chlorine, this jet of burning hydrogen continues to burn, forming hydrogen chloride.

3. Chlorine combines with the hydrogen of certain compounds. If turpentine, for example, is poured on a piece of filter paper, and the paper is thrust quickly into a jar of chlorine, a flash of yellow flames flares up and a large amount of black smoke is formed:

$$C_{10}H_{16} + 8Cl_2 \rightarrow 16HCl + 10C$$

A lighted candle burns in a jar of chlorine with a very smoky flame forming similar products.

4. Chlorine combines with most of the nonmetals. It forms compounds with oxygen and nitrogen only indirectly. It combines with phosphorus to form phosphorus trichloride.

$$P_4 + 6Cl_2 \rightarrow 4PCl_3$$

5. Chlorine "adds" to many compounds; for example:

$$2FeCl_2 + Cl_2 \rightarrow 2FeCl_3$$
$$2CuCl + Cl_2 \rightarrow 2CuCl_2$$

6. Chlorine is a bleaching agent. When chlorine is dissolved in water, hydrochloric and hypochlorous acids are formed; the hypochlorous acid formed is unstable and decomposes yielding atomic oxygen:

$$Cl_2 + H_2O \rightarrow HCl + HClO$$
$$HClO \rightarrow HCl + (O)$$

The atomic oxygen has the ability to combine with the coloured matter in many substances. After such treatment, the substances are whiter in appearance and are said to have been bleached.

7. Chlorine is poisonous. Even in small quantities chlorine attacks the moist membranes of the respiratory system. One part of chlorine in 30 000 parts of air is a lethal mixture.

Uses
1. In industry, chlorine is used for bleaching cotton and wood pulp, but not for bleaching wool or natural silk, as it hardens and destroys these materials. If chlorine is passed over calcium hydroxide (slaked lime), a compound known as *chloride of lime* is formed:

$$Ca(OH)_2 + Cl_2 \rightarrow CaOCl_2 + H_2O$$

Then, the $CaOCl_2$ reacts with an acid to cause bleaching action:

$$CaOCl_2 + H_2CO_3 \rightarrow CaCO_3 + HCl + HClO$$
$$\text{(from air)}$$

The hypochlorous acid formed is the actual cause of the bleaching action.

Laundry bleach or Javel water is made by adding chlorine to cold sodium hydroxide solution:

$$2NaOH + Cl_2 \rightarrow NaClO + NaCl + H_2O$$
$$\text{Sodium}$$
$$\text{hypochlorite}$$

2. Chlorine is a good disinfectant, since it destroys bacteria. It is used to purify drinking water and water in swimming pools. In communities where it has been added to the water supply, typhoid fever and dysentery have been practically eliminated. Only about one kilogram of chlorine is needed to disinfect three million litres (3×10^6 L) of water.

3. Chlorine is used to make many useful materials such as carbon tetrachloride, CCl_4, and chloroform, $CHCl_3$, solvents; and hydrochloric acid, HCl.

Thus chlorine can cause great discomfort or even death, as well as contribute to the comfort and health of people.

27:3 Sodium Chloride

Anyone who thinks of salt usually visualizes sodium chloride, NaCl. This compound of chlorine is one of the most useful and most abundant compounds utilized by man. In ancient Rome salt was so important that soldiers received a special pay called *salarium* for the purchase of this commodity. The word "salary" was derived from *salarium*; and the expression "He is not worth his salt" is common today.

Sodium chloride is found in sea water, salt lakes, and deposits formed by the evaporation of inland seas many thousands of years ago. Sea

Courtesy The Canadian Salt Company Limited
Interior of a salt mine near Windsor, Ont.

water contains on the average about 3 per cent salt, while the Dead Sea and Great Salt Lake contain about 20 per cent. Canadian deposits of rock salt, or halite, are found at Windsor, Ontario; Unity, Saskatchewan; and Malagash, Nova Scotia. An area of about 250 000 km² under Texas, Oklahoma, and Kansas is occupied by a deposit of salt about 150 m in thickness.

In some cases, where a deposit of salt is easily accessible, salt is mined by excavation. Usually, however, a well is drilled down to the deposit of salt. The well consists of two pipes, one inside the other. Water, which is forced down the outside pipe at high pressure, dissolves the salt; and the brine (salt solution) is forced up the inner pipe. The brine is placed in tanks where insoluble substances settle out and where it may be treated chemically to remove other impurities. It is then filtered and evaporated under vacuum. When salt crystallizes from the solution, it is dried, screened, and packaged.

It is too costly to separate salt from any solution by artificial evaporation if the solution contains less than 17 per cent salt. In hot countries where rock salt is not available, sea water is run into shallow basins and the heat of the sun evaporates the water.

Sodium chloride crystallizes into cubic crystals which melt at 800°C. These crystals usually contain some water mechanically enclosed in tiny droplets inside the crystal lattice. When rock salt is heated, or when a salt solution is evaporated, the crystals fly apart with a crackling sound caused by the changing of this water to steam.

Sodium chloride is quite soluble in water; 35.7 g dissolve in 100 g of water at 0°C, and 39.8 g at 100°C. This is unusual, because most solids are much more soluble in hot water than in cold.

Pure sodium chloride is non-hygroscopic and does not cake unless the humidity is very high. Salt usually hardens because of impurities in it, such as calcium or magnesium chloride, which absorb moisture. "Free-running" salt is prepared by precipitating the calcium and magnesium from the original salt solution before evaporation.

Very pure sodium chloride may be obtained by adding hydrochloric acid to a saturated solution of the salt. The excess of chloride ion from the salt and the acid decreases the solubility of the salt so that it precipitates.

Physiological saline is the name of a salt solution, 0.9 per cent NaCl by mass, used frequently in medicine. The special property of this solution is that it has the same osmotic pressure as the cells, tissue, and blood of the human body. Solutions of the same osmotic pressure are called *isotonic*.

To prevent water entering or leaving the tissues, adjoining solutions have to be of equal osmotic pressure. This is the chief reason for the use of isotonic solutions for drops applied to the eyes, nose, and ears, and for injection of drugs.

An adult needs about one teaspoon of salt per day. From this, gastric cells produce the hydrochloric acid essential for digestion. Perspiration contains salt; in hot weather a greater-than-normal intake of salt is necessary to maintain physical well being.

Salt is used for curing fish, meat, and hides. It is a raw material in the industrial manufacture of sodium hydroxide, sodium carbonate and bicarbonate, hydrochloric acid, sodium metal, chlorine, soap, glass, and enamel. In fact, sodium chloride is the ultimate source of pratically all compounds containing sodium or chlorine.

Salt melts ice even in freezing weather because of its great attraction for water. It forms bonds with the water molecules in the ice crystal causing the ice to melt. A solution may thus be obtained with a freezing point as low as −22°C. Salt has been used for a long time on streets, walks, and railway tracks to remove ice. Freezing mixtures are made with it for cold storage plants and in the manufacture of artificial ice and the making of ice cream.

27:4   Hydrogen Chloride

Pure hydrogen chloride is a colourless gas with a sharp, irritating odour. It is heavier than air. It is extremely soluble in water; approximately 500 litres of the gas dissolve in one litre of water at STP. A saturated solution contains about 39 per cent of the gas, but the laboratory acid has about 37 per cent. Because of its great affinity for water, the gas fumes in moist air, owing to the formation of a mist of hydrochloric acid.

The gas cannot be boiled out of its solution entirely because a constant boiling mixture* is formed which boils at 110°C. This solution contains about 20 per cent of HCl by mass.

The large solubility of hydrogen chloride in water may be demonstrated with a "fountain experiment." The apparatus is assembled as shown in Fig. 27.3 and the flask is filled with dry hydrogen chloride. A little water is placed in the medicine dropper. When the bulb of the dropper is squeezed, the ejected water dissolves some of the hydrogen chloride, thus lowering the pressure. This causes the air to push water up through the jet in fountain-like fashion.

Chemical Properites of Hydrogen Chloride and its Water Solution
On the one hand, anhydrous hydrogen chloride is a stable gas, is a poor conductor of electricity, and does not even attack metals at low temperatures; on the other hand, when it comes in contact with water, it acts as proton donor and forms hydrochloric acid (Chapter 25).

27:5   Hydrochloric Acid

Hydrochloric acid is the most important manufactured halogen compound. It has been known for a

---

* A constant boiling mixture is one whose vapour has the same composition as the liquid solution. Therefore, no change in composition occurs as boiling proceeds, and the boiling temperature remains constant.

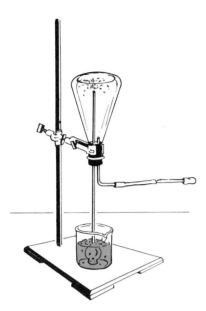

Fig. 27.3:
The hydrogen chloride fountain

is added to the water in which the tendons are heated. Glucose is made from starch in a similar manner. In these processes the acid acts as a catalyst.

Hydrochloric acid is used to remove oxides from metals, a procedure that must be done before one metal is plated with another. The process is called "pickling." A cheaper substitute for pickling is sulfuric acid, but hydrochloric acid is preferred because it forms soluble chlorides whereas sulfuric acid forms insoluble sulfates.

A chloride is a salt formed by replacing the hydrogen of hydrochloric acid with a metal or positive radical. Examples are zinc chloride ($ZnCl_2$) and ammonium chloride (NH_4Cl). All common chlorides are soluble excepting silver chloride ($AgCl$), mercury (I) chloride (Hg_2Cl_2), and lead chloride ($PbCl_2$). The latter is slightly soluble in cold water but much more soluble in hot.

very long time: the alchemists prepared it by the reaction of sulfuric acid on salt.

Hydrochloric acid is a typical strong acid. It readily displaces weaker acids from their salts. It reacts with the metals above hydrogen in the Electromotive Series to form hydrogen:

$$Zn + 2HCl \rightarrow ZnCl_2 + H_2\uparrow$$

It neutralizes bases:

$$NaOH + HCl \rightarrow NaCl + H_2O$$

Like other acids it affects indicators:

$$HCl + Ind^- \rightarrow HInd + Cl^-$$

where HInd and Ind− are the different forms of the indicator which are differently coloured.

Uses
Hydrochloric acid is used as a laboratory reagent for testing and analysis.

In forming gelatin and glue from the tendons of animals, a small amount of hydrochloric acid

27:6   Test for Chlorides

To test for the chloride ion, a solution of silver nitrate is added to the solution to be tested. The resultant double decomposition precipitates insoluble white silver chloride:

$$AgNO_3 + Cl^- \rightarrow AgCl\downarrow + NO_3^-$$

The precipitate is divided into three portions: the first is kept for comparison; to the second is added a little nitric acid; and to the third is added some concentrated ammonium hydroxide. Silver chloride is insoluble in the nitric acid but dissolves in the ammonium hydroxide. The test with nitric acid and ammonium hydroxide is necessary because white silver salts other than the chloride are insoluble in water, but are soluble in nitric acid.

It will be noted that silver chloride darkens on exposure to light, for light slowly reduces the salt to metallic silver. This reaction is the basis of photography.

QUESTIONS

1. What is the meaning of the term *halogen*?

2. List the halogens in decreasing order of chemical activity.

3. Why is fluorine more active than chlorine?

4. Describe how chlorine was discovered.

5. Is chlorine found free in Nature? Explain your answer.

6. Account for the active nature of chlorine.

7. What compounds of chlorine are commonly found in nature?

8. (i) Describe, with the aid of a labelled diagram, the laboratory preparation of chlorine from manganese dioxide and hydrochloric acid. Write the equation for the reaction.
   (ii) Show how this reaction is an oxidation-reduction type.

9. Write the equations to show how chlorine may be prepared by heating sulfuric acid, sodium chloride, and manganese dioxide together.

10. Write the equation for the reaction of chlorine with water.

11. Balance the following:
$$KMnO_4 + HCl \longrightarrow KCl + MnCl_2 + Cl_2\uparrow + H_2O$$
$$PbO_2 + HCl \longrightarrow PbCl_2 + Cl_2\uparrow + H_2O$$

12. Give the equation representing the electrolysis of fused sodium chloride.

13. What are the products of the electrolysis of brine?

14. Faraday liquefied chlorine in 1823. Why was it the first gas to be liquefied?

15. Why should precautions be taken when working with chlorine?

16. How could one safely show that hydrogen and chlorine have a strong chemical affinity?

17. Write the equation to show the reactions between chlorine and each of the following: carbon monoxide; iron (II) chloride; copper (I) chloride. Name the products in each case.

18. How much MnO_2 would be required to release 10L of chlorine from sufficient HCl, if the chlorine is measured at 20°C and 104 kPa?

19. What volume of chlorine could be obtained from 20 g of sodium chloride by electrolysis, if the chlorine is measured at −10°C and 97.7 kPa?

20. Obtain information about the introduction of chlorine as a water disinfecting agent. What changes did chlorine bring about? Why is it said that without chlorine, it is doubtful whether large cities would be possible?

21. The excessive use of chlorine as a disinfecting agent for water carries some dangers with it. Research this problem to determine under what conditions such excessive use might take place, and what the dangers involved might be. Is there an actual case where this problem has arisen?

22. Prepare reports on the use and hazards of the following substances:
    (i) Polyvinyl chloride
    (ii) Freon

(iii) Chlorinated hydrocarbons used as pesticides

(iv) Polychlorinated biphenyls (PCB's)

23. Is there a relation between the use of chlorine in industry and mercury pollution? Explain.

24. What mass of hydrogen chloride could be made from 10 L of chlorine, if the chlorine is measured at 25°C and 102 kPa pressure?

25. What is the simplest formula of a compound which contains 79.7% chlorine and 20.3% aluminum?

26. If 8 mL of chlorine and 3 mL of hydrogen are mixed in the dark and then exposed to light, what gases would result and what would be their volumes?

27. Write a note on the occurrence of sodium chloride.

28. Define the term *salt*.

29. What fundamental processes are involved in producing table salt from brine?

30. Why does freezing brine make it more concentrated?

31. (i) Why does salt cake in moist weather?

(ii) How is "free running" salt made?

(iii) How is pure salt made?

(iv) Is NaCl a molecular formula? Explain your answer.

(v) What is the physiological importance of salt?

(vi) List several uses of salt.

32. How does salt melt ice?

33. (i) List the physical properties of hydrogen chloride.

(ii) List the chemical properties of hydrogen chloride and its water solution.

(iii) Why is hydrochloric acid termed a "typical strong acid"?

(iv) Write a paragraph on the uses of hydrochloric acid.

34. In terms of electronegativity, how can one explain that NaCl is ionic and CCl_4 is covalent?

35. Which chlorides are insoluble?

36. Outline the test for the chloride ion.

CHAPTER

28

SULFUR

28:1   The Sulfur Family

The elements of group VI of the periodic table are oxygen (O), sulfur (S), selenium (Se), tellurium (Te), and polonium (Po). The distribution of electrons in the atoms of these elements is given in Table 28.1.

The atoms of these elements all have six electrons in their outer shell. This explains the combining capacity and the oxidation numbers of these elements.

Oxygen was discussed in Chapter 9. Selenium and tellurium are rare, and polonium is exceedingly rare. In their physical and chemical properties, selenium and tellurium resemble sulfur. A peculiar feature of selenium atoms is that they lose their outer electrons when exposed to light. Hence, selenium is useful for making photoelectric cells, which pass an electric current when light shines on them.

28:2   Occurrence of Sulfur

As long ago as 1000 B.C., the yellow, brittle, lustrous, solid element sulfur was burned and used as a fumigant. In the free state it was used as a medicine. Early myths considered sulfur to be an essential part of all matter that could be burned; that is, it was the element of fire. It was, in fact, called brimstone (fire-stone).

A useful element that can make rubber tires tough and strong for the job they have to do. Unfortunately, some sulfur compounds cause difficult pollution problems.

Sulfur is one of the most abundant elements, making up about 0.1 per cent of the Earth's crust. It occurs in the free state in Sicily, Japan, Spain, Iceland, Mexico, and the United States. It is found much more widely distributed in the compound form as sulfates in gypsum ($CaSO_4 \cdot 2H_2O$) and barite ($BaSO_4$), and as sulfides in galena (PbS), cinnabar (HgS), zinc blende (ZnS), and iron pyrites (FeS_2). Many ores, such as those of silver and copper, contain sulfides. Sulfur is also present in some proteins.

28:3   Physical Properties

Sulfur is an allotropic element; that is, it exists in several crystalline and amorphous forms. It is a pale yellow, soft, brittle solid when in a crystalline form, but is plastic or pliable in the amorphous form. All forms are practically insoluble in water.

The familiar rhombic crystal type of sulfur is odourless and tasteless and very soluble in carbon disulfide (CS_2). Rhombic crystals may be made by

TABLE 28.1

Electrons in the Atoms of the Sulfur Family

Element	Atomic Number	Shell Number					
		1	2	3	4	5	6
Oxygen	8	2	6				
Sulfur	16	2	8	6			
Selenium	34	2	8	18	6		
Tellurium	52	2	8	18	18	6	
Polonium	84	2	8	18	32	18	6

dissolving sulfur in carbon disulfide and allowing the liquid to evaporate. This form of sulfur is made up of ring-shaped molecules consisting of eight atoms each.

When rhombic sulfur is maintained at a temperature between 95.5°C and 114.5°C for some time, it slowly changes to monoclinic or prismatic crystals (see Fig. 28.1). The *transition point* is the temperature at which an allotropic element changes its crystalline form. At 95.5°C, a transition point for sulfur, the element changes from rhombic to monoclinic form.

Monoclinic crystals may be made by melting sulfur and pouring it into a filter paper folded for filtering. When the sulfur is partly solidified and the paper is opened out, the monoclinic crystals may be seen. This form of sulfur is darker than the rhombic form. It melts at 119°C. If allowed to stand for several days, it will revert to the rhombic form; it is stable only above 95.5°C. Monoclinic crystals consist of an eight-membered ring molecule.

When heated rapidly, sulfur melts at 114.5°C to form a straw-coloured liquid. If heated slowly, a large part of the sulfur would change to the monoclinic form that melts at 119°C. In the molten condition, it consists of ring-shaped S_8 molecules, as it did in the crystalline form. Its fluidity results from the sulfur rings being able to roll over one

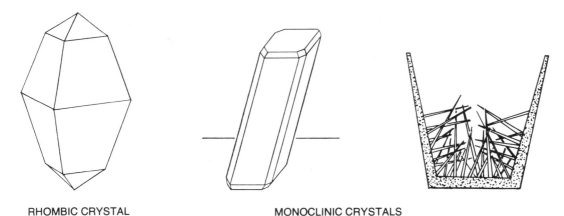

RHOMBIC CRYSTAL   MONOCLINIC CRYSTALS

Fig. 28.1:
Crystalline forms of sulfur

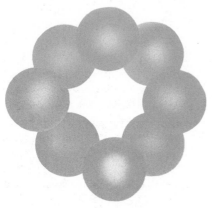

Fig. 28.2:
Two representations of the S_8 molecule

another easily. As the temperature is raised, the S_8 molecules begin to break up, and open chains of sulfur atoms form. As the ring molecule opens, the two atoms that are separated each have an un-shared electron. These atoms form bonds with atoms from other ring molecules, and long chains may result.

These chain-like molecules form a dark brown substance that is viscous, owing to the length of the molecules. At a temperature of around 200°C, the sulfur can hardly be poured. Above 200°C the sulfur becomes less viscous as the long molecules begin to break up. Sulfur boils at 445°C, forming a yellow vapour, which consists of S_8 molecules.

When sulfur at the boiling point is poured into cold water, it solidifies to form an amber-coloured plastic mass which may be stretched like rubber; it is called plastic or amorphous sulfur. The plastic property results from the sudden cooling which did not allow ring molecules to re-form. This form of sulfur is insoluble in carbon disulfide. Upon standing for a few days, it slowly changes to rhombic crystals because the chains re-form S_8 molecules. (Fig 28.2)

28.4   The Oxidation Numbers of Sulfur

With six electrons in the outer shell, sulfur commonly shows an oxidation number of 2⁻ and several positive oxidation numbers as shown in Table 28.2.

TABLE 28.2

Main Oxidation Numbers of Sulfur

Oxidation Numbers	Examples
2−	H_2S, hydrogen sulfide
	Na_2S, sulfide salts
	S^{2-} sulfide ion
0	S^0, S_8, atomic and molecular sulfur
4+	SO_2, sulfur dioxide
	H_2SO_3, sulfurous acid
	Na_2SO_3, sulfite salts
	$NaHSO_3$, hydrogen sulfite salts
	SO_3^{2-}, HSO_3^-, sulfite and hydrogen sulfite ions
6+	SO_3, sulfur trioxide
	H_2SO_4, sulfuric acid
	Na_2SO_4, sulfate salts
	$NaHSO_4$, hydrogen sulfate salts
	SO_4^{2-}, HSO_4^-, sulfate and hydrogen sulfate ions

28:5   Chemical Properties

1. Sulfur unites with many metals. If these metals are finely divided, the reaction may be very vigorous, resulting in combustion:

$$Fe + S \rightarrow FeS$$
$$2Cu + S \rightarrow Cu_2S$$
$$Zn + S \rightarrow ZnS$$

2. It combines with hydrogen slowly at high temperature to form hydrogen sulfide. The reaction is rapid if hydrogen is bubbled through boiling sulfur:

$$H_2 + S \rightarrow H_2S$$

3. Sulfur combines with some non-metals as does oxygen. A highly heated mixture of coke and sulfur forms carbon disulfide, CS_2. This is a colourless liquid with a bad odour. It vapourizes easily, and the vapours are poisonous and highly inflammable. Its principal use is as a solvent for waxes and gums.

    Sulfur burns with a pale blue flame in air or oxygen to form sulfur dioxide:

$$S + O_2 \rightarrow SO_2$$

Here the oxidation number of the sulfur is $4+$. Sulfur trioxide. SO_3 (oxidation number $6+$), may be formed by special procedures as will be seen in section 28.8.

28:6   Vulcanization

The vulcanization of rubber was discovered by Charles Goodyear in 1839 while experimenting with rubber mixtures; he accidentally dropped some rubber and sulfur on a hot stove. Without sulfur, rubber is brittle in winter and sticky in summer. Vulcanization converts the sticky mass of raw rubber into the tough, yet elastic, familiar substance in use today. Rubber tires for cars, trucks, and airplanes are made by vulcanization.

28:7   Sulfur Dioxide

Sulfur dioxide, SO_2, is usually present in gases from volcanoes and in water from certain sulfur springs. Coal contains sulfur in the combined form, and this produces sulfur dioxide when the coal is burned. Even small amounts of this gas in the city air are a serious pollutant.

Preparation
LABORATORY
Salts containing the SO_3^{2-} ion are called sulfites. They are derivatives of sulfurous acid, H_2SO_3, a weak acid. If any of these salts are treated with strong acids, sulfurous acid is formed, which breaks down to form water and sulfur dioxide. Gentle heat is needed to make the reaction go to completion. Sodium sulfite is usually treated with sulfuric or hydrochloric acid:

$$Na_2SO_3 + H_2SO_4 \rightarrow Na_2SO_4 + H_2O + SO_2\uparrow$$

Sulfur dioxide is collected by the upward displacement of air because, like hydrogen chloride it is heavier than air and very soluble in water. When the bottles are filled may be determined by the use of moist blue litmus paper, which, because of the formation of sulfurous acid, turns red on contact with the gas:

$$H_2O + SO_2 \rightleftharpoons H_2SO_3$$

Physical and Chemical Properties
Sulfur dioxide is a colourless gas with a strong, choking odour like that of burning matches. It is heavier than air and is very soluble in water because it reacts with water. It can be liquefied at $20°C$ with a pressure of three atmospheres.

    Sulfur dioxide is a stable compound. It does not burn or support combustion. A catalyst, like platinum or vanadium pentoxide, causes sulfur dioxide to combine with oxygen to form sulfur trioxide, SO_3.

Chemical Test for a Sulfite

Sulfite salts, sulfurous acid, and sulfur dioxide all produce a marked colour change with potassium permanganate solution, and this is the basis of the chemical test for these compounds. The reaction is an electronic exchange in which the sulfur compounds transfer electrons to the permanganate ion. The latter ion gives a purple colour to its solution. When it gains electrons it changes to the colourless manganese (II) (Mn^{2+}) ion. This colour change identifies sulfite salts, sulfur dioxide, and sulfurous acid. The equation representing the reaction is:

$$\overset{7+}{2KMnO_4} + \overset{4+}{5H_2SO_3} \rightarrow$$

$$\uparrow \qquad\qquad \downarrow$$
$$2 \times 5e = 5 \times 2e$$

$$\overset{6+}{K_2SO_4} + \overset{2+}{2MnSO_4} + \overset{6+}{2H_2SO_4} + 3H_2O$$

When carrying out this test, hydrochloric acid is added to the unknown salt, and the mixture is warmed in a flask or test tube. Any evolved gas is passed through potassium permanganate solution. If the solution is decolourised, the original material contained a sulfite.

$$SO_3^{2-} + 2H_3O^+ \rightarrow 3H_2O + SO_2\uparrow$$
$$SO_2 + H_2O \rightarrow H_2SO_3$$

Uses

The most common use of sulfur dioxide is for making sulfuric acid. It is used to some extent as a refrigerant in mechanical refrigerators. While it absorbs less heat in evaporating than do some gases, such as ammonia, it liquefies so easily that it is a convenient gas to use. The use of sulfur dioxide in the bleaching and preservation of food has already been discussed.

Sulfite pulp, a very important material for making high quality paper, consists of a long fibre of cellulose, which gives paper high tensile strength. Wood in its natural state consists principally of cellulose fibres and a glue-like substance called lignin. To convert the wood into sulfite pulp, the wood is first chopped into tiny chips. Then the chips are placed in a heated calcium hydrogen sulfite solution, which is made by bubbling sulfur dioxide through a suspension of calcium hydroxide. The lignin dissolves in the solution leaving free cellulose fibres.

Sulfur dioxide is used in making sulfites which are, in turn, important for producing small amounts of sulfur dioxide, as, for instance, in the laboratory. Cotton is normally bleached by means of chlorine, but if any chlorine remains on the cloth, the cloth will be slowly destroyed. The chlorine is usually removed by passing the cloth through a sulfite solution. When used in this way, the sulfite is called an *antichlor*:

$$Na_2SO_3 + Cl_2 + H_2O \rightarrow Na_2SO_4 + 2HCl\uparrow$$

28:8   Sulfuric Acid

Sulfuric acid is one of the most important compounds of chemistry. It is difficult to name one modern manufactured article that does not make use of this acid directly or indirectly at some stage. The standard of living or industrial activity of any

Courtesy Canadian Industries Limited

A view of a modern contact plant

country can be judged by the per capita consumption of sulfuric acid.

Sulfuric acid is manufactured by two methods; these are the newer Contact Process and the old Lead Chamber Process.

The Contact Process

(a) Sulfur is burned in dry air and sulfur dioxide is formed:

$$S + O_2 \rightarrow SO_2\uparrow$$

(b) The sulfur dioxide and excess air are passed through a hot gas filter where most impurities are removed. The gases then pass into the main reactor, called the Contact Tower. This tower contains perforated shelves supporting a catalyst.

(c) When the gases come in contact with the catalyst, the union of sulfur dioxide and oxygen produces sulfur trioxide.

$$2SO_2 + O_2 \rightarrow 2SO_3\uparrow$$

Vanadium pentoxide or platinized silica gel are now used as the catalyst instead of the platinum metal used formerly. These are less expensive and more resistant to any impurities still present in the mixture of reacting gases. Such impurities are trace amounts of arsenic, antimony, selenium, and chlorine.

The temperature must be about 450°C. Above this temperature some of the sulfur trioxide is decomposed, while below this temperature some of the sulfur dioxide remains unchanged.

(d) The sulfur trioxide is cooled and then passed to the absorption towers. Concentrated sulfuric acid is pumped into the top of the towers, and as this liquid descends the tower, it absorbs the sulfur trioxide gas to form "fuming sulfuric acid" or oleum:

$$SO_3 + H_2SO_4 \rightarrow H_2SO_4 \cdot SO_3 \text{ (oleum)}$$

Concentrated sulfuric acid needs to be used in the absorption towers because pure water tends to form a fine mist which is difficult to precipitate. Thus, concentrated acid needs to be used to manufacture more sulfuric acid.

Fuming sulfuric acid, called oleum, is the pro-

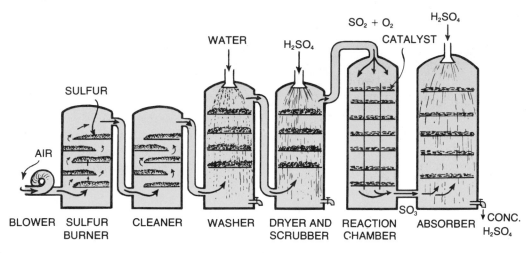

Fig. 28.3:
The contact process for making sulfuric acid

duct obtained from the absorption towers. It fumes in air because some of the sulfur trioxide dissolved in it escapes into the air where it reacts with the water vapour:

$$SO_3 + H_2O \rightarrow H_2SO_4$$

The oleum is finally diluted to the desired concentration:

$$H_2SO_4 \cdot SO_3 + H_2O \rightarrow 2H_2SO_4$$

Pure H_2SO_4 is properly called hydrogen sulfate.

Physical Properties

Sulfuric acid is a colourless, odourless, syrupy, heavy liquid with a density of 1.84 g/mL. It has long been called oil of vitriol because of its appearance. It boils at 338°C. A great deal of heat is liberated when sulfuric acid is diluted with water, due to the donation of protons to the water molecules, as well as the hydration of the sulfate ion. For this reason, the acid must be added to the water, so that the heavy acid sinks through the water and the heat is evenly dispersed. If the water is added to the acid, the first few drops of water are changed to steam, which will splatter acid from its container.

Chemical Properties

DILUTE SULFURIC ACID

When sulfuric acid is added to water, it donates protons to the water molecules in two steps, first producing the hydrogen sulfate ion, and second giving the sulfate ion:

$$H_2SO_4 + H_2O \rightarrow HSO_4^- + H_3O^+$$
$$HSO_4^- + H_2O \rightarrow SO_4^{2-} + H_3O^+$$

Dilute solutions of the acid are completely ionized. The dilute acid reacts with metals above hydrogen in the Electromotive Series to yield hydrogen (Chapter 34).

$$Zn + H_2SO_4 \rightarrow ZnSO_4 + H_2\uparrow$$

Dilute sulfuric acid neutralizes bases:

$$2NaOH + H_2SO_4 \rightarrow Na_2SO_4 + 2H_2O$$

It reacts with metallic oxides:

$$CuO + H_2SO_4 \rightarrow CuSO_4 + H_2O$$

Because sulfuric acid has such a high boiling point, it liberates other acids from their salts.

Examples

$$FeS \quad + H_2SO_4 \rightarrow FeSO_4 \ + H_2S\uparrow$$
$$2NaCl \ + H_2SO_4 \rightarrow Na_2SO_4 + 2HCl\uparrow$$
$$Na_2SO_3 + H_2SO_4 \rightarrow Na_2SO_4 + H_2SO_3$$
$$then \ H_2SO_3 \rightarrow H_2O + SO_2\uparrow$$
$$2NaNO_3 + H_2SO_4 \rightarrow Na_2SO_4 + 2HNO_3\uparrow$$

CONCENTRATED SULFURIC ACID

Pure hydrogen sulfate or concentrated sulfuric acid is a good oxidizing agent. This is due to the high oxidation number of 6+ of sulfur in the sulfate ion. In this condition, the sulfur atom is apt to gain electrons, and as a result hot concentrated H_2SO_4 reacts even with copper, a metal below hydrogen in the Electromotive Series. It should be noted that no hydrogen is produced in this reaction. Instead, sulfur changes in its oxidation state from 6+ to 4+, resulting in the formation of sulfur dioxide gas.

$$\begin{array}{ccccc} 0 & 6+ & 2+ & 4+ \\ Cu + 2H_2SO_4 & \rightarrow & CuSO_4 + & SO_2 + 2H_2O \\ \downarrow & & & \uparrow \\ 2e & & & 2e \end{array}$$

When metals above hydrogen in the Electromotive Series react with hot concentrated H_2SO_4 both sulfur dioxide and hydrogen are produced.

At 450°C and atmospheric pressure, sulfuric acid decomposes into sulfur trioxide and water. This accounts for the white fumes formed when the acid is evaporated. The reaction is reversible:

$$H_2SO_4 \rightleftharpoons H_2O + SO_3\uparrow$$

Sulfuric acid is a strong dehydrating agent; gases may be dried by passing them through it.

When the concentrated acid comes in contact with carbohydrates, it decomposes them so that the hydrogen and oxygen present in the carbohydrates are removed as water, and a black residue of carbon remains:

$$(C_6H_{10}O_5)_n \xrightarrow{H_2SO_4} n(5H_2O + 6C)$$
$$\text{cellulose}$$

$$C_{12}H_{22}O_{11} \xrightarrow{H_2SO_4} 11H_2O + 12C\downarrow$$
$$\text{sucrose}$$

Proteins are also charred by the concentrated acid.

Test for a Sulfate

If a few drops of barium chloride reagent are added to the solutions being tested, and a white precipitate forms, the presence of a sulfate is indicated:

$$BaCl_2 + H_2SO_4 \rightarrow BaSO_4\downarrow + 2HCl$$

It is necessary to test the solubility of the precipitate in hydrochloric acid because certain other materials, such as carbonates, may give a white precipitate with the barium chloride. Such precipitates dissolve in hydrochloric acid.

Uses of Sulfuric Acid

About one-quarter of the sulfuric acid made is used to produce fertilizer. Phosphorus is an essential element for plant growth, but it is easily depleted from the soil. Rock phosphate, $Ca_3(PO_4)_2$, is a plentiful mineral, but it is insoluble. However, when treated with sulfuric acid, it changes to calcium dihydrogen phosphate, which is soluble and useful to plants. The product is called superphosphate and is used as fertilizer.

$$Ca_3(PO_4)_2 + 2H_2SO_4 \rightarrow 2CaSO_4 + Ca(H_2PO_4)_2$$
$$\text{superphosphate}$$

The dehydrating action of sulfuric acid makes it a necessity in the nitration of glycerol, cotton, toluene, and other compounds from which explosives are made. Sulfuric acid is also used to make cellulose film and rayon.

The acid is often used to clean or "pickle" metals before they are plated with another metal. Of the hundreds of other processes using sulfuric acid, a few are the making of sulfate salts, paper, leather, dyes, drugs, paints, and other acids. The acid is used as the electrolyte in lead storage batteries.

QUESTIONS

1. Write a paragraph on the occurrence of sulfur.

2. List the allotropic forms of sulfur.

3. Explain how two crystalline forms of sulfur may be made and give the physical properties of each. Draw a diagram of each type of crystal.

4. How may amorphous sulfur be prepared? What are its chief properties?

5. (i) Describe the changes in sulfur as it is heated to its boiling point.
   (ii) Account for these changes.

6. Define transition point and apply this term to sulfur.

7. (i) In what ways are sulfur and oxygen similar?
   (ii) Account for this similarity.

8. Give formulas of compounds to show where sulfur has oxidation numbers of $2-$, $4+$, and $6+$.

9.   Draw an electronic diagram to show the structure of H_2S.

10. List three chemical properties of sulfur.

11. What is vulcanization and how was it discovered?

12. What is the most important compound of sulfur?

13. What mass of elemental sulfur would be obtained from 110 g of gypsum, $CaSO_4 \cdot 2H_2O$?

14. Calculate the simplest formula of a compound that contains 23.1 per cent magnesium, 30.7 per cent sulfur, and 46.2 per cent oxygen.

15. How many kilograms of PbS would be required to yield 10 kg of sulfur?

16. Where does sulfur dioxide occur naturally?

17. (i) List three methods of preparing sulfur dioxide.
     (ii) Describe the laboratory method in detail giving the equation.

18. Give five physical properties of sulfur dioxide.

19. List the properties of sulfurous acid.

20. Describe the chemical test for a sulfite.

21. Name as many uses of sulfur dioxide as you can.

22. Show electronically how hydrogen and sulfur combine chemically.

23. "Sulfur oxides" are often listed among air pollutants. Consult some references to help you identify these oxides, and write a report of the scope of the problems they cause and what can be done about them.

24. Prepare a report on the hazards involved in the transportation of sulfuric acid. What special precautions are necessary?

25. Why is sulfuric acid so important to humanity?

26. Describe the contact process of manufacturing sulfuric acid in detail, giving the equations and a sketch of the apparatus.

27. (i) Give the physical properties of sulfuric acid.
     (ii) Explain how it should be diluted.

28. List the chemical properties of dilute sulfuric acid and illustrate each with an equation when possible.

29. Give the chemical properties of concentrated sulfuric acid. Account for its strong oxidizing properties.

30. What is the test for a sulfate?

31. What is superphosphate?

32. Give as many uses of sulfuric acid as you can.

33. Find the molarity of a sulfuric acid solution, if 10 mL of it are neutralized by 7 mL of a 0.2 mol/L solution of sodium hydroxide. Assume the salt produced is $NaHSO_4$.

34. Find the relative rates of diffusion of hydrogen sulfide and sulfur dioxide.

35. Suppose that a farmer wishes to place 10 kg of available phosphorus on each hectare of his field. Find the mass of superphosphate per hectare required (1 ha $= 10^4 m^2$).

5
ORGANIC COMPOUNDS

Photosynthesis converts solar energy, CO_2, and H_2O into food in the form of chemical compounds.

CHAPTER

29

CARBON AND ORGANIC COMPOUNDS

The element that forms more compounds of greater variety than any other.

29:1   The Element and its Occurrence

Carbon is present in approximately 1 000 000 known compounds, and new carbon compounds are being synthesized all the time. Many carbon compounds are used daily in various forms and are, indeed, essential to our existence. Although forming so many important and varied compounds, it is estimated that carbon constitutes only 0.03 per cent of the Earth's crust. It occurs in coal, wood, petroleum, and natural and artificial gas. Vast deposits of metal carbonates are found, mainly those of calcium and magnesium which make up limestone and dolomite.

29:2   Physical and Chemical Properties

All forms of carbon are similar in that they are insoluble in water, acids, bases, and other materials. They are all black or greyish-black solids, except diamond which is colourless when pure. They are odourless and tasteless. The microcrystalline forms of carbon dissolve in some molten metals such as iron. When heated out of contact with air, carbon does not melt; instead it vaporizes. Under great pressure carbon can be melted. Its melting point, although not yet accurately determined, is about 3500°C.

All forms of carbon burn in ample air or oxygen to form carbon dioxide. Carbon monoxide forms if the oxygen or air supply is limited.

Carbon is a good reducing agent and is commonly used to reduce oxide ores to metals:

$$\overset{3+}{Fe_2}O_3 + \overset{0}{3C} \rightarrow \overset{0}{2Fe} + \overset{2+}{3CO}$$

$$\overset{2+}{2Cu}O + \overset{0}{C} \rightarrow \overset{0}{2Cu} + \overset{4+}{CO_2}$$

$$\overset{4+}{CO_2} + \overset{0}{C} \rightarrow \overset{2+}{2CO}$$

Carbon reacts with some elements to form carbides:

$$CaO + 3C \rightarrow CaC_2 + CO$$
$$\text{calcium carbide}$$

$$SiO_2 + 3C \rightarrow SiC + 2CO$$
$$\text{silicon carbide}$$

Some carbides are of great commercial value because of their hardness.

29:3 Allotropic Forms of Carbon

There are two allotropic forms of crystalline carbon — diamond and graphite. All the other forms of free carbon, as found in coal, coke, charcoal, boneblack, and lampblack, are usually called amorphous or non-crystalline forms. There is strong evidence to show that the so-called amorphous forms are in reality microcrystalline, composed of crystals too small to be seen by ordinary optical methods, but whose structure is revealed by X ray analysis.

29:4 Diamond and Graphite

The carbon atoms in diamond have the tetrahedron geometrical structure. They are held together in a lattice by covalent bonds, which are extremely effective with such small atoms as carbon. As a result, diamond has many striking properties: it is the hardest substance known; it has a higher melting point than any other element; and it is a non-conductor of electricity. These properties exist because the electrons cannot move freely from one atom to another, all outer electrons being in covalent bonds.

The weakness of the bond between layers of the graphite crystal allows the planes to slide over one another. This gives graphite a soft, greasy, and slippery feeling. Since the electrons in this bond may be moved freely, graphite is a good conductor of electricity.

Occurrence, Production, and Uses of Diamond
The principal diamond-producing regions of the world are South Africa and Brazil. The largest diamond ever found has a mass of 623 g.

In Africa, diamonds are found in blue-coloured earth. This is mixed with water and run over grease-covered trays. The diamonds stick in the grease, while the earth is washed away. The com-

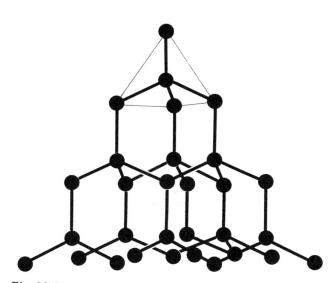
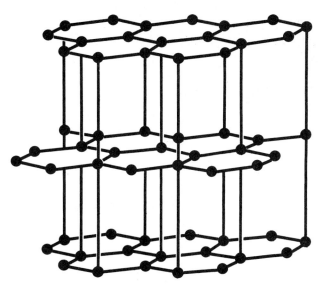

Fig. 29.1:
Diamond and Graphite

position of this blue earth indicates that it was originally mineral-bearing volcanic rock. Most likely the diamonds were formed because this rock, when molten, came in contact with some coal deposits, dissolving the carbon of the coal. As the rock cooled, the carbon crystallized under great pressure into diamond. Later, weathering actions caused the disintegration of the rock, leaving the diamond.

Henri Moissan attempted to make small diamonds in 1893. He prepared pure carbon by charring sugar. He dissolved this in molten iron and plunged the mass of iron into cold water. The outer part of the mass solidified and contracted producing great pressure. After cooling, the iron was dissolved in hydrochloric acid, and if any diamonds were recovered, they were too small to be of any practical use.

In 1956 a group of scientists at the General Electric Company discovered a process for making diamonds commercially. The diamonds produced, although too small for gems, are large enough for many practical uses. By 1960 these diamonds were being produced at a price lower or comparable to the cost of the natural product.

The value of the diamond as a gem is largely due to its very high refractive index; that is, the amount of bending that light undergoes in passing through a material. For use as a gem, the diamond is shaped so that it has a number of flat surfaces (facets) meeting at angles. The surfaces act as internal reflectors, and light entering the diamond is effectively separated into its colours giving the gem a great brilliance. The flat surfaces are formed by allowing a steel disc coated with oil and diamond dust to rotate against the diamond, which is held in a clamp.

The diamond is essential to modern industry. Many machine parts are fashioned with grinding wheels, which are composed of materials so hard that they themselves can be cut only by diamond. Diamond drills are used in mining for obtaining ore samples. A diamond drill consists of diamonds set into the end of a cylinder. As the drill revolves, it bites into the rock, leaving a solid core of sample material inside the cylinder. The core is examined to determine its mineral content.

Occurrence, Production, and Uses of Graphite
Graphite is found in many parts of the world, but chiefly in Canada, Siberia, and Ceylon. It, too, was probably formed by volcanic heat in contact with coal deposits. The natural form contains grit and many other impurities.

Synthetic graphite is prepared by means of an electric furnace. In the furnace a core of loosely packed carbon is placed between two electrodes and is surrounded by a packing of coal. The heat

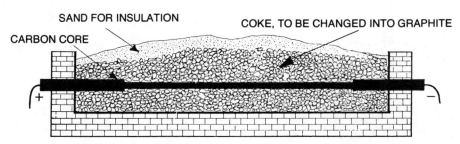

Fig. 29.2:
The manufacture of graphite
Heat is developed because of the high resistance of the carbon core

produced by the passage of electricity between the electrodes forms the graphite from the coal surrounding the carbon core. Air is excluded by covering the coal with a layer of sand (see Fig. 29.2). The graphite produced by this process is very pure and free from grit.

Graphite, a black, shiny, soft solid, leaves a mark when it is drawn across a paper. The name graphite comes from the Greek word meaning "to write." Because it was originally thought to be a form of lead, it is sometimes called plumbago or black lead. The lead of a pencil is a mixture of graphite, clay, and wax heated in a mould. Hard lead contains more clay than does soft lead.

Graphite is an excellent dry lubricant because its crystalline structure allows one layer to slide over another. It is sometimes mixed with oil to form a high-temperature lubricant. Because it is a good conductor of electricity, graphite is often used for

electrodes. A non-conductor may be made conductive by coating it with graphite. Graphite is therefore used in electroplating and electrotyping. Graphite crucibles are used for making high-grade steel and other alloys. Certain oil-retaining bearings contain graphite. It is also used as a pigment in black paint and as an ingredient of dry cells.

29:5   Coal

Coal may be regarded as a mixture of carbon plus remains of organic matter. Many millions of years ago the growth of vegetation was much more prolific than it is now. In many places a considerable depth of decaying vegetation was built up, and, where these deposits became permanently flooded

The primeval forest whose vegetation changed to coal and oil over long stretches of geological time
Taken from *Chemistry: A Humanistic Approach* by L. M. Vallarino and J. V. Quagliano, Copyright 1975, with permission of Webster/McGraw-Hill

for some reason, swamps were formed. Decomposition of the plant matter, aided by bacteria and fungi, caused its transformation first into peat and then into lignite. Gradually the deposits became covered over with silt, sometimes to a great depth. The mass of the silt and water above the deposit caused pressure and heat which gradually changed the lignite into soft bituminous coal. If the soft coal were then subjected to greater pressure or heat, it changed into anthracite, or hard coal. Deposits of peat, lignite, and bituminous and anthracite coal are widespread throughout the world.

Soft coal is often inefficiently burned passing much carbon and many carbon compounds into the air as smoke. Where soft coal is a major fuel, smog (a mixture of smoke, fog, and sometimes dangerous oxides) is often a problem.

Smoke from the combustion of coal can be controlled by down-draft combustion or by smoke precipitators. In a down-draft furnace, air is forced through the burning coal from the top. This results in more complete combustion.

Combustion of coal supplies about 20 per cent of the world's energy requirements. The rest comes from natural gas, petroleum, water power, and nuclear energy. The major use of coal is in generating electrical energy, and about one-quarter of the bituminous coal mined is used in making coke for the iron and steel industry.

In 1931, Bergius, a German chemist, patented a process for making gasoline from coal. Powdered coal mixed with heavy oil is heated to about 4000°C at 200 atm of pressure, in contact with hydrogen and a catalyst. The carbon of the coal and the hydrogen combine to form various hydrocarbons. These can be separated by distillation, and one of the products is gasoline.

Another process called the Fisher-Tropsch process uses coal and steam to produce a mixture of carbon monoxide and hydrogen:

$$C + H_2O \rightarrow CO\uparrow + H_2\uparrow$$

These gases are then converted into hydrocarbons with the aid of a catalyst:

$$7CO + 15H_2 \xrightarrow[\text{catalyst}]{\text{iron}} C_7H_{16} + 7H_2O$$

The above processes produce gasoline of good quality, but it is more expensive than the petroleum product. The processes could be used, however, in the event of a petroleum shortage. In fact, Germany made practically all its gasoline and oil by these methods during the Second World War.

Experimental work is going on at the present time to produce industrial gas from coal deposits without mining. The coal is ignited and supplied with air from pipes leading down to the coal:

$$2C + O_2 \rightarrow 2CO\uparrow$$

The resultant gas is then forced up other pipes to the surface. Pure oxygen in place of air is found to be more effective. Low grade or inaccessible coal seams may thus become valuable assets.

29:6   Renewed Interest in Coal as a Source of Energy

The world is now in the midst of an energy crisis resulting from its heavy use of petroleum for supplying energy for heating, transportation, industry and agriculture. Faced with the dwindling supplies of petroleum, nations everywhere, including Canada, are turning again to coal as a source of energy.

Coal is found in Nova Scotia, Alberta and British Columbia, and is used extensively to generate electricity in a number of Canadian provinces.

While coal is more abundant than oil, it is also a finite resource and there are a number of disadvantages involved with its use:

1. Coal needs to be mined and the safety of the miners must be assured.

2. Its transportation is costly.
3. It needs to be converted into a liquid or gas if it is to be used as a fuel in transportation and this may also prove costly.
4. Pollutants such as sulfur are more difficult to remove from a solid than from a liquid or gas.
5. The world population has almost doubled since 1940 when the Germans liquified coal for use in transportation. We have no experience in the liquification of coal on the large scale which modern transportation demands. We must expect that much research is necessary to solve these problems.
6. Large scale coal mining will have to be done by the strip mining method. This method involves the removal of vegetation and soil for several hundred metres to reach the coal. The removal of the coal will cause huge cavities underground, as well as despoiling the surface.

29:7   Coke, Charcoal, and Adsorptive Carbon

Coke, a form of carbon of great industrial importance, is generally obtained by heating soft coal in ovens, thus driving off the volatile constituents of the coal. This process is called *destructive distillation*. The residue of the destructive distillation of coal is coke.

Coke is used mostly to reduce metals, especially iron, from ores. It burns with practically no flame and leaves little residue.

If the process of destructive distillation is applied to wood, charcoal is obtained. It burns with no smoke and leaves little ash. During the first part of the Industrial Revolution, the stately oaks of England practically disappeared to make charcoal for reducing iron ore. Fortunately, it was soon discovered that coke could be used successfully for this purpose.

Powdered charcoal is frequently pressed into briquettes. These find a wide use as fuel for barbeques.

All forms of amorphous carbon have high adsorptive power. This means they can collect thin layers of molecules of various materials on their surface. This property is mostly due to the large surface the carbon presents because of its porous structure. Thus, poisonous or odourous gases may be removed from air by passing the air through layers of charcoal. Portable gas masks contain charcoal made from coconut shells because such charcoal is more resistant to breakage than is wood charcoal. It thus retains its porous structure and its adsorptive power longer. Charcoal may be used also to decolourize and deodorize liquids. Many industrial solvents and waste substances are adsorbed by charcoal, and in the field of biochemistry charcoal is used to adsorb the antibiotic streptomycin from its mould culture. Other forms of adsorptive carbon are used in industry for purification of products.

29:8   The Many Carbon Compounds

The carbon compounds and their mixtures provide the tissues of our bodies, the foods we eat, and the textiles we wear. Paper, rubber, plastics, gasoline, oil, dyes, explosives, and almost all medicines are composed of carbon compounds. About one million such compounds have been prepared and studied. Why is carbon able to form so many compounds?

One reason is that carbon atoms can form stable covalent bonds with one another. This permits chains and rings of carbon atoms to form, and these can grow in length and complexity, giving rise to a large number and variety of molecules. The stability of the carbon-to-carbon bond is explained by the *intermediate* electronegativity of carbon. It is not as highly electron-attracting as the halogens or poorly electron-attracting as the metals. The carbon-to-carbon bond is therefore both non-polar and stable. In addition, carbon forms stable covalent bonds with hydrogen, oxygen, and nitrogen. These elements have electronegativity values of about the same order as carbon. The resulting bonds are not highly polar.

29:9   Organic Chemistry

Because of the large number, variety, and importance of carbon compounds, they have been grouped together as a field of special interest. Their study is called *organic chemistry*. The name arises from an old belief that such compounds were formed only in plant and animal organisms. The chemistry of living organisms supposedly needed some vital force, since life is such an unusual phenomenon.

Today organic chemistry is the study of the behaviour of the compounds formed by carbon with, mainly, hydrogen, oxygen, and nitrogen, as well as with other elements to a lesser degree. The study of the chemistry of living processes is called *biochemistry*, a field overlapping biology and chemistry.

29:10   Organic Compounds

Some General Properties
Large numbers of organic compounds could hardly be expected to show exactly the same properties. Yet if allowance for obvious differences is made, it is interesting to see how consistent the properties of organic compounds actually are.

(a) They are largely non-polar. The carbon and hydrogen particularly form non-polar bonds because of their almost equal electronegativity (H = 2.1 and C = 2.5).

(b) Organic compounds tend to be insoluble in water. Since they are non-polar they cannot

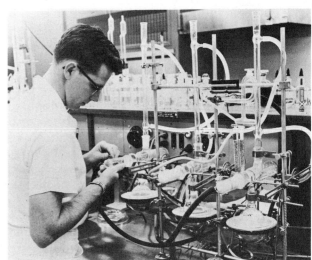

Courtesy Chas. Pfizer and Company, Incorporated
Organic chemist studying synthesis of new resins for paints.

form bonds with water molecules. In view of this, no energy is available to separate the hydrogen bonds of the water; therefore, the organic molecules and the water molecules cannot mix.

If, however, the organic molecule contains one or more hydroxyl groups, as in the case of ethanol or sucrose, hydrogen bonds may form between them and water molecules. This enables such substances to dissolve in water.

(c) Organic compounds tend to be soluble in organic liquids. Since the non-polar organic substances are held together by weak intermolecular forces, their molecules intermingle readily.

(d) Their melting and boiling points are low. Only when the molecule contains an OH or NH group, which permits hydrogen bonding, is the compound not so volatile.

(e) They are, for the most part, non-electrolytes. As mentioned previously, the bond between hydrogen and carbon is extremely stable and is not likely to be split by ionization for proton donation, that is, to act as an acid. Nor is the hydrogen able to donate a pair of electrons; that is, to function as a base. When, however, the molecule contains a hydroxyl OH group, or an amino NH_2 group, or other similar groups, then acid, base, oxidizing or reducing properties may appear. There are many important organic acids and bases.

Molecular structure and Homologous series

Owing to the ability of the carbon atom to add to itself, organic molecules may become complex. To help visualize the molecule, it is written structurally with bonds connecting atoms and groups. Molecules having similar atoms and differing only by adding more carbon atoms (plus the correct number of hydrogen atoms) are said to make up a *homologous series*.

A good example is the homologous series of the hydrocarbons, called alkanes, discussed in the next chapter.

Sources

Petroleum, coal, wood, plants, and animals are the main natural sources of organic compounds. All of these sources yield mixtures of organic compounds, some of which can be used without further separation. Often, however, pure compounds must be separated from the raw material. With these pure compounds, the organic chemist synthesizes textiles, plastics, rubber, detergents, and a large number of other useful products.

QUESTIONS

1. Organic compounds are defined as those containing carbon, hydrogen and a few other elements. What other definitions can you find of the word "organic" in a good dictionary? What other words can you recall that might be related in meaning to the word organic (such as organism)? Do you see anything common to these words?

2. Give a brief account of the importance of carbon and its compounds.

3. What are the allotropic forms of carbon?

4. Describe the electronic structure of carbon.

5. List the properties of diamond and graphite.

6. Explain why diamond and graphite exhibit different properties.

7. List the common physical properties of carbon.

8. Summarize the common chemical properties of carbon.

9. (i) Write the equations for the reduction of Fe_2O_3 and CuO by carbon.
   (ii) In what processes are these reactions used?

10. Account for the formation of diamonds in Nature.

11. Describe how artificial diamonds are produced.

12. Why is the diamond valued as a gem?

13. How are diamonds used in industry?

14. How is graphite made synthetically?

15. (i) List the principal properties of graphite.
    (ii) What are the uses of this material?

16. Account for the formation of coal deposits.

17. Contrast the properties of anthracite and bituminous coal.

18. Write a paragraph on the importance of coal.

19. Name and describe two processes of making gasoline from coal.

20. Describe how coke is made. Of what importance is this material?

21. Define *adsorption*.

22. Explain how a gas mask works.

23. Find the volume of carbon dioxide, measured at STP, obtained from burning 5 g of carbon completely.

24. Calculate the mass of silicon carbide that could be obtained from 350 g of silicon dioxide.

25. Find the volume of carbon dioxide measured at 313°C and 95 kPa pressure obtained by burning 0.5 g of carbon.

26. A gaseous compound contains 92.3 per cent carbon and 7.7 per cent hydrogen. One litre of the gas at STP weighs 1.16 g. Find its molecular formula.

27. Explain clearly why carbon forms so many compounds.

28. Why are carbon-to-carbon bonds quite stable?

29. Why are bonds between carbon and hydrogen, oxygen, or nitrogen not highly polar?

30. Define the terms *organic chemistry* and *biochemistry*.

31. Why are organic compounds usually soluble in organic liquids?

32. Why are the boiling and freezing points of ethane, C_2H_6, lower than those of ethanol, C_2H_5OH?

33. Explain why most organic compounds are non-electrolytes.

34. What general groups of organic compounds are usually electrolytes?

35. What are the principal sources of organic compounds?

CHAPTER
30

HYDROCARBONS AND FUELS

Will we freeze in the dark? When? 198...?

30:1 Various Hydrocarbons

Hydrocarbons, the compounds that contain hydrogen and carbon only, are present in natural gas, petroleum or crude oil, and coal deposits. Some plant hydrocarbons are of great value — rubber latex and turpentine are two examples.

Hydrocarbons that contain only single bonds between the carbon atoms are called *saturated*, while those containing one or more double or triple bonds are said to be *unsaturated*. The saturated hydrocarbons are called *alkanes*.

30:2 Methane

The simplest alkane has the formula of CH_4 and is called methane. Experimental evidence for its formula is its molar mass of 16 g/mol and its percentage composition of 75 per cent carbon and 25 per cent hydrogen. It should be kept in mind that all chemical formulas are based on such experimental evidence.

In methane the carbon atom is attached by four covalent bonds to the hydrogen atoms, building a molecule that is tetrahedral in shape (Chapter 19). Its structure may be represented as in Fig. 30.1.

The molecule is non-polar and therefore has the following properties: (a) it has a low boiling point (−161.4°C), evidence of poor intermolecular attraction; (b) it does not dissolve in water because it does not interact with water; (c) it is a non-electrolyte, and (d) it is chemically inert; methane and other hydrocarbons of its class are called *paraffins* (of little affinity) for this reason.

The methane molecule reacts with chlorine at high temperature and pressure by substituting a chlorine atom in place of a hydrogen atom. This is called a *substitution reaction*:

The organic product is CH_3Cl, called methyl chloride, a refrigerant. More hydrogen atoms in the methane molecule may also be replaced, and the final product formed is CCl_4, carbon tetrachloride.

Methane burns to form carbon dioxide and water. This reaction produces much heat:

$$CH_4 + 2O_2 \rightarrow CO_2\uparrow + 2H_2O + Heat$$

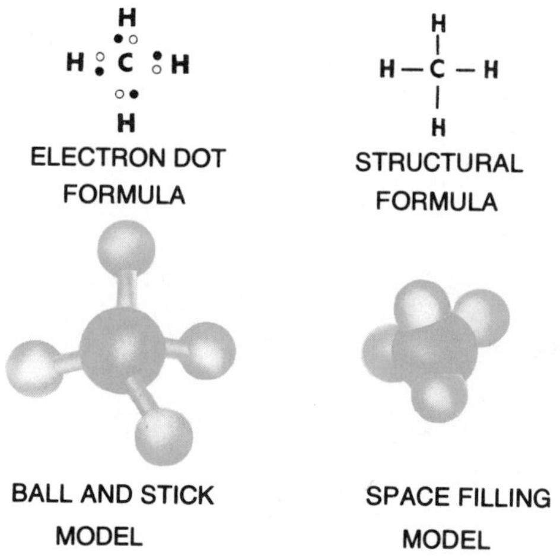

ELECTRON DOT
FORMULA

STRUCTURAL
FORMULA

BALL AND STICK
MODEL

SPACE FILLING
MODEL

Fig. 30.1:
Molecular representations of methane

30:3   The Alkane Hydrocarbons

All the above physical and chemical properties are characteristic of the alkane hydrocarbons which resemble methane (Table 30.1).

Alkane hydrocarbons conform to a general formula C_nH_{2n+2}, where n is the number of carbon atoms in the molecule. Each member of this series differs from methane by one or more CH_2 groups, thus forming a *homologous series*. (See Fig. 30.2.)

30:4   Isomerism

Experiments show that two compounds both having the same molecular formula of C_4H_{10} exist with slightly different physical properties. One has a boiling point of 0.6°C and the other of 12°C, so that there can be no doubt about their difference. The reason for the difference can soon be found by examining the possible structures of such molecules. There are two ways in which the molecule of C_4H_{10} can be drawn: in the first, the four carbon atoms are in one line or chain; in the

TABLE 30.1

Series of Alkane Hydrocarbons

Name	Formula	Molar Mass g/mol	B.P.	Normal State
Methane	CH_4	16	−161.4°C	Gas
Ethane	C_2H_6	30	− 88.3	Gas
Propane	C_3H_8	44	− 44.5	Gas
Butane	C_4H_{10}	58	− 0.6	Gas
Pentane	C_5H_{12}	72	36.2	Liquid
Hexane	C_6H_{14}	86	69.0	Liquid
Heptane	C_7H_{16}	100	98.4	Liquid
Octane	C_8H_{18}	114	124.6	Liquid
Hexadecane	$C_{16}H_{34}$	226	Melts at 18°C	Solid
Hexacentane	$C_{60}H_{122}$	842	Melts at 102°C	Solid

second, only three are in one line, and the fourth is attached to the middle carbon:

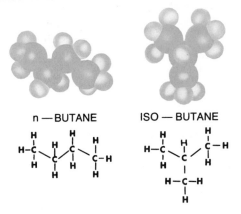

n — BUTANE   ISO — BUTANE

Compounds having the same molecular formulas but different structures are called *isomers*, and the phenomenon is called *isomerism*. As the complexity of molecules increases so does the possibility of isomerism. There are thirty-five known organic compounds with the molecular formula C_9H_{20}!

30:5   Organic Groups or Radicals

To name organic compounds and their isomers, we require a simple way of naming groups of atoms that recur frequently. For example, the CH_3- group

ETHANE C_2H_6

PROPANE C_3H_8

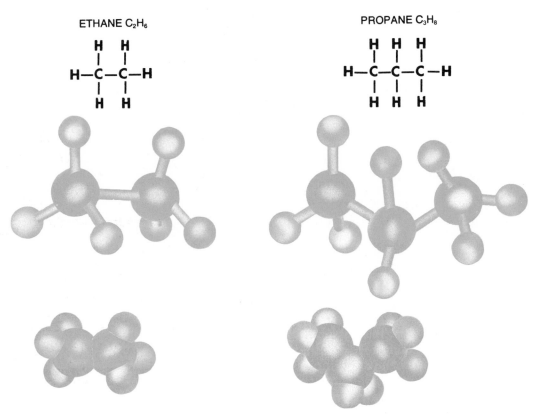

Fig. 30.2:
Molecular representations of ethane and propane

TABLE 30.2

Alkanes and Alkyl Groups

Methane	CH_4	Methyl	CH_3-
Ethane	C_2H_6	Ethyl	C_2H_5-
Propane	C_3H_8	Propyl	C_3H_7-
Butane	C_4H_{10}	Butyl	C_4H_9-

occurs three times in the isomer of butane. CH_3- is called the methyl group.

An *organic* group or *radical* may be considered a molecule minus one (or more) hydrogen atoms. They are named accordingly by replacing the *ane* ending by *yl*.

The groups are themselves attached to larger molecules and should not be confused with ions. Their general name is the *alkyl group* and they are represented by *R*.

30:6 Physical Properties of the Alkanes

Reference to Table 30.1 shows that the state and boiling point of the hydrocarbons are related to molecular mass and chain length. The first four members of the series are gases at ordinary temperature and pressure. Those from C_5 to C_{20} are liquids, less dense than water, whereas those with more than twenty carbon atoms are wax-like solids. Isomers have slightly different physical properties. In general, the more branched the chain, the lower the boiling point.

Other physical and chemical properties of the entire series resemble those of methane because of the similar electronic structures: they are water insoluble; they dissolve in organic solvents; they are non-electrolytes; they are chemically unreactive, except at high temperature and pressure; they react by substitution of their hydrogen atoms; and they burn readily to liberate much heat and are, therefore, good fuels.

30:7 Natural Gas

Natural gas, largely methane, has, to a great extent, replaced coal gas as an industrial and domestic fuel. This gas is found wherever oil and coal occur, and it issues from the Earth when porous rocks, saturated with it, are tapped. Most oil wells produce some natural gas.

Formerly, natural gas was burned as waste at oil wells, but when the value of this material was realized, controls were established, and the wasteful burning of natural gas has greatly diminished.

Natural gas is stripped of its heavy molecules before it is piped to the consumer. Butane and propane, which readily liquefy under pressure, are separated and are used as liquid fuels.

The origin of natural gas is likely the same as that of petroleum, i.e. the incomplete decomposition of vegetable or animal matter, either with or without bacterial action.

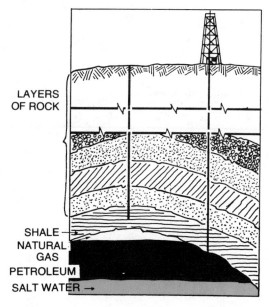

Fig. 30.3:
Typical structure of Earth's strata in natural gas fields and oil fields

30:8   Petroleum

Crude oil is a mixture of gaseous, liquid, and solid hydrocarbons. Petroleum comes from two Latin words, *petra* meaning rock and *oleum* meaning oil. This material is well named as can be seen by studying Fig. 30.3.

Likely oil-bearing strata are found by air photography, surface examination of rock, outcroppings, core drillings, and seismographic mapping of the Earth's strata. The latter process consists of exploding dynamite in holes in the Earth's crust. The reflections of the shock waves from rock layers, on being recorded, allow a geologist to map the substrata.

When a well enters oil strata, gas pressure may be sufficient to force oil to the surface. Such a well is called a gusher. Usually, however, pumps must be used to lift the oil to the surface. The oil is stored in large steel tanks until it is sent to the refinery.

Fractional Distillation

After undesirable impurities, such as sulfur, wax, and clay, are removed, the crude oil is separated into fractions, which consist of mixtures of hydrocarbons having different boiling points. In this process, known as fractional distillation, the oil is heated in a pipe-still consisting of many pipes inside a gas-fired furnace. It is then discharged into the bottom of a fractionating or "bubble" tower where the volatile components form vapours which ascend the tower. The more volatile the vapour, the higher it rises before condensing to a liquid. In this way fractions of the hydrocarbons are sorted out according to their boiling points (Fig. 30.4)

The heavier fractions with the highest boiling points condense on the lower trays. Several gases, from methane to butane, are collected at the top of the tower. The main products in descending order are naphtha, gasoline, kerosene, heating oil, lubricating oil, waxes, tars, and asphalt.

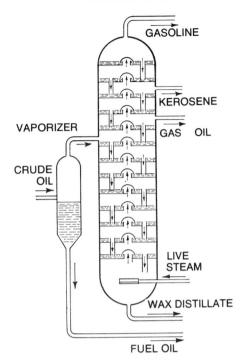

Fig. 30.4:
Bubble tower for the fractional distillation of petroleum

Gasoline

Today, gasoline is the most important single product obtained from crude oil. It is a mixture consisting chiefly of hexane C_6H_{14}, heptane C_7H_{16}, and octane C_8H_{18}. The boiling point of the mixture is about 80°C.

Simple distillation produces only about 5L of gasoline from 42L of crude oil. The yield of gasoline is increased per barrel by *catalytic thermal cracking* of heavy molecules. If hydrocarbons of large molecular mass are heated to a high temperature in the absence of air, the molecules disintegrate or "crack" into several small fragments.

Example:

$$C_{16}H_{34} \rightarrow C_8H_{18} + C_8H_{16}$$

Molecules with 16 carbon atoms cannot be used as gasoline, but molecules with 8 carbon atoms can. Catalysts have been developed that allow this process to be carried out at fairly low temperatures.

Another method of increasing the yield of gasoline is *polymerization*, the opposite of cracking. In this process, small molecules of similar structure are joined to form larger ones. *Alkylation* is a process of joining saturated and unsaturated hydrocarbons to form larger molecules. About 16 per cent of our gasoline is obtained by cooling and compressing natural gas. The resulting product is *casing head gasoline*. Enriched gasolines with better engine-performance properties are produced by isomerization of straight chain molecules into branched chains.

GASOLINE AS AN ENGINE FUEL

Any combustible gas can cause an explosion if intimately mixed with air in the right proportions and ignited. The gaseous fuel and oxygen combine almost instantly, and the gases produced by the reaction are greatly expanded by the heat.

However, it has been found in research on the relative merits of the individual hydrocarbons as fuels for internal combustion engines, that those compounds with straight chain molecules tend to explode too rapidly and burn too unevenly upon ignition. Such rapid combustion causes fuel knock in a motor, accompanied by loss of power or damage to the motor.

For maximum power the gas-air mixture should burn quickly in a combustion wave spreading smoothly in all directions from the spark plug. This should occur only when the piston has reached the top of its compression stroke.

OCTANE NUMBERS

The octane number refers to the anti-knock quality of a motor fuel. A branched-chain isomer of octane is an excellent motor fuel, whereas straight-chain heptane is a very poor motor fuel, as mentioned above. By mixing these liquids and using the resultant fuel in a test engine, it is possible to compare the anti-knock qualities of this mixture with those of any other gasoline. The particular mixture of heptane and octane which has the same anti-knock qualities as the gasoline being examined is noted. The percentage of octane in the reference mixture is called the *octane number*, and this number is affixed to the gasoline being compared. A gasoline with an octane rating of 90 ("90 octane") means that this gasoline has the same anti-knock quality as a mixture of 90 per cent octane and 10 per cent heptane. Gasoline quality is supervised by the government, and the octane number of the gasoline sold must be exhibited on the gas pump. Aviation fuels may have an octane rating of 100 or more. These fuels are composed, for the most part, of carefully selected branched molecules.

Unleaded gasoline

In 1921 Thomas Midgely discovered that as little as 1 mL of tetraethyl lead, $(C_2H_5)_4Pb$, per litre of gasoline greatly improved its anti-knock properties.

By 1970 the amount of tetraethyl lead used in the cars of Canada and United States was over 350 million kilograms per year. When the fuel is burned in the car engine, the added lead forms a gaseous compound which becomes part of the waste exhaust gases, adding to air pollution. Government regulations have ordered that engines in new cars should be designed to operate only with unleaded gasoline to combat this health hazard.

30:9   Petrochemistry

Natural gas and petroleum are now used in increasing amounts to make organic compounds: included among these are ethanol, glycerol, acetone, ethylene glycol, benzene, and toluene. Such compounds used to be obtained from a variety of sources but are now available directly or indirectly from petroleum. Rubber, plastics, detergents, insecticides, and synthetic fibres, like orlon, dacron and nylon, are synthesized from the above compounds. The industry based on converting petroleum by-products to useful substances is called the *petrochemical industry*.

30:10   Unsaturated Hydrocarbons

The unsaturated hydrocarbons are those which contain double or triple bonds between some of the carbon atoms in their molecules. The simplest examples are ethene (or ethylene) C_2H_4 and ethyne (or acetylene) C_2H_2.

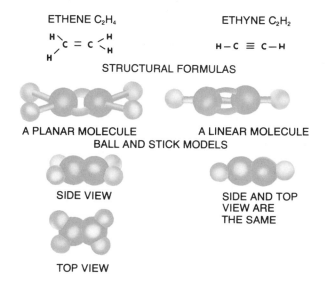

ETHENE C_2H_4 ETHYNE C_2H_2

STRUCTURAL FORMULAS

A PLANAR MOLECULE   A LINEAR MOLECULE
BALL AND STICK MODELS

SIDE VIEW   SIDE AND TOP
VIEW ARE
THE SAME

TOP VIEW

Chemical Evidence for Double and Triple Bonds
Why do we believe that double and triple bonds are present in the molecules of these compounds? What chemical evidence can be offered to back up our belief in these structures?

The saturated hydrocarbons react slowly by substituting one of the atoms already present in the molecules with another. The unsaturated hydrocarbons, being more reactive, react by *adding* other atoms to their molecules. This is explained by the "saturating" of the double bond. In this process one of the bonds is left intact between the carbon atoms, while new atoms or groups are added to the open bond. Thus a molecule of ethene adds a molecule of hydrogen to form a molecule of ethane.

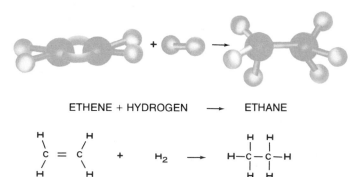

ETHENE + HYDROGEN   ⟶   ETHANE

Similarly, a molecule of ethyne adds two molecules of hydrogen to form a molecule of ethane:

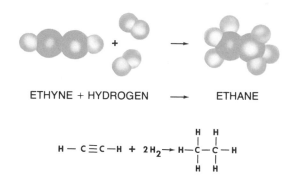

ETHYNE + HYDROGEN   ⟶   ETHANE

Because of its reactivity, ethene is used for the preparation of many synthetic products: for example, at high temperature, ethene reacts with water vapour to form ethanol;

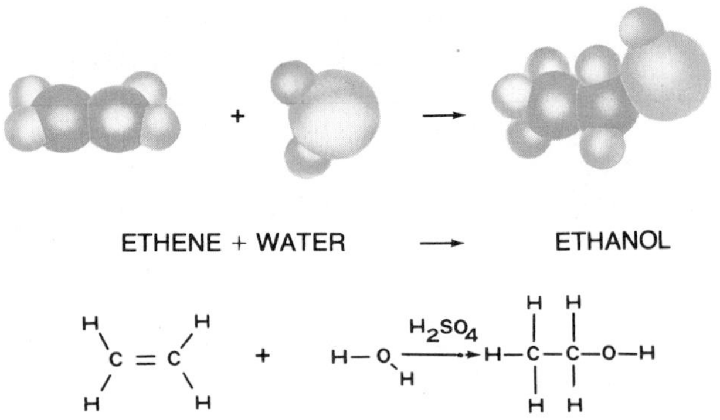

ETHENE + WATER ⟶ ETHANOL

Molecules with double bonds are often able to add to each other just as they add other atoms to themselves. The large molecules formed in this way are called *polymers* (*poly*—many, *mers*—units), and the process of combining many small molecules into large ones is called *polymerization*. It is through polymerization that plastics, rubber, and textiles are produced synthetically.

Ethene molecules may add to each other and thereby form a large molecule containing as many as 1000 ethene molecules linked together. The resulting product is *polythene* (or polyethylene) which is used in a great assortment of products; for

instance, squeeze bottles, ice-cube trays, and large sheets used for insulating buildings under construction.

The formation of polythene from ethene may be represented as below.

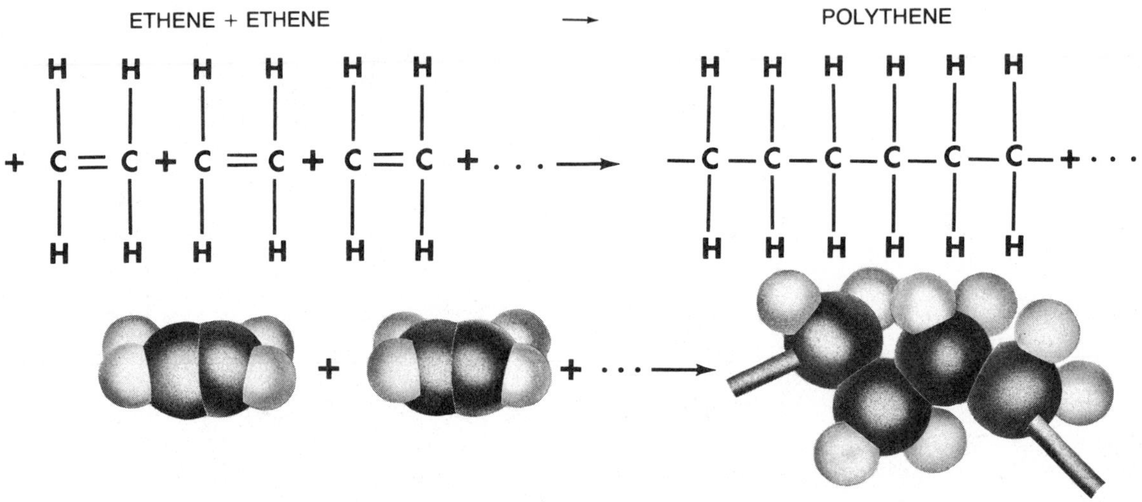

30:11 Petroleum: Resource and Pollutant

In the past, petroleum was found in many parts of the United States as well as in the western provinces of Canada, especially Alberta, where there are large quantities. With this resource, North America had large amounts of cheap energy and used it to develop industry, transportation, housing, agriculture and commerce. At the present time, these supplies are no longer sufficient for our demands. Oil must be imported from the small number of countries in which there is still a surplus for export, such as the Near East, North Africa, and Venezuela. Some oil will also be obtained from Alaska and possibly from the Canadian North in the future. Other industrialized nations such as Japan and the European countries also have to import vast quantities of oil. However,

ETHENE + ETHENE ⟶ POLYTHENE

the oil is a finite and limited non-renewable resource, resulting from slow processes of chemical decomposition over some 300 million years. All in all, the world's oil reserves are about 36 billion tonnes and the world's consumption is about 1 billion tonnes per year. With increasing world population, the rising material standard of living, and greater numbers of cars on roads and highways everywhere, the oil usage rate is growing. Even if some new oil-producing fields are discovered, it is clear that the world's present rate of using petroleum will soon cause the exhaustion of this valuable resource.

Consider only a few of the long list of products obtained from petroleum—heating oil, gasoline, lubricating oil, and grease. Heating oil provides warmth for the winter months and its absence would mean great hardship in northern countries like Canada. Gasoline makes possible the large scale transporation of people, goods, and food. Cars, jet planes, trains, ships, and motor bikes as we know them today must have a fluid to supply their engines with energy. Lubricating oils and grease are used in every machine that has moving parts. Without such lubricants, the machinery for agriculture, industry, transportation, and domestic use would not function.

Vast amounts of the vitally needed petroleum are pumped from deep wells drilled into the Earth on land and in the coastal waters where the ocean meets the land. The oil is transported by tanker, pipeline, rail, and truck to refineries. Here it is separated into heating oil, gasoline and lubricating oil, and other valuable products. These are further

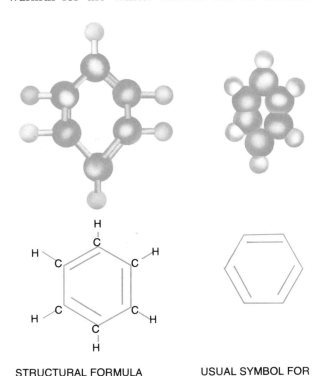

STRUCTURAL FORMULA
FOR BENZENE

USUAL SYMBOL FOR
BENZENE MOLECULE

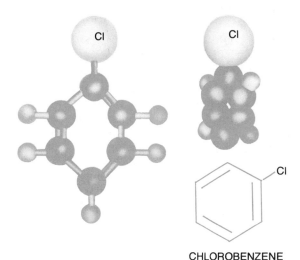

CHLOROBENZENE

Fig. 30.5:
The ring structure of benzene

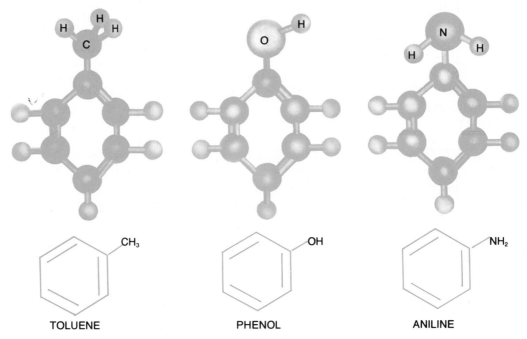

Fig. 30.6:
Derivatives of benzene

transported to homes, factories, gas stations, and farms.

Unfortunately, it is inevitable that some spillage occurs from tankers wrecked by storms, blowouts at sea, or leakage from pipelines and vehicles. Every year it is estimated that about 5 million tonnes pollute the ocean. The oil forms a large slick or floating film on the water that interferes with the exchange of oxygen and carbon dioxide between the air and water. Many fish and waterfowl die as a result. Cleanup crews try to contain the slick and to absorb the oil using straw or sawdust. Every effort must be made by the nations of the world to minimize oil spills and to take measures to eliminate the destruction of wildlife and pollution of beaches and estuaries as well as of the ocean itself.

Finally, when the fuel from petroleum is burned in an engine or furnace, it gives off a mixture of exhaust gases containing carbon dioxide, carbon monoxide, cyclic hydrocarbons and others. While carbon dioxide is a normal constituent of the atmosphere needed for photosynthesis, excessive amounts placed into the air over long periods of time may cause an intense greenhouse effect that will upset the factors that regulate the temperature of the Earth. Carbon monoxide is a toxic gas that displaces oxygen from hemoglobin in the blood, thereby preventing the normal transport of that vital gas to the cells of the body. Cyclic hydrocarbons are complex compounds of carbon and hydrogen that cause cancer. Furthermore, the mixture of these exhaust gases with smoke and fog produce smog, a mixture of about fifty different compounds reacting among themselves in the presence of sunlight to form pollutants that irritate the eyes and lungs.

Many critical problems concerning petroleum and energy will demand great research efforts and new ideas from scientists, engineers, health workers, and social scientists. Much attention is already directed toward conservation of fuel by the insulation of homes and office buildings, and higher efficiency of transportation, introduction of renewable sources of energy, and reduction of demand for energy on the part of the public as a whole.

Aromatic Hydrocarbons

Another class of hydrocarbons of great industrial and theoretical interest is related to benzene, C_6H_6, a liquid obtained in the destructive distillation of coal. These are termed the aromatic hydrocarbons, and a large number of dyes, perfumes, medicines, and explosives have been obtained from them.

Benzene is the parent of the aromatic compounds just as methane is the parent of the open-chain substances. Benzene is the simplest of the aromatic compounds which, in turn, may be regarded as derived from the parent substance.

C_6H_6—A Puzzle

The formula of benzene, C_6H_6, baffled the early organic chemists when they attempted to write its structure as they would write the structure of, say, hexane C_6H_{14}:

$$H-\overset{\overset{\displaystyle H}{|}}{\underset{\underset{\displaystyle H}{|}}{C}}-\overset{\overset{\displaystyle H}{|}}{\underset{\underset{\displaystyle H}{|}}{C}}-\overset{\overset{\displaystyle H}{|}}{\underset{\underset{\displaystyle H}{|}}{C}}-\overset{\overset{\displaystyle H}{|}}{\underset{\underset{\displaystyle H}{|}}{C}}-\overset{\overset{\displaystyle H}{|}}{\underset{\underset{\displaystyle H}{|}}{C}}-\overset{\overset{\displaystyle H}{|}}{\underset{\underset{\displaystyle H}{|}}{C}}-H$$

Obviously, there were "too few" hydrogen atoms in the C_6H_6 molecule for it to be written as a straight line.

The difficulty was finally overcome by Kekulé, a German chemist, who suggested that the six car-

bon atoms were arranged in a closed hexagonal ring, joined by alternate double and single bonds.

This would explain why benzene had only one isomer when one hydrogen was replaced by a chlorine atom to form chlorobenzene.

Apparently, there is no difference between the positions around the hexagon to which the chlorine atom could be attached.

Compounds Related to Benzene

Toluene is a liquid similar to benzene in properties, having a methyl, CH_3-, group in place of one of the hydrogen atoms of benzene.

Trinitrotoluene, a high explosive, is made from this compound.

Phenol is a hygroscopic solid, having a hydroxyl, $OH-$, group in place of one of the hydrogens of benzene (Fig. 30.6). It is used as a disinfectant and as a raw material for making plastics, but is a highly poisonous substance. Its presence in lake water is toxic to fish. It is also toxic to plants and humans. Unfortunately phenol occurs in the waste water of some industrial processes and since it is extremely difficult and costly to remove, it has been allowed to enter lakes and rivers. Government and industry are attempting to improve ways of recovering such toxics from waste water. Aniline is a liquid having an amino, NH_2-, group in place of one of the hydrogen atoms of benzene. Many dyes and drugs are made from aniline and its derivatives.

QUESTIONS

1. (i) What are hydrocarbons?
    (ii) Mention some important hydrocarbons.

2. Distinguish between saturated and unsaturated hydrocarbons.

3. What are the alkanes?

4. Describe the structure of methane, using a diagram.

5. List the principal physical properties of methane. Why does methane have these properties?

6. How may methyl chloride and carbon tetrachloride be made from methane?

7. Summarize the chemical properties of methane.

8. Illustrate how methane, ethane, and propane are part of a homologous series.

9. Define and give an example of isomerism.

10. What are alkyl radicals? Illustrate your answer with an example.

11. Summarize the general rules of naming organic compounds.

12. What are the common properties of the saturated hydrocarbons?

13. Write a note on the importance of natural gas.

14. Account for the origin of natural gas.

15. From your reading of current articles, write a note on oil exploration and discovery.

16. Describe the operation and construction of a bubble tower.

17. List the main products separated from petroleum by distillation.

18. What are the most important components of gasoline?

19. List and describe briefly the methods of increasing the yield of gasoline from petroleum.

20. Explain clearly the cause and effects of engine knock.

21. Explain how the octane number of a motor fuel is determined.

22. What is the importance of petrochemistry?

23. What are some possible substitutes for petroleum products?

24. What facts support the belief that unsaturated hydrocarbons contain a double or triple bond?

25. (i) Write the structural formulas for ethene and ethyne.
    (ii) What are some uses of these compounds?

26. Define *polymerization*. Illustrate your answer by reference to the formation of polythene.

27. Give two examples of cyclic hydrocarbons.

28. (i) What is an example of an aromatic hydrocarbon?
    (ii) Draw its structural formula.

29. A gaseous compound contains 85.72 per cent carbon and 14.28 per cent hydrogen. A litre of the gas at STP weighs 2.50 g. Find its molecular formula.

30. $CaC_2 + 2H_2O \rightarrow Ca(OH)_2 + C_2H_2$
    Calculate the mass of calcium carbide required to yield two moles of acetylene.

31. Find the density of the gas butane, C_4H_{10}, at STP in g/L.

32. Find the mass in grams of 10^{18} molecules of methane.

33. Gasoline, obtained from fossil fuels, is the source of energy for cars, buses, trucks, and planes. Recently, some attention has been paid to the possibility that methanol might be able to substitute for gasoline as a source of energy for vehicles. Prepare a report on this proposal.

34. It is said that when our oil supplies run out, we can use coal as an equivalent source of energy. Discuss this proposal after you have done some research on it.

35. Consult references to find out what experts think about how much longer our supply of fossil fuels will last. What consequences do you foresee from your findings?

CHAPTER

31

OXYGEN-CONTAINING ORGANIC COMPOUNDS

Will one of them, methanol, replace gasoline?

31:1 Alcohols

When one or more of the hydrogen atoms in a hydrocarbon molecule is replaced by a hydroxyl OH− group, the molecule that results represents a new type of compound called an *alcohol:* These compounds form a homologous series.

Functional Group
The entry of the polar hydroxyl group into the molecule permits hydrogen bonding. For this reason, alcohols are very different from hydrocarbons. Alcohols are liquids while hydrocarbons with an equal number of atoms in their molecules are gases. The alcohols of lower molecular mass dissolve in water and react with sodium to liberate hydrogen. Hydrocarbons do neither.

It is the hydroxyl group that gives alcohol its distinctive properties. A group that is characteristic of an entire series is called a *functional group*. The hydroxyl OH is the functional group of the alcohols. If R stands for any alkyl group, the alcohols may be represented by ROH.

Naming Alcohols
The longest chain of carbon atoms that includes the hydroxyl group is the basis for the name of an alcohol. This name has the ending — *ol*. The position of the hydroxyl group is indicated by the number of the carbon atom to which it is attached.

While alcohols are derivatives of hydrocarbons, the substitution of a hydroxyl radical for a hydrogen is done by indirect means. This can be seen in the preparation and properties of the two most common alcohols, methanol and ethanol.

Methanol
Most of the methanol used today is produced synthetically by passing a mixture of carbon monoxide and hydrogen over a catalyst consisting of the oxides of zinc, copper, and chromium. A temperatre of 400°C and a pressure of 150 atm are used. The following reaction occurs:

$$CO + 2H_2 \rightarrow CH_3OH$$

This compound is also known as wood alcohol because a small amount is obtained when wood is destructively distilled.

Methanol is a colourless liquid, miscible with water in all proportions. It boils at about 66°C and has a characteristic odour. Both the liquid and vapour are poisonous and are capable of causing blindness or death. Methanol burns with a pale blue flame:

$$2CH_3OH + 3O_2 \rightarrow 2CO_2\uparrow + 4H_2O$$

Methanol is used as a raw material in the manufacture of formaldehyde, HCHO, from which some plastics are made. It is used as a solvent for shellac and varnishes and as a fuel additive in aircraft when extra power is needed, such as at take-off. Much methanol is also used to denature grain alcohol. Denaturing renders grain alcohol unfit for drinking but does not interfere with most of its industrial uses.

Ethanol

More than 50 per cent of the ethanol produced is made from ethene. The simplified equation for its production is as follows:

Esso Research and Engineering Company

A scientist is studying a motor driven by a fuel cell battery. This device converts chemical energy from a liquid fuel, methanol, directly into electricity.

$$\underset{\substack{|\;\;\;|\\H\;\;H}}{\overset{\substack{H\;\;H\\|\;\;\;|}}{C=C}} + H-O-H \xrightarrow{H_2SO_4} \underset{\substack{|\;\;\;|\\H\;\;H}}{\overset{\substack{H\;\;H\\|\;\;\;|}}{H-C-C}}-OH$$

This alcohol is commonly produced by fermentation, a chemical change brought about by the growth of bacteria, yeasts, or moulds. These living organisms produce enzymes.

Ethanol is obtained when glucose, $C_6H_{12}O_6$, a monosaccharide (Chapter 32), is fermented. Since glucose occurs in a large number of fruit juices, any of these may be used to prepare ethanol. The process is catalyzed by an enzyme called zymase found in yeast:

$$\overset{zymase}{C_6H_{12}O_6 \rightarrow 2C_2H_5OH + 2CO_2\uparrow}$$

Wines are prepared by such fermentation of fruit juice.

Starch, a polysaccharide (Chapter 32) obtained from corn, barley, rice, wheat, and potatoes, may also ferment to produce ethanol.

However, when starch is used, its large molecule must first be broken into molecules of glucose. This is done with the aid of diastase, an enzyme found in malt, which is obtained commercially from sprouting barley seeds.

In making beer, the starch is first fermented to glucose with the aid of diastase; then the glucose is fermented to alcohol with the aid of zymase:

$$\overset{diastase}{(C_6H_{10}O_5)_n + nH_2O \rightarrow nC_6H_{12}O_6}$$
Starch

$$\overset{zymase}{nC_6H_{12}O_6 \rightarrow n(2C_2H_5OH + 2CO_2)}$$
Glucose   Ethanol

It is also possible to obtain ethanol from sucrose.

SOME COMMON ALCOHOLS

NAME AND FORMULA   MOLECULAR STRUCTURE

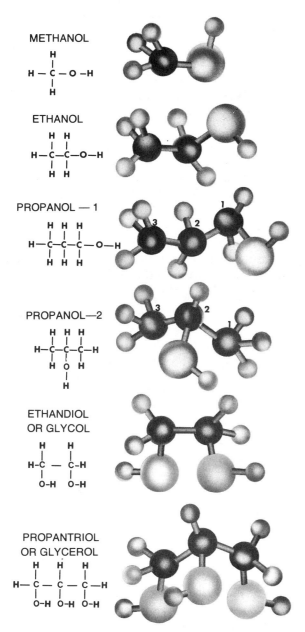

METHANOL

ETHANOL

PROPANOL — 1

PROPANOL—2

ETHANDIOL
OR GLYCOL

PROPANTRIOL
OR GLYCEROL

Fig. 31.1

In this case, the sucrose, a disaccharide, must first be broken down to glucose and fructose of which it is composed. This is done with the aid of invertase, another enzyme found in yeast. Thus the addition of yeast, which contains both invertase and zymase, breaks down the sucrose to a simpler sugar and then uses it to produce ethanol. Molasses, a by-product in the refinement of sucrose from sugar cane, is fermented to ethanol in this way.

Fermentation stops when the concentration of ethanol reaches 12 per cent. The alcohol is distilled from the mixtures and may be thus concentrated to about 95 per cent. A 95 per cent ethanol-water mixture is constantly boiling and cannot be further separated by distillation. Calcium oxide, CaO, may be added to remove the water if absolutely pure ethanol is required. The calcium oxide does not combine with the alcohol; nor is it soluble in the alcohol.

PROPERTIES OF ETHANOL

Ethanol is a colourless liquid with a characteristic odour and burning taste. It is miscible with water in all proportions, but it is lighter than water; it boils at about 78°C, and it burns with a pale blue flame as follows:

$$C_2H_5OH + 3O_2 \rightarrow 2CO_2\uparrow + 3H_2O$$

Ethanol is next to water in importance as a solvent. It is also used in the preparation of rubber, ether, vinegar, chloroform, perfumes, medicines, varnishes, lacquers, and antifreeze.

Ethylene Glycol and Glycerol

Ethanol and methanol have one hydroxyl group in their molecules and are, therefore, termed monohydroxy alcohols. Ethylene glycol, or ethanediol, $C_2H_4(OH)_2$, is an example of a dihydroxy alcohol. Its two hydroxyl groups are present on adjacent carbon atoms.

$$
\begin{array}{ccc}
& H & H \\
& | & | \\
H - & C - & C - H \\
& | & | \\
& OH & OH
\end{array}
$$

Ethylene glycol is used as permanent antifreeze because it has a low freezing point and it does not evaporate readily. The two hydroxyl groups increase the hydrogen bonding in the liquid, thereby causing ethylene glycol to have higher viscosity than ethanol.

Glycerol, or propanetriol, is the most important trihydroxy compound. Its structural formula is

$$
\begin{array}{cccc}
& H & H & H \\
& | & | & | \\
H - & C - & C - & C - H \\
& | & | & | \\
& OH & OH & OH
\end{array}
$$

This alcohol has long been produced as a by-product of the soap industry.

Due to hydrogen bonding, glycerol is a thick, syrupy liquid, heavier than water, and mixes with water in all proportions. It is colourless and has a sweet taste. Because it is hygroscopic (that is, it absorbs and retains moisture), it is used in ointments, medicines, cosmetics, tooth paste, candy, adhesives, and leather. Its chief use, however, is in making nitroglycerine, commonly used in dynamite. When used to make dynamite, glycerine is treated with a mixture of sulfuric and nitric acid:

$$
\begin{array}{c}
H_2SO_4 \\
C_3H_5(OH)_3 + 3HNO_3 \rightarrow C_3H_5(NO_3)_3 + 3H_2O \\
\text{glycerol} \qquad\qquad\qquad \text{nitroglycerine}
\end{array}
$$

The sulfuric acid absorbs the water formed. This reaction must be conducted with rigid temperature control to prevent premature explosion. The nitroglycerine must be highly purified after its formation, otherwise it is not safe to handle. Minute amounts of impurities have been found to render it unstable. When nitroglycerine explodes, it disintegrates into gaseous products.

For use in dynamite, the nitroglycerine is absorbed in some material like starch or wood pulp. Dynamite is quite safe to handle because the absorbed nitroglycerine is very resistant to detonation unless subjected to the explosive force of a percussion cap.

31:2 Oxidation of Organic Compounds

When methane is ignited, it burns to produce carbon dioxide (CO_2), and water. Carbon dioxide represents the most complete state of oxidation of carbon. If, however, the oxidation is carried out more gently, compounds other than carbon dioxide are formed.

Suppose it were possible to introduce one oxygen atom at a time into each of the carbon-hydrogen bonds of methane. In the first step methanol would be obtained from methane:

$$
\begin{array}{ccc}
H & & H \\
| & O & | \\
H - C - H & \rightarrow & H - C - OH \\
| & & | \\
H & & H
\end{array}
$$

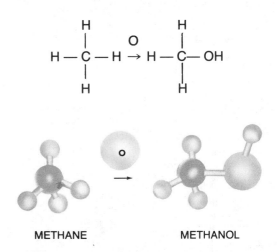

METHANE   METHANOL

where O is the symbol for introducing an oxygen atom.

In the second step, the following structure would result:

$$\begin{array}{ccc} H & & OH \\ | & O & | \\ H-C-OH & \rightarrow & H-C-OH \\ | & & | \\ H & & H \end{array}$$

METHANOL   UNSTABLE MOLECULE

Now there are two OH groups on the same carbon atom. Owing to hydrogen bonding and their proximity to each other, these form a molecule of water which breaks away from the rest of the molecule leaving:

$$\begin{array}{c} H \\ | \\ H-C=O \end{array}$$

METHANAL   +   WATER
(FORMALDEHYDE)

This compound is the first member of the *aldehyde* (*al*cohol-*dehyd*rate) series. Its name is *methanal* or *formaldehyde*. The functional group of the aldehyde series is:

$$\begin{array}{c} -C=O \\ | \\ H \end{array}$$

and it is written as $-CHO$, not as $-COH$, to avoid confusing this functional group with that of the alcohols.

The next stage of the oxidation would produce the acid:

$$\begin{array}{ccc} H & & OH \\ | & O & | \\ H-C=O & \rightarrow & H-C=O \end{array}$$

METHANAL ————————→ METHANOIC OR FORMIC ACID

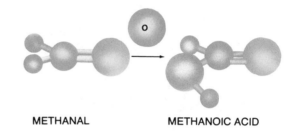

METHANAL   METHANOIC ACID

Aldehydes and Ketones
Methanal, CH_2O, is made by the partial oxidation of methanol, achieved by passing vapourized methanol and air over a catalyst such as vanadium at a temperature of $250-300°C$.

Methanal is a colourless gas. Without OH there is no hydrogen bonding in the molecule, so that the boiling point of formaldehyde is relatively low. Methanal is very soluble in water and its solution is called *formalin*. It is used as a disinfectant, an embalming fluid, a preservative for specimens, and as an ingredient of Bakelite. Another of its products is phenolic resins. These substances have a variety of uses such as adhesives in the manufacture of weatherproof plywood.

Ketones are compounds having the general formula:

$$\begin{array}{c} R \\ \diagdown \\ C=O \\ \diagup \\ R \end{array}$$

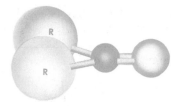

They resemble aldehydes except that the hydrogen of the aldehyde group is replaced by an alkyl group.

The simplest ketone is acetone:

ACETONE

This compound is formed in small amounts when wood is destructively distilled. It is made by special fermenting bacteria from isopropyl alcohol, obtained from petroleum. It is a colourless, fragrant, inflammable liquid which is an excellent solvent for acetylene, oil, resins, explosives, lacquers, nail polish, and other organic compounds.

31:3   Organic Acids

The most common functional group of organic acids is the carboxyl group:

$$\begin{matrix} & O \\ & \| \\ -&C-O-H \end{matrix}$$

This group has a double bond consisting of four electrons between a carbon and an oxygen atom. Such double bonds have the effect of withdrawing electrons from adjacent atoms. In this way, the bond between the hydrogen and the oxygen of the OH group is weakened, and ionization results. This causes the compound to be an acid. Nevertheless, the effect is rather limited; hence organic acids are weak electrolytes.

Note that the acid hydrogen is attached to an oxygen atom, not to a carbon atom. The C—H bond is too non-polar for it to form hydronium ions in solution readily.

Three examples of organic acids are lactic acid in sour milk, tartaric acid in many fruits, and citric acid in lemons.

Acetic Acid
Dilute solutions of ethanol, if allowed to remain exposed to air, slowly turn sour. Examination of the material shows that the sour taste results from acetic acid. It is known that spores of *bacillus aceti* are present in the air. When they grow in a solution containing ethanol they produce an enzyme which causes the oxidation of ethanol to acetic acid:

$$C_2H_5OH + O_2 \quad \rightarrow \quad CH_3COOH + H_2O$$
ethanol   acetic acid

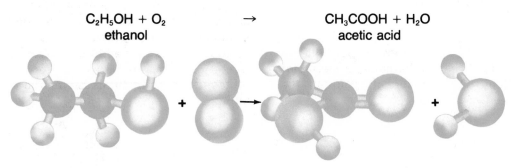

This reaction explains why wine and cider may turn sour. Our grandparents used to make their own vinegar by inoculating solutions of sugar with bacillus aceti which they called "mother of vinegar." A bottle of bacillus used to be a common pantry article.

About 50 per cent of the commercial acetic acid used today is made from fermentation of sugar solutions. The rest is made synthetically as a by-product of the petroleum industry.

Pure acetic acid is a liquid that solidifies at 16.7°C to form ice-like crystals; hence its name, *glacial acetic acid*. The acid has an odour like vinegar, which is not surprising since vinegar is a five per cent acetic acid solution. Glacial acetic acid boils at 118°C. Its high boiling point is due to hydrogen bonding. It mixes with water, alcohol, and ether in all proportions, and is a weak acid.

Acetic acid is used widely in foods, and it is used to make many synthetic products such as artificial silk, dyes, drugs, and white lead, a common ingredient of paints.

Esters

If the hydrogen of a carboxyl radical is replaced by an alkyl radical, the resultant material is called an *ester*. Esters are made most easily by allowing an organic acid to react with an alcohol. This reaction is analogous to neutralization. But an ester is not a salt; it is a covalent compound and does not form ions. To make the reaction go to completion, it is necessary to remove the water that forms by means of concentrated sulfuric acid. Otherwise, the ester has a tendency to react with the water, and an equilibrium is established. The formation of esters is called *esterification*. A typical example of esterification would be:

$$\text{Esterification}$$
$$H_2SO_4$$
$$CH_3COOH + C_2H_5OH \rightleftharpoons CH_3COOC_2H_5 + H_2O$$
$$\text{acetic acid} \quad \text{ethanol} \quad \text{ethyl acetate}$$
$$\text{Hydrolysis}$$

The reaction of the ester with water is called *hydrolysis*.

31:4 Fats and Oils

Animal and vegetable fats and oils are mixtures of esters. They are made of glyceryl radicals attached to complex acid radicals like palmitic, stearic, and oleic.

These fats hydrolyze slightly in hot water. The glycerol formed gives a sweet taste to cooked fats on roast meats.

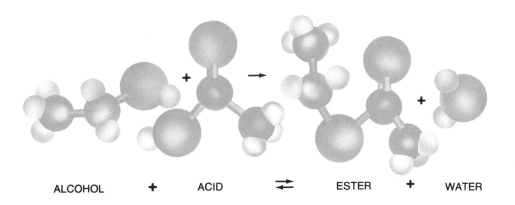

ALCOHOL + ACID ⇌ ESTER + WATER

Soap

Animal and vegetable fats react chemically with bases to form soap and glycerol. A *soap* is a metallic salt of a fatty acid. A good example of a reaction forming soap is the following:

$$C_3H_5(C_{17}H_{35}COO)_3 + 3NaOH \rightarrow$$
$$\text{stearin, a fat}$$

$$3C_{17}H_{35}COONa + C_3H_5(OH)_3$$
$$\text{sodium stearate,} \quad \text{glycerol}$$
$$\text{a soap}$$

This type of reaction is called *saponification*.

Crude soap has been known for centuries and was likely first discovered when fats were accidentally spilled on hot ashes. Potassium carbonate found in ashes would saponify the fat. Modern factories make soap by heating fats from animals, plants, and even fish, with sodium carbonate.

The essential steps in making soap are the following.

1. *Saponification:* A solution of sodium carbonate is boiled with fat by passing steam into the mixture.
2. *Salting Out:* Soap is not soluble in salt solution; therefore brine is added to the mixture, and curds of soap collect below in a water layer.
3. *Soap Treatment:* The curds of soap are then treated with steam and water to remove the impurities. The melted soap is run into containers where colouring matter, perfume, medicants, and sometimes a filler such as talc are added. The soap is finally cooled and cut or pressed into bars.

HOW SOAP CLEANS

The most outstanding characteristic of soap is that its long molecule is non-polar at one end and polar at the other.

When soap is added to an insoluble mixture of oil or grease and water, the non-polar end goes to the oil portion while the polar end remains in the water. This means that the soap molecule must

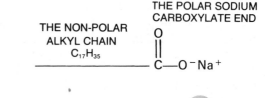

THE NON-POLAR
ALKYL CHAIN
$C_{17}H_{35}$

THE POLAR SODIUM
CARBOXYLATE END

$$\begin{array}{c} O \\ \| \\ \rule{3cm}{0.4pt}\ C{-}O^-Na^+ \end{array}$$

A MOLECULE OF SOAP
(HYDROGEN ATOMS ARE OMITTED)

place itself at the boundary between the oil and the water. It weakens the boundary of separation and permits the oil droplets to disperse in the water. This is called *emulsification*. The resulting *emulsion* is water soluble and may be flushed away with a stream of water.

Soap solutions also have a very low surface tension, which allows such solutions to wet a surface more easily than water. The combination of low surface tension and emulsifying power accounts for the cleaning power that soap has.

Hard water usually contains Ca^{2+}, Mg^{2+}, or Fe^{3+} ions. These ions precipitate soap in the form of curds, thus destroying its cleaning power. A typical reaction would be:

$$2C_{17}H_{35}COONa + Ca^{2+} \rightarrow$$
$$\text{sodium stearate}$$
$$\text{(soluble)}$$

$$(C_{17}H_{35}COO)_2Ca\downarrow + 2Na^+$$
$$\text{calcium stearate}$$
$$\text{(insoluble)}$$

When these ions are present, the soap cannot do its cleaning job. It is possible, however, to eliminate these ions from hard water by some water softening process.

31:5   Ethers

Ethers are compounds with this general formula, $R — O — R$.

In water, the oxygen atom is joined to two hydrogen atoms; in alcohol, it is joined to one hydrogen and one carbon atom; in ether, it is joined to two carbon atoms:

Water $H — O — H$

Alcohol $R — O — H$

Ether $R — O — R$

In this example R represents the alkyl group symbol.

With the elimination of OH, there is almost no possibility of hydrogen bonding, and therefore ether is far more volatile than either alcohol or water. It does not dissolve in water. On the other hand, molecules of organic compounds find it easy to separate the weakly attracted molecules of ether. Many organic substances dissolve in ether that cannot dissolve in water.

Diethyl ether's main use is to extract organic products from plants or other materials. Ether is still used to some extent as an anaesthetic. Its boiling point of 35°C makes ether easy to remove from its extracts.

Because ether is very volatile and its heavy vapours are highly inflammable, great care must be exercised in its use.

QUESTIONS

1. What is an *alcohol*?

2. (i) Write a note on the naming of alcohols.
    (ii) Name the following: C_3H_7OH; C_4H_9OH.

3. (i)   Write the structural formula of methanol.
    (ii) How is methanol made?
    (iii) Write the equation for the burning of methanol.

4. What is *fermentation*?

5. Write the structural formula of ethanol.

6. Outline the production of ethanol from starch, giving the names of the principal enzymes involved.

7. Write the equation for the production of ethanol from ethene.

8. (i) Write the equation for the burning of ethanol.
    (ii) Give the main uses of ethanol.

9. (i) Write the structural formula for glycerol.
    (ii) What is the source of this material?

10. What are the uses of glycerol?

11. What functional group is found in all organic acids?

12. Why are organic acids weak electrolytes?

13. Give the names and formulas of three organic acids.

14. Butane's formula is C_4H_{10}. What should be the formula for butanoic acid?

15. Explain clearly why wine or cider may turn sour on standing.

16. Write the equation for the formation of acetic acid from ethanol.

17. What are the sources of acetic acid?

18. What is *glacial acetic acid*?

19. What is an *ester*?

20. Write an equation to illustrate esterification.

21. Write an equation to illustrate saponification.

22. Describe the steps in commercial soap making.

23. Give some uses of soap other than for cleaning.

24. Explain clearly how soap cleans.

25. What ions are usually present in hard water?

26. What different compounds could be formed by the stepwise oxidation of methane? Illustrate your answer with equations.

27. (i) Describe the commercial production of methanal (formaldehyde).
    (ii) List the uses of this material.

28. What are *ketones*?

29. (i)   Write the structural formula of acetone.
    (ii) What are the sources of acetone?
    (iii) List the properties and uses of this material.
    (iv) Why is acetone a good solvent of organic materials?

30. Alcohol contains 52.12 per cent carbon, 13.13 per cent hydrogen and 34.74 per cent oxygen: the molar mass is 46 g/mol. Find its true formula.

31. Glucose ferments as follows:

$$C_6H_{12}O_6 \ \rightarrow \ 2C_2H_5OH + 2CO_2$$

How many litres of carbon dioxide could be obtained from 12 g of glucose, if the gas is measured at 19°C and 102.7 kPa pressure?

32. Methanol burns as follows:

$$2CH_3OH + 3O_2 \ \rightarrow \ 2CO_2 + 4H_2O$$

What mass of water is formed by burning 50 g of methanol?

33. How does the breathalyzer test work, and has it been successful in reducing car accidents?

CHAPTER

32

CARBOHYDRATES, PROTEINS, AND FOOD

Carbohydrates and proteins are important ingredients in our food.

32:1 Carbohydrates

This class of compounds is made up of molecules containing carbon, hydrogen, and oxygen. The hydrogen and oxygen atoms are usually present in the ratio of two to one, as they are in water. Sugars, starches, and celluloses are the most common carbohydrates.

The different properties possessed by sugars and starches are due to the size of the molecules of these substances. Glucose, the unit that builds many carbohydrate and sugar molecules, is an example of a *monosaccharide*. Sucrose (table sugar) is a disaccharide consisting of a molecule of glucose linked to one of fructose. Starch, which is a long chain or polymer, each unit of which is a glucose molecule, is a *polysaccharide*.

Glucose, a Monosaccharide
Pure glucose, sometimes called dextrose, is a white, crystalline material with the molecular formula $C_6H_{12}O_6$. Each molecule contains five hydroxyl groups and one aldehyde group. For simplicity it is represented by G-OH.

The blood normally contains about 70 to 90 mg of glucose per 100 mL. Glucose is oxidized in the body to form carbon dioxide and water, as energy is released for keeping the body warm and allowing it to work.

Commercially, glucose is made by the decomposition of starch by a process called hydrolysis. The action is catalyzed by dilute hydrochloric acid:

$$(C_6H_{10}O_5)_n + nH_2O \rightarrow nC_6H_{12}O_6$$
starch $\qquad\qquad$ glucose

Glucose is not as sweet as cane sugar, but it is nevertheless used in candy, jams, jellies, ice cream, soft drinks, and table syrups. The glucose used in food is often made from corn.

Fructose is another monosaccharide and is an isomer of glucose. Its formula is therefore $C_6H_{12}O_6$ as well, and may be represented by F — OH.

Sucrose, a Disaccharide
A disaccharide consists of two monosaccharide

units joined together. This is done by the removal of a molecule of water between glucose and fructose:

$$G—O\boxed{H + HO}—F \rightarrow G—O—F + H_2O$$

When sugar is eaten and digested, its molecule is split by the re-introduction of the molecule of water. This is an example of hydrolysis. All digestive processes are hydrolyses and are catalyzed by enzymes.

Sucrose is obtained from sugar cane and sugar beet. It is also present in maple sugar. Sucrose changes to glucose and fructose during digestion or if it is heated with a small amount of hydrochloric acid:

$$C_{12}H_{22}O_{11} + H_2O \rightarrow C_6H_{12}O_6 + C_6H_{12}O_6$$

sucrose   glucose   fructose

Most molasses produced is used in making ethanol, but it is also a valuable food for both humans and cattle.

Starches, Polysaccharides

Starch is the stored carbohydrate in many plants, and it forms a high percentage of the composition of cereals, potatoes, corn, and rice.

The granules of starch from various sources differ in both size and appearance.

The chemical structure of all starches is similar but not identical. It has been determined that starch molecules consist of glucose units, chemically united. The molecular mass of starch molecules varies from 10 000 to 1 000 000. The glucose units may be arranged in chains as much as 30 glucose units long. Branched chains account for the presence of as many as 6000 glucose units in a given starch molecule. The formula of starch is usually written as $(C_6H_{10}O_5)_n$.

Starch is called a *polysaccharide* because it is built up in plants from many glucose molecules.

Each glucose molecule is attached to the chain by removal of a molecule of water. The molecule of starch may therefore be represented by

$$—G—O—G—O—G—O—G—O—$$

where $G—O—$ is the remainder of a glucose molecule and stands for $C_6H_{10}O_5$.

During digestion, the bonds in starch are broken by hydrolysis. Parts of water molecules are re-introduced into the severed fragments of the starch molecules which eventually are completely broken down into glucose. It is then released from the digestive tract to enter the blood stream.

$$G—O—G—O—G—O—G \rightarrow {}_n(G—O—H)$$
$$H—O—H \quad H—O—H$$

Starch is tasteless and odourless. In hot water the starch granules break up and thus some starch dissolves, but most starches do not dissolve in cold water. When mixed with iodine, starch turns bluish-black in colour. This is frequently used to test for starch.

Heating to about 200°C causes the molecules of starch to break down into fragments with smaller molecular mass. The mixture of fragments is called *dextrin*. Dextrins are used in infant foods and malted milk because they are more easily digested than starch.

Cellulose

This material is the main constituent of cotton, wood, linen, straw, and many other substances. It is the structural material of plant life and, like starch, consists of chains of glucose units, though the units are combined differently and the cellulose chains are not branched. The molecular mass of cellulose is from 500 000 to 3 000 000, depending on chain lengths. As a result, there are many classes of cellulose. The formula of cellulose is often written as $(C_6H_{10}O_5)_n$.

Cotton is about 95 per cent cellulose with impurities of fats and wax. When these impurities are removed, the product is called *absorbent cotton*. Linen is also a cellulose material but it has a higher percentage of impurities than cotton. The cellulose of wood is essential to the paper-making industry.

Making paper, one of Canada's chief industries, requires separating the cellulose of the wood from the other constituents, called lignin. This is done by grinding the wood into small chips, and cooking these at high pressure and temperature with chemicals which attack and dissolve the lignin. The cellulose fibres are removed, washed, and bleached, and form a product called *pulp*. This is suspended in water, and other ingredients such as size, fillers, and a little glue are added. The suspension is agitated and deposited on a rapidly moving screen. As the water drains away, the remaining mat of paper is pressed and dried by passing it through hot rollers.

32:2   Proteins

The chief constituent of animal cells is *protein*. Proteins contain carbon, hydrogen, oxygen, nitrogen, and in some cases sulfur and phosphorus. Proteins are essential components of the jelly-like material that is found in the cells of all living matter. Some examples of protein are egg albumen, casein of milk, glutenin of wheat, gelatin in bones, insulin of the pancreas, and haemoglobin of the blood.

Muscle and skin are mostly protein, and even silk and wool are members of this class of compounds. Molecular mass of proteins range from about 5000 to about 6 700 000. These compounds are very sensitive to heat. For example, the protein in raw egg is soluble, but heating makes it insoluble. Drying proteins also makes them insoluble.

When concentrated nitric acid comes in contact with a protein, a yellow compound called *xanthoproteic acid* is formed. This reaction is frequently used as a test for proteins. The skin and finger nails turn yellow on contact with nitric acid as a result of this reaction.

Plants are able to synthesize proteins from inorganic materials such as soluble nitrates, carbon dioxide, and water. Animals cannot do this; so they must depend upon plants or other animals for their protein supply.

In the digestive process, certain enzymes, such as *pepsin* in the stomach and *trypsin* in the small intestine, break proteins down into simpler substances called *amino acids*. The amino acids combine to form proteins by the elimination of a molecule of water between every pair of combining amino acids (Fig. 32.1). These amino acids pass through the intestine walls into the blood stream, and after being transported to the cells, they are synthesized into the proteins of the body.

32:3   Amino Acids

The amino acids, out of which nature builds all the proteins of the plant and animal world, are remarkably consistent in their structure.

Imagine that in the methane molecule,

$$H - \underset{\underset{H}{|}}{\overset{\overset{H}{|}}{C}} - H$$

one hydrogen atom is replaced by the acidic carboxyl group $-\overset{\overset{O}{\|}}{C} - O - H$, and another by the basic amino group—NH_2. The other two bonds may remain as they are, attached to hydrogen atoms, or they may be attached to alkyl groups. The resulting molecule would be:

$$H - N - \overset{\overset{\displaystyle R}{|}}{\underset{\underset{\displaystyle H}{|}}{C}} - \overset{\overset{\displaystyle O}{\|}}{C} - O - H$$

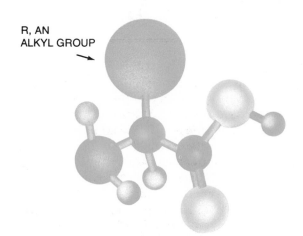

R, AN
ALKYL GROUP

GENERAL STRUCTURE
OF AN AMINO ACID

By changing this R group, nature produces about 25 different amino acids, which become the building blocks of thousands of proteins for an unlimited number of species of living organisms.

Protein is digested by the reintroduction of the molecule of water.

32:4   The Food Problem

Importance of Photosynthesis

Photosynthesis was mentioned in Chapter 9. Through this process, green plants can be considered as chemical factories in which sunlight, water, carbon dioxide, and the chlorophyll contained in the cells of the plants combine to synthesize sugars and starches and evolve oxygen:

$$6\,CO_2 + 6\,H_2O \xrightarrow{\text{sunlight}} \underset{\text{glucose}}{C_6H_{12}O_6} + 6\,O_2 \uparrow$$

$$n\,C_6H_{12}O_6 \rightarrow \underset{\text{starch}}{(C_6H_{12}O_6)_n} + n\,H_2O$$

While there are many steps in the photosynthetic process, the overall reaction is endothermic—absorbing heat. The energy required to make the reaction proceed is supplied by sunlight.

The importance of photosynthesis cannot be overestimated. All animals obtain their food from plants, while plants are dependent on the complex photosynthetic reactions through which they manufacture sugars, starches, and cellulose. Proteins, fats, vitamins, and other foods are formed by further natural chemical reactions. Practically all naturally occurring organic substances are directly or indirectly the result of photosynthesis.

WATER MOLECULE REMOVED AS TWO
AMINO ACIDS COMBINE

Fig. 32.1:
Bonds between the amino acids of a protein molecule

Food: A Source of Nourishment

Humans and animals need a well-balanced diet in order to obtain the energy and the raw materials necessary to keep the body functioning properly.

FOOD AS SOURCE OF ENERGY

Fats and carbohydrates are the two main classes of substances found in food that supply the energy the body requires. The body needs energy to keep warm, to do work and to keep the essential organs functioning. This energy is supplied when the complex molecules of fats and carbohydrates are broken down into simpler substances.

In the case of malnutrition, the body could use some of its protein reserves as a source of energy. On the other hand, if the quantity of carbohydrates absorbed by the body exceeds the daily requirements, the organism changes them into fats.

FOOD AS A SOURCE OF PROTEINS

Proteins are the main *body builders*. The proteins found in food supply the body with amino acids which are the most important building blocks of cell materials. The body uses these amino acids to build up its own proteins.

Depending on their nature, proteins have many functions. Some help the body keep both *material* and *energy* in reserve for later use. For example, the proteins found in egg white, in milk, and in the seeds of plants fill that purpose. Other proteins act *as carriers*. For example, the haemoglobin in the blood is a protein that transports oxygen to various parts of the body. A third type of protein could be labelled *structural* proteins. The human skin and the web material of spiders are typical examples of structural proteins. Finally, another group of proteins *regulate the functions* of the body. Insulin, secreted in the pancreas, belongs to this group. It promotes the utilization of sugar in the organism. Insulin can be extracted from natural sources and used in the treatment of diabetes.

FOOD AS A SOURCE OF VITAMINS

The many vitamins known are not chemically related among themselves; they are complex substances that seem to *help enzymes* in their catalytic action. As their name suggests, vitamins play a vital role in maintaining health and growth.

Although the specific roles of many vitamins are not yet established, the pathological consequences of the lack of certain vitamins are well known. For example, the lack of vitamin B_1 (thiamine) can cause beriberi (inflammation of the nerves) while a deficiency in vitamin C causes scurvy (hemorrhage of the skin and mucous membranes).

Vitamins are needed by the body in only very small quantities and most are usually available in a normal varied diet.

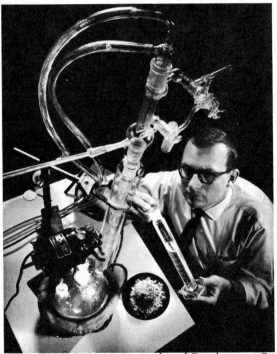

Courtesy General Electric Research and Development Centre

A scientist separates synthetic amino acids for study of their individual properties.

FOOD AS A SOURCE OF MINERAL SALTS

Besides organic compounds, the body must absorb a great variety of inorganic salts that supply such elements as sodium, potassium, magnesium, calcium, iron, phosphorus, fluorine, chlorine, bromine, and iodine. These elements play an important *physiological role*. For example, calcium in the form of calcium phosphate, is the main constituent of bones, while iron is necessary in the formation of the haemoglobin in the blood. Milk, fruits, and green vegetables contain calcium phosphate while whole wheat, meats, and fish contain iron.

A diet deficient in certain mineral salts can cause important physiological disorders. For example, the thyroid gland requires iodine to make thyroxin, one of the regulators of metabolism. If iodine is lacking, the gland enlarges in an effort to make more thyroxin, and a goitre results. Because most foods contain no iodine, sodium or potassium iodide may be added to salt to alleviate the dietary deficiency. This product is known as iodized salt.

Food Crisis Ahead

As already mentioned, the body needs food to produce energy, build tissues, and regulate metabolism. All types of foods furnish energy, but proteins are needed for growth and building body tissue. The body cannot synthesize all the different amino acids it needs. Hence, some protein containing these indispensible amino acids must be present in the diet for nutrition to be adequate. Vitamins and minerals must also be supplied since they also are not synthesized by the body.

The modern sciences of agriculture and chemistry, aided by technology and large inputs of fossil fuel energy, have made great progress in increasing the amount and variety of food that can be grown. However, it must be remembered that ultimately all foods must either be grown on the land or obtained from the sea, lakes, and rivers.

The amount of arable land is limited and is being diminished by the growth of cities. The oceans, lakes and rivers are overfished and polluted.

Furthermore, protein is obtained from animals which themselves need food. Thus, the provision of protein for man requires more land, grain, water, and other resources than simply the supply of carbohydrates in the form of, say, wheat. All the while the demand for food is growing. The world population is now about 4 billion people, increasing nearly 2% per year. This means that almost 80 million additional human beings need food each year! Hopefully, the world's people look forward to a rising standard of living, but this also places more demands on the food supply.

A large part of the success of modern agriculture, particularly in North America, is due to the cheap energy of the past 25 years. This made possible the use of large farm machines, the production of fertilizers, the building of storage facilities, the transportation of food by train, boat, and trailer truck, the processing of food in factories, and the driving of the consumer in the family car to the supermarket to purchase the food.

This system is based on trading the energy of petroleum for the energy content of food. This exchange is accepted because of the importance of having the food despite the fact that its production consumes more energy than it provides.

Through mechanized agriculture, Canada, the United States, Australia, New Zealand, and Argentina are able to produce a surplus of food for export sale on the world market. However, these are only five countries out of the 150 countries in the world today.

With the approaching end of the petroleum era, a drastic change will have to occur in order for mankind as a biological species to return to a more harmonious coexistence with the limitations of the biosphere and the natural processes, which are dependant on solar energy, for the supply of food.

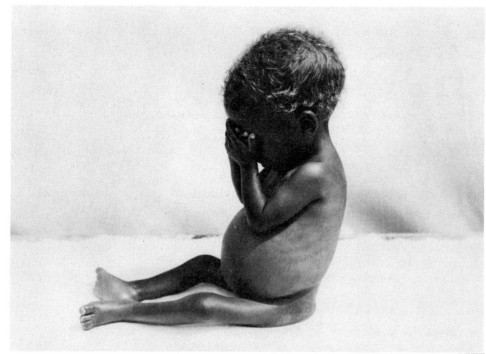

UNICEF Photo

A child suffering from Kwashiorkor (protein malnutrition). Kwashiorkor is the Ghanaian name meaning "displaced infant" and refers to the fact that it attacks children when they are weaned, often because a sibling is on the way.

QUESTIONS

1. What are *carbohydrates?*

2. (i) Why is glucose called a monosaccharide?
    (ii) How is glucose involved in vital processes?
    (iii) How is this sugar made commercially?
    (iv) What are some uses of glucose?

3. What is *fructose?*

4. What is a *disaccharide?*

5. What change occurs when sucrose is digested?

6. How is the starch molecule related to sugar?

7. Write a note on the occurrence of starch.

8. What is the test for starch?

9. What is *dextrin* and how may it be formed?

10. Describe the digestion of starch.

11. (i) Write a note on the importance and occurrence of proteins.
    (ii) What are some properties of proteins?
    (iii) What is the test for protein?

12. From what raw materials do plants synthesize protein?

13. Explain the digestion of proteins.

14. Describe the structure of amino acids.

15. Would you consider agriculture to be an industry? Make a list of the similarities and differences between agriculture and industry. Also, indicate the nature of the "food industries." Consult references to find out what they are and how they do or do not work well together.

16. How does the growth of a large city influence the surrounding agricultural area? Farmers often say that city-dwellers take food for granted. Is this charge justified?

17. Make a list of the factors necessary for good production of food. Check your list with someone who is knowledgeable about the subject. Search out whether the factors listed are likely to become more or less available in the future in Canada and elsewhere.

18. Make a similar list of the factors that make up the demand for food. Once again, check your list by consultation, and evaluate the factors as to whether they will create a greater or smaller demand for food in the future.

19. What has your research shown you about the world food situation?

20. Canada has always been a world leader in industries based on forest products. After researching this statement, write a report on Canada's present position in this respect.

Ontario Ministry of Agriculture and Food

CHAPTER
33

SYNTHETIC PRODUCTS

Convenient materials for daily living. Some cause special waste disposal problems because they are not biodegradable.

33:1   Synthetic Detergents

A large number of synthetic detergents are now on the market, and many of them are better cleaning agents than soap. Detergents consist of molecules designed along similar lines to soap molecules; that is, they have a long non-polar carbon chain of 12 to 18 atoms and a highly polar group at one end of the molecule. The advantage that these materials have over ordinary soap is that they do not form insoluble precipitates with calcium, magnesium, and iron (III) ions and, as a result, they work equally well in hard or soft water. At the present time in Canada the consumption of detergents far exceeds the consumption of soap.

One of the most commonly used synthetic detergents is sodium lauryl sulfate:

$$CH_3(CH_2)_{10}CH_2OSO_2O^-Na^+$$

The long non-polar hydrocarbon chain is grease soluble and the polar sodium sulfate end is water soluble. In the manufacture of this material, fats, treated with sodium hydroxide, are decomposed to long-chain acids and glycerol. The acids are then changed to alcohols by reacting them with hydrogen over a nickel catalyst. One of these alcohols is lauryl alcohol, $CH_3(CH_2)_{10}CH_2OH$, which is treated with sulfuric acid to form lauryl hydrogen sulfate:

$CH_3(CH_2)_{10}CH_2OH + HOSO_2OH \rightarrow$
lauryl alcohol   sulfuric acid
$CH_3(CH_2)_{10}CH_2OSO_2OH + HOH$
lauryl hydrogen sulfate

Next, the lauryl hydrogen sulfate is treated with sodium hydroxide to form the sodium lauryl sulfate:

$CH_3(CH_2)_{10}CH_2OSO_2OH + Na^+OH^- \rightarrow$
$CH_3(CH_2)_{10}CH_2OSO_2O^-Na^+ + H_2O$
sodium lauryl sulfate

Several detergents with this same general structure may be formed from other long-chain molecules.

Another important group of detergents is made by the alkylation of benzene with propene or another similar unsaturated compound. The product is then treated with sulfuric acid and sodium hydroxide to form the following material:

R —⟨ ⟩— SO$_2$O$^-$Na$^+$

sodium alkylaryl sulfonate*

where R is an alkyl group

33:2   Polythene

Ethene gas is capable of combining with itself by polymerization to form chains 2000 or more carbon atoms in length. The product of this combination is called polythene. Originally, this could be done only at high temperatures and pressures, but quite recently catalysts have been discovered which make this reaction possible at room temperature and atmospheric pressure.

Although like paraffin wax in appearance and

Courtesy Mobil Oil Corporation

A tube of polythene film being extruded

touch, polythene is strong and melts at 110-120°C. This material can be moulded, extruded, and spun into filaments in the same manner as many other plastics. When in the form of sheets or pipes, it can be welded into complex articles by hot-air (150°C) torches. It makes an excellent packaging material, is very inert chemically, and does not dissolve in solvents at room temperature. These properties make it a good material for handling chemicals. It is even used in drains and pipes. Polythene is an excellent insulator and, as a result, it is used to insulate underwater telephone cables.

33:3   Rubber

Columbus was the first European to become acquainted with rubber. The natives of the West Indies had toys made of it. Eventually, some of this natural rubber, which was obtained from the sap of certain tropical trees, was taken to England. Priestly found it was of great value in rubbing away pencil marks from paper, and so he gave it its name.

Natural rubber is a polymeric material of a high molecular mass. The unit of this polymer is called *isoprene*, which has the formula

$$CH_2 = C - CH = CH_2$$
$$\overset{\displaystyle CH_3}{\underset{\displaystyle |}{}}$$

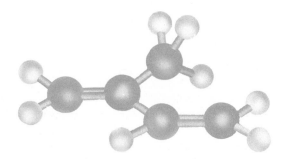

* The sulfonate group is the residue left when one OH is removed from H_2SO_4.

There may be as many as 2000 isoprene units in one rubber molecule combined as follows:

$$x \; \underset{\substack{| \\ H}}{\overset{\substack{H \quad CH_3}}{C}} = \underset{}{C} - \underset{}{C} = \underset{\substack{| \\ H}}{C} \longrightarrow \left[\underset{\substack{| \\ H}}{\overset{\substack{H \quad CH_3}}{C}} - C = C - \underset{\substack{| \\ H}}{C} \right]_x$$

The elastic character of rubber is due to the shape of the molecule. It is in the form of a fairly compact coil. The application of a stretching force causes this coil to lengthen, and the removal of the force allows the coil to return to its original size.

Crude rubber is found suspended in the latex obtained from various trees and plants. For example, the sap of milkweed and dandelion contains crude rubber, but not in sufficient amount to be used commercially. Raw rubber may be precipi-

Courtesy Du Pont of Canada Limited

Production of neoprene rubber film.

Courtesy Polymer Corporation Limited

The synthetic rubber plant of Polymer Corporation, Sarnia, Ontario
The storage spheres hold the alkene hydrocarbons to be polymerized into rubber. The towers serve to concentrate butene by distillation.

tated from the latex by acidifying it or by passing an electric current through it.

Crude rubber precipitated from latex is sticky when warm and brittle when cold. It is very easily severed, and it deteriorates because of slow oxidation. About 120 years ago Charles Goodyear discovered *vulcanization*. In this process, rubber is heated with sulfur. It is known that the sulfur atoms form cross links between the isoprene chains, which makes the rubber more stable, so that it is not soft in hot weather or brittle in cold weather.

Various fillers and pigments are added to rubber during vulcanization to increase the wearing qualities of rubber or to give it a desired colour. Some of these materials are carbon black, zinc oxide, antimony sulfide, and white lead.

At the present time there are many rubbers which have important uses; for example, in the making of automobile tires. Butyl rubber is a copolymer of butadiene and isobutene, obtained from petroleum cracking processes.

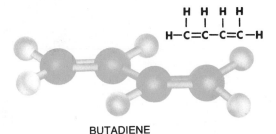

$$H-C=C-C=C-H$$

BUTADIENE

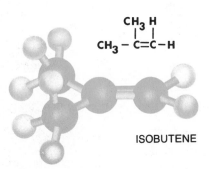

$$CH_3 - C=C-H$$

ISOBUTENE

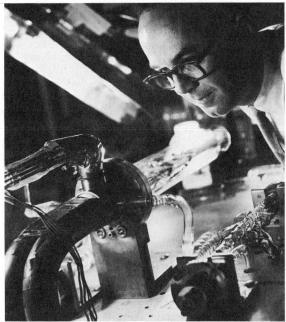

Courtesy General Electric Research and Development Centre

A scientist studies a new family of plastic materials. These are produced as films only a few millionths of a centimetre thick and have possible uses ranging from superior electrical insulation to corrosion-resistant protective coatings for metals.

This rubber is resistant to chemical action and impervious to gases. It is widely used for inner tubes.

Neoprene was the first American synthetic rubber. It is a polymer of *chloroprene*, which is made from acetylene and hydrogen chloride. Chloroprene differs from isoprene only in that chlorine replaces the methyl radical. The unit is thus:

$$\left[CH_2 - \overset{\overset{\textstyle Cl}{\textstyle |}}{C} = CH - CH_2 \right]$$

Because of its strength, its chemical inertness, and its insolubility in petroleum products, neoprene is used in gaskets, boots and shoes, gasoline hose, and floor tiles.

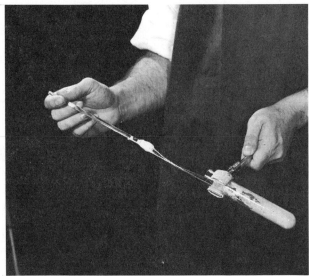

Courtesy Du Pont of Canada Limited

A manufactured fibre is born.
It was an experiment such as this that suggested the fibre-forming possibilities of nylon. Here, in its most elementary form, is the birth of a man-made fibre in a research chemist's test tube.

QUESTIONS

1. What advantages have detergents over soaps?

2. How are soaps and detergents similar?

3. (i)   List the properties of polythene.
    (ii) Discuss the uses of polythene.
    (iii) Why is polythene an efficient insulator?

4. What is *isoprene*?

5. Account for the elasticity of rubber.

6. What different properties does rubber have after vulcanization?

7. Write a note on synthetic rubber.

8. Prepare a report on some aspect of these subjects:
    (i)   The industrial use of plastics;
    (ii) The extent of the use of plastics in packaging and bottling;
    (iii) The disposal of non-biodegradable plastic containers thrown into garbage, or of solid wastes;
    (iv) Biodegradable plastics.

6
METALS AND RADIOACTIVITY

Metals like aluminum and steel make the modern city possible.

CHAPTER

34

THE METALS

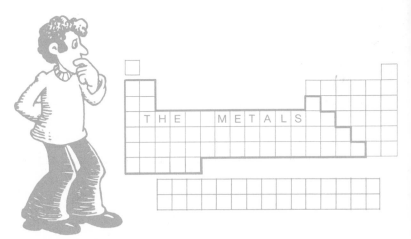

34:1 The Importance of Metals

About 80 of the elements are metals, some of which are among the most useful substances of our industrial civilization. In the ancient world, gold, silver, and copper were well-known and used as ornaments. Such metals were found free in Nature because of their chemical inertness. Iron, lead, tin, and mercury were also known and used, but to a smaller degree. In the modern world, iron, copper, aluminum, nickel, chromium, zinc, and lead are among the most important metals in general use, but many others are also used for special purposes.

34:2 What is Metallurgy?

Metallurgy is the science that deals with the recovery of metals from their ores and the alloying of these metals for their many uses.

Metals are usually found in combined form. Often they are themselves part of mixtures, called ores, which have various percentages of metal content, sometimes as low as two per cent of the mass of the ore. Metal is recovered from ores by both physical and chemical means. The physical methods are used to separate the ore from the rock, where this is possible, while the chemical change is one of converting the metallic ion to the atom by

Metals are good conductors of electricity, and the majority are strong and flexible.

donating electrons to it. Chemically, this is an example of reduction.

34:3 Properties of Metals

Metals generally may be recognized by their appearance. They have a lustre or shiny reflection which non-metals like sulfur, or salts like sodium chloride, do not possess.

Metals are good conductors of electricity and heat, whereas non-metals are poor conductors and, therefore, make good insulators. Copper and aluminum are two of the best conductors of electricity, which is why they are used extensively in electrical wiring. The ability of an element to conduct current is a good test of its metallic nature. The few intermediate elements that conduct electricity only to a small extent are called *metalloids*.

Metals show other properties as well. They can be hammered into different shapes or drawn into long thin wires; hence they are said to be *malleable* and *ductile*. Some are so hard that they can be made into tools such as hammers and chisels. Yet there are metals which are soft; for example, the alkali metals can be cut with a knife. Metals, as a rule, have a high melting point, with the result that furnaces, engines, and radiators are made of metals. However, there are metals that have a low melting point. Mercury, for instance, is a liquid at room temperature.

Many metals have a high density; gold has a density of 19 300 kg/m³. On the other hand, some metals have a low density. Garden furniture is made of aluminum because it is light, among other reasons. There are other metals that are lighter than aluminum and most of the alkali metals are even lighter than water.

Chemically, all metallic atoms have one important property in common: they all become positive ions, or cations, in binary salts.

34:4 The Metal Bond

The electronic structure of the atoms of metals is a satisfactory explanation for the large variation in properties shown by metals and for their formation of cations in binary salts, such as Na^+Cl^-.

The atoms of metals have relatively few outer electrons and, what is most important, these electrons are not confined to any particular atom. Instead, they move freely from atom to atom, and their motion has been compared to that of the molecules of a gas.

Since the outer electrons are not attached to atoms, the atoms should be considered to be positively charged ions. *Electronically, therefore, a metal is defined as a substance consisting of positively charged ions, fixed in the crystal lattice, with negatively charged electrons moving freely through the crystal.* The free electrons act as a cohesive force, without which the positive ions alone would repel each other. For this reason the mobile electrons are said to be the *metallic bond*.

34:5 Explanation of Metallic Properties

Lustre
Metallic lustre is explained by the free electronic motion. The electrons readily absorb light falling upon them, whereupon they assume a higher energy level. They do not remain at this higher level but fall back to a lower one immediately. This is accompanied by the emission of the light absorbed. Thus, most of the light is readily re-emitted, causing the metallic lustre.

Conductivity
Metals are good conductors of electricity because of the freedom of the electrons to move through the crystal lattice.

When a negative electrode comes in contact with the metal at one end and a positive electrode contacts the other end, electrons move through the lattice almost without resistance. If electrons enter one end of a conducting metal, an equivalent number of electrons are drained off at the other end. Heat conductance results because thermal energy is transferred from one mobile electron to another when the metal is heated. Electrical resistance increases with a rise of temperature because the metallic ions vibrate more vigorously about their lattice points in the crystal, thus interfering with the movement of the electrons.

Malleability and Ductility
Since the metallic bond is cohesive but not rigid, when a metal is hammered into a different shape it is merely necessary for the atoms to assume different positions. No fixed covalent bonds, such as those of carbon or sulfur, are present to prevent the atoms from assuming different positions. For this reason metals are malleable and ductile, whereas non-metals are brittle.

Melting Points of Metals

All metals except mercury are solids at room temperature. In general, the larger the atomic radius of a metal, the lower its melting point. This is so because as the atoms become more massive, the force of cohesion by the electrons becomes less effective, with the result that less heat is needed to break metal bonds.

Many transition metals have an unfilled inner shell of electrons. While this inner shell is not filled, its electrons are free to move about from atom to atom, acting as a cohesive force or metal bond. When the inner shell is filled to a capacity of 18 electrons, the electrons tend to remain close to individual atoms. When this occurs, the metal must depend on the limited number of outer electrons, only two per atom, for bonding. The metal bond is thus weakened and the melting point of the metal is lowered. This explains why mercury is a liquid. In mercury atoms, the inner shell is full to its capacity of 18 electrons. Zinc and cadmium, whose inner shells are filled with 18 electrons, are also easily melted.

On the other hand, iron, cobalt, and nickel have incomplete inner shells. Their electrons are free to move about and thus act as part of the metal bond. Indeed, there are enough electrons even to form some covalent bonds. Consequently, these metals have very high melting points.

Hardness and Density

Hardness and high density may be explained in the same way. The alkali metals have only one outer electron per atom. The "electron pool" is low and the metal bond is weak, hence the metals are soft and of low density. Generally, the more outer electrons a metal has per atom, the harder the metal will be and the greater will be its density.

Electromotive Activity Series

Metals are the elements whose atoms most readily lose their electrons; therefore they have low electronegativity. This easy loss of electrons determines the chemical properties of the metals and causes them to become positive ions.

The ability of a substance to lose electrons is relative; there must be another substance able to receive the electrons being lost by contact with the first. The two systems can be connected together electrically to form a continuous flow of electrons

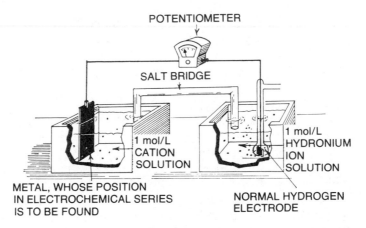

Fig. 34.1:
Experimental determination of the electromotive activity series

from one electrode to another, during which movement the electrons possess energy and can do work. Such work is measured as *voltage*. The voltage of a battery represents the number of units of work done (in *joules*) for the passage of each unit of electric charge (in *coulombs*).

By measuring the voltage in cells that use different metals as one electrode and hydrogen as the other, an accurate measure of the chemical activities of the metals can be obtained.

Hydrogen gas has the property of adsorbing on platinum metal. A glass tube with a side arm is sealed to a strip of platinum and hydrogen gas is admitted under one atmosphere of pressure. This apparatus, immersed in a 1 mol/L solution of strong acid, is called the Standard Hydrogen Electrode, with which other electrodes are coupled.

The metals that give the highest voltage when used as electrodes are placed at the top of the series called the *Electromotive Activity Series* (Table 34.1). This series is useful for remembering the chemical properties of the metals: the higher a metal is in the series, the more easily it becomes an ion; any metal will displace one below it from its solution; any metal above hydrogen will displace hydrogen from acids.

34:6   Alloys

A substance consisting of two or more metallic elements which are soluble in each other when molten, or which do not separate into distinct layers when solid, is called an *alloy*. One of the first alloys ever made was bronze, consisting of tin and copper. This alloy was so important to progress that a pre-historic period is known as the Bronze Age.

Some alloys may be considered as *solid solutions*. Brass, consisting of copper and zinc, has some zinc atoms in place of copper atoms in the cubic structure characteristic of pure copper.

TABLE 34.1

The Electromotive Activity Series

Lithium	Li
Potassium	K
Calcium	Ca
Sodium	Na
Magnesium	Mg
Aluminum	Al
Zinc	Zn
Iron	Fe
Tin	Sn
Lead	Pb
Hydrogen	H
Copper	Cu
Mercury	Hg
Silver	Ag
Platinum	Pt
Gold	Au

TABLE 34.2

Some Alloys

Alloys	Components
Simple brasses	Cu, Zn
Tin brasses	Cu, Zn, Sn
Nickel silver (German silver)	Cu, Ni, Zn
Ordinary bronze	Cu, Sn
Phosphor bronze	Cu, Sn, P
Zinc bronze	Cu, Sn, Zn, (P)
Aluminum bronze	Cu, Al
	Cu, Al, (Fe, Mg, Mn, Ni, Pb, Si)

Alloys of Gold, Silver, and Copper	
Name	Percentage Composition
18-carat gold	Gold, 75%; copper, silver
14-carat gold	Gold, 58%; copper, silver
Gold coin	Gold, 90%; copper, 10%
Silver coin	Silver, 90%; copper, 10%
Nickel coin	Copper, 75%; nickel, 25%
Sterling silver	Silver, 92.5%; copper, 7.5%

Sterling silver, consisting of silver and copper, is another example. Steel is also a solid solution in that the carbon atoms are located in some of the spaces between the iron atoms. Copper and gold may be mixed in all proportions.

Some alloys consist of crystals of the elements, heterogeneously mixed. Bismuth-cadmium alloys are examples of these. Other alloys are like compounds in that the composition is definite. Sodium-zinc or magnesium-copper mixtures are examples.

The properties of an alloy may be radically different from those of the elements that compose it. Alloys are usually harder and more resistant to the breakage and wear than the pure elements. Pure iron is so soft that it is useless for many purposes; if, however, it is alloyed with silicon, carbon, manganese, chromium, and vanadium, the resultant chrome-vanadium steel is so hard that it may be used for making gears or tools which will withstand enormous pressures without breakage. Pure aluminum is very soft, but when mixed with copper, manganese, and magnesium it forms "duralumin," a light but tough product used for aircraft and other structural purposes. Our modern industrialized civilization would be impossible without alloys.

QUESTIONS

1. Write a paragraph on the importance of metals.

2. How do metals usually occur in Nature?

3. Define these terms: *metallurgy, metalloids, malleable, ductile.*

4. What common properties do metals have?

5. Define the term *metal*, and describe the metallic bond.

6. Explain the following terms by means of the electronic theory in reference to metals: *lustre, conductivity, malleability, ductility.*

7. Why is electrical conductance of a metal less at a higher temperature?

8. Why do zinc, cadmium, and mercury have low melting points?

9. Why do some metals, such as iron, cobalt, and nickel, have a relatively high melting point?

10. Why are some metals, such as sodium, soft while others are hard?

11. (i) What is voltage?
    (ii) Relate voltage released by metals used in an electrical cell to the activity of a metal.

12. Define the term *electromotive series* and give an example to show the meaning of this term.

13. Define *alloy*. Give two examples of alloys.

14. Write a paragraph on the structure of alloys.

15. Why are alloys so useful? Give specific examples of their usefulness.

16. If 0.8 g of a certain metal liberates 442 mL of hydrogen from hydrochloric acid when the hydrogen is measured over water at 22°C and 101.6 kPa pressure, find the mass of the metal that will liberate a mole of gas at STP.

17. What mass of silver could be obtained from 100 mL of a 0.2 mol/L solution of silver nitrate by precipitation with excess sodium chloride?

18. Give the mass of the metal ion in each of the following solutions: (i) 250 mL of 0.2 mol/L $AgNO_3$; (ii) 50 mL of 0.5 mol/L $CdCl_2$; (iii) 125 mL of 1.5 mol/L $CuSO_4$.

19. Write the oxidation number of each atom in the following: (i) $Zn(IO_3)_2$; (ii) $NaAlO_2$.

20. Write an essay on the ways that metals affect our daily lives.

21. Search out some of the changes that are taking place at the present time in the nickel mining and refining industry. Compile a report on the problem.

22. If the technology of mining the ocean bed for metallic minerals becomes practical, what changes do you foresee for the Canadian North?

23. Make a list of industries that use metals to a major extent.

24. What types of pollution are associated with industries that mine and refine metals?

25. Metallic particulates in the air have been cited as pollutants. Consult some references to help identify these particulates and write a report on the scope of the problems they cause and what can be done about them.

CHAPTER
35

THE NUCLEUS AND RADIOACTIVITY

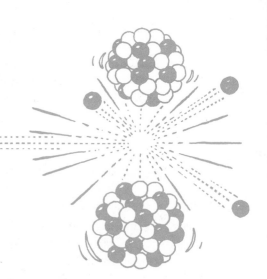

What happens when atomic nuclei break up?

35:1   Nuclear Change

In physical changes, the size, shape, or state of a substance is altered but not its composition. In chemical reactions, the composition of a substance changes. There is yet another type of change which is neither physical nor chemical. Because it involves the nucleus of the atom, it is termed *nuclear*.

Categories of nuclear changes may be classified as:

a. *Transmutation*, in which an isotope of an element is changed into another isotope of about the same atomic number;

b. *Fission*, in which an isotope of an element is split into smaller fragments;

c. *Fusion*, in which the nuclei of smaller atoms combine (or fuse together) to form a larger nucleus. In such reactions, tremendous amounts of energy are released, far in excess of the greatest energies of a physical or chemical change. Such energy is termed *atomic or nuclear energy*.

35:2   Discovery of Radioactivity

In 1896, the French physicist Becquerel (Chapter 5) found that a salt of uranium placed on a photographic plate left its picture on the film as if it had been photographed. After careful experiments had shown that the same effect could be had even if the photographic plates were wrapped in thin metal sheets, Becquerel concluded that the uranium compound emitted rays that were able to penetrate metal foil.

Becquerel also found that an electrically charged electroscope was discharged by the mere presence of the uranium compound. He concluded that the rays emitted by the uranium salt had the ability to change the molecules of air into ions. These ions were then attracted to the charged electroscope, thus discharging it.

This property of a substance, the emitting of rays without stimulus from any external source, was termed *radioactivity*. From the modest beginnings described above, the phenomenon of radioactivity has grown into the powerful source of energy known the world over as *nuclear energy*.

Pierre and Marie Curie – the pioneers of research into radioactivity
Ambassade de France, Ottawa

35:3   The Discovery of Radium

Pierre Curie and his wife, Marie, who were colleagues of Becquerel, extended the study of radioactivity. Using the ore from which the uranium compound was obtained, Marie Curie discovered two other elements, *radium* and *polonium*, which were even more radioactive than uranium. In order to accomplish this, Marie Curie had to purify about one tonne of ore to recover 0.1 g of radium and an even smaller amount of polonium. The life of Marie Curie is a truly inspiring one of perseverance and courage.

35:4   Radiations from the Radioactive Elements

What are the radiations coming from such radioactive elements as uranium, polonium, and radium? What is their nature and their origin?

The eminent British scientist Ernest Rutherford began his study of radioactivity to find answers to such questions. In the course of his research, he made many fundamental discoveries about atomic structure (Chapter 6). Rutherford placed a few grains of radioactive matter in a thick-walled lead container open only at the top, as illustrated in Fig. 35.1. Above the opening was a screen with a coating of zinc sulfide. He discovered that when rays from radioactive elements struck this screen, tiny flashes of light, called *scintillations,* could be observed. In studying the rays, Rutherford found that when a strong magnetic or electrostatic field was placed around the beam of radiation, three spots appeared on the zinc sulfide screen. Rutherford concluded that the beam of radiation contained three rays. One of these was positively charged, another negatively charged, and a third was neutral. He named them *alpha* (α), *beta* (β), and *gamma* (γ) rays and undertook further study to identify them.

The alpha rays were found to be a stream of helium nuclei, He^{2+}. Their positive charge was shown by their attraction to the negative electrode in the above experiment. They travel at high speeds and strongly ionize air or any gas through which they pass.

Alpha particles may be observed indirectly in a cloud chamber (Fig. 35.2). This apparatus contains air saturated with water vapour and is filled with a cooling device which may be a movable piston, a rubber bulb, or a cube of dry ice. A small source of alpha particles is present in the air chamber. To make the paths of the alpha particles visible, the air is cooled directly by the dry ice, or by suddenly increasing its volume by the motion of the piston, or by the action of the rubber bulb. As the tempera-

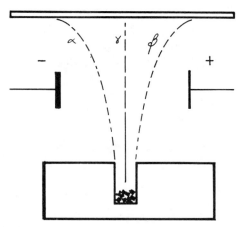

Fig. 35.1:
Separation of alpha, beta, and gamma rays

ture drops, water condenses on the ions of air formed along the paths of the particles, thus making the paths visible.

The beta rays were found to be electrons travelling even faster than alpha particles. Their negative charge was shown by their attraction to the positive electrode. Beta rays consist of electrons travelling at high velocities, in some cases approaching the speed of light. Beta rays have higher penetrating power than do alpha rays, but their ionizing power is much less, and they produce only faint tracks in a cloud chamber.

Gamma rays are similar to X rays except that they have a shorter wave length and greater energy and penetrating power. They are not affected by either magnetic or electric fields.

A single element does not emit both alpha and beta particles as a rule. Gamma rays are emitted with either alpha and beta radiation.

35:5   Geiger Counter

A valuable instrument for measuring radioactivity is the Geiger counter. It consists of a metal cylinder, the cathode, and a fine tungsten wire along the

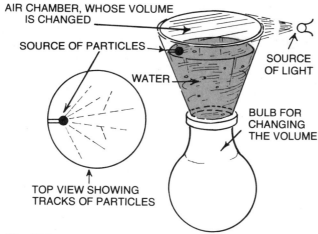

Fig. 35.2:
The cloud chamber

axis of the cylinder, the anode. Both cathode and anode are enclosed in a thin-walled, glass tube filled with gas (usually argon) at low pressure.

The anode is charged to a high voltage of about one thousand volts. This is not enough to ionize the argon; so no current flows. If, however, an alpha or a beta particle enters the tube, electrons are knocked out of the atoms of argon by collision with the high energy particles. Such electrons rush toward the positively charged anode and a pulse of electric current flows through the tube. Thus even a single alpha or beta particle could be detected since it may cause the pulse or current. The pulses may be amplified, recorded, or flashed.

35:6   The Unusual Features of Radioactivity

In the studies on radioactivity by Becquerel, Curie, and Rutherford, much evidence had been collected that indicated that radioactivity was not just another chemical reaction:

1. Radioactive materials emit rays of unusual nature.

2. Temperature and pressure have no effect on the intensity of radioactivity, whereas these factors, particularly temperature, influence chemical reactions.
3. All the compounds of a radioactive element are radioactive.
4. The energy of radioactivity is about 100 000 times as great as that of chemical reactions.

35:7   Rutherford's Theory of Radioactivity

Radioactivity is the process whereby the atoms of one element change into the atoms of another.

Radioactivity causes the nucleus of the atom to be altered. To illustrate, radium belongs to the same family of elements as magnesium; namely, group II of the periodic table. In radioactive change, radium is changed to radon, a Rare Gas. In the process, the atom of radium has changed to the atom of radon. In the same process, an alpha particle has been emitted. This is an instance of radioactive change called the *transmutation* of

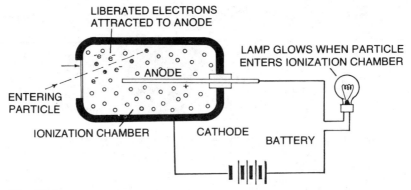

Fig. 35.3:
Geiger counter

atoms. It is caused by changes in the nucleus of the atoms and is accompanied by the emission of alpha, beta, or other particles along with gamma rays.

Since alpha and beta particles are charged, their emission from an atom results in a change in the nuclear charge and, therefore, in the atomic number. Hence an isotope of an element has been produced that is different from the original. When an atom emits an alpha particle from its nucleus, the resulting nucleus has two less positive charges, and the new atom has an atomic number two less and a mass number four less than the original.

The transmutation of radium to radon could therefore be represented by the equation:

$$_{88}^{226}Ra \rightarrow _{86}^{222}Rn + _{2}^{4}He$$

Nuclear reactions may be written like chemical reactions, with equations to show what change has taken place. One obvious difference is that all the terms of the equation are symbols, since these changes involve only atoms, not molecules. It is of course necessary to identify the particular isotope of the element that enters the reaction. This is done by a number in the upper left hand corner of the symbol. Finally, it is also necessary to show the

atomic numbers of the atoms involved, since protons are given out in some nuclear reactions. Atomic numbers are usually shown in the lower left hand corner.

In the preceding equation, the superscript refers to the mass number and the subscript to the atomic number. The mass number is the nearest integral value of the mass of an isotope in atomic mass units. Inspection shows that the atomic numbers and the atomic masses balance:

88p		86p		2p
138n	$\rightarrow$	136n	+	2n
226		222		4

35:8   The Rate of Nuclear Change

Rutherford studied the nuclear changes in three series of elements found to be naturally radioactive. He identified about 40 elements in the step-by-step alteration of the nucleus of larger atoms to smaller ones. He also determined the rate at which each radioactive isotope changed to its successor, and reported such rates of change in terms of the *half-life* of the isotope.

The rates at which nuclear changes occur vary

widely — ^{238}U disintegrates very slowly while ^{110}Ag, on the other hand, disintegrates very rapidly. In all cases, however, the number of atoms of any radioactive element that changes in unit time is a constant fraction of the total number of atoms of the isotope present. As more and more atoms change, the number changing per unit time decreases. For this reason, the rates of nuclear change are expressed by means of the *half-life*, defined as the time required for half of the isotope in any given sample to disintegrate. The half-life for ^{238}U is 4.5×10^9 y and for ^{110}Ag is 24 s.

If a radioactive element has a half-life of one year, then the record of its disintegration would be as shown in Table 35.1, if one started with 1 g on January 1, 1979.

TABLE 35.1

Date	Mass of Radioactive Element
Jan. 1, 1979	1 g
Jan. 1, 1980	0.5 g
Jan. 1, 1981	0.25 g
Jan. 1, 1982	0.125 g

35:9   Nuclear Structure and Binding Energy

What is the nucleus of the atom, and what is its source of energy? Although all the particles composing the nucleus have not yet been identified (even the discovery of such important particles as the neutron is fairly recent), a tentative picture of nuclear structure might be suggested.

As stated earlier, atomic nuclei are made up of protons and neutrons, held together by powerful forces which are not entirely understood, but which are known to be different from the familiar gravitational and electrostatic forces. The small size of the nucleus would indicate that nuclear forces operate over very short distances only. Newly discovered particles, such as *mesons,* are also present and they may help explain how the nucleus holds together.

It is significant that the mass of an atomic nucleus is generally less than the sum of the mass of protons and neutrons which are present. For example, the helium nucleus contains two protons and two neutrons. The sum of the masses of these particles is $2(1.0073) + 2(1.0087)$ or 4.0320 u. The helium nucleus has a mass of only 4.0017 u. Apparently 0.0303 u of mass were lost in the formation of the nucleus of a helium atom.

The explanation of this loss is provided by the principle that mass and energy are interconvertible according to the equation:

$$E = mc^2$$

where E is energy in joules, m is mass in kilograms and c is the speed of light in metres per second. Since the speed of light is very great, 3×10^8 m/s, a small mass could produce a large amount of energy. According to this equation, the conversion of one kilogram of mass to energy should yield 25 billion (2.5×10^{10}) kilowatt-hours of electrical energy. This is equal to the total output of electric power in Canada for a two-year period. The formation of one mole of helium from protons and neutrons would liberate 2.7×10^{12} J of heat. The conversion of hydrogen nuclei to helium nuclei is the source of the sun's energy and is an instance of *atomic fusion.*

Research is being done to learn how to harness this type of energy for electric power.

The *binding energy* is the energy equivalent to the difference between the actual mass of the nucleus of an isotope and the sum of the masses of the protons and neutrons that compose it, expressed as energy. The binding energy is greatest for the elements of atomic mass from 40 to 100, and gradually decreases for both the very large and the very small atoms.

35:10   Nuclear Reactions

Radioactivity and nuclear change were first discovered with the elements of high atomic number. Nuclear physicists were always curious to find out whether the atoms of any element could be made to undergo nuclear change or become radioactive as well.

In 1919, when Rutherford bombarded nitrogen with alpha particles ($_2^4$He) from a radioactive substance, he found that a minute amount of oxygen of atomic mass 17 was formed—an isotope of ordinary oxygen. A proton was also liberated in this nuclear reaction, the first successful artifical transmutation:

$$_7^{14}N + _2^4He \rightarrow _8^{17}O + _1^1H$$

The alpha particles used by Rutherford were not effective in producing much change. Since they were liberated by the naturally occurring radioactive elements, they were the only projectiles available for nuclear experiments until 1932.

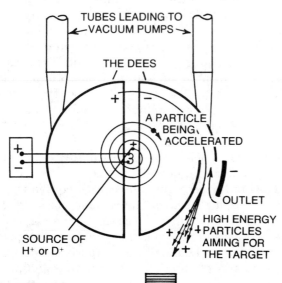

Fig. 35.4:
The cyclotron

35:11   The Cyclotron

With the invention of the cyclotron in 1932 by Professor E. O. Lawrence, it became possible to accelerate charged particles, such as protons H$^+$ and deuterons D$^+$, the heavy isotope of hydrogen, to such velocities that they could be used in similar nuclear experiments. The cyclotron consists of a pair of semicircular metal chambers, called *dees* because of their shape, mounted between the poles of an extremely powerful electromagnet (Fig. 35.4). A high frequency alternating current is passed through them, causing their polarity to change rapidly. A charged particle, such as a proton, is liberated near the centre of one of the dees, and the alternating current causes it to go in a circular path from one dee to the other and back. Each time the particle passes from one dee to the other it is given an additional electrical boost to make it go faster. Finally, it emerges with a velocity nearly equal to that of light and strikes the target with enough energy to penetrate the nucleus and to cause nuclear change.

35:12   Discovery of the Neutron

Scientists realized that the ideal particle for use as an atomic projectile would be a neutral one. Its lack of a positive charge would permit it to enter the nuclei of atoms freely; but without an electrical charge, this particle was difficult to detect and to manage. Finally, in 1932, it was discovered by physicists that when a light element like magnesium was bombarded with alpha particles, transmutation of magnesium to silicon occurred, and at the same time, a stream of neutrons issued from the reaction. The reaction could be represented by this equation:

$$_{12}^{24}Mg + _2^4He \rightarrow _{14}^{27}Si + _0^1n$$

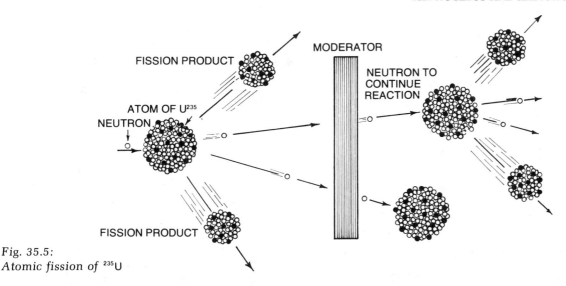

Fig. 35.5:
Atomic fission of ^{235}U

The silicon nucleus thus produced is unstable, and it undergoes radioactive disintegration according to the equation:

$$^{27}_{14}\text{Si} \rightarrow ^{27}_{13}\text{Al} + ^{0}_{1}\text{e}$$

This nuclear change was important for the following reasons:

1. A method was provided for obtaining neutrons.
2. Both transmutation and radioactivity had been achieved artificially.
3. An element was prepared whose atom was larger than the original.

Scientists did not believe at first that neutrons were produced in this manner, but careful experimentation showed that this was indeed the case.

35:13   Atomic Fission

In the reaction of magnesium with the alpha particle, a silicon atom is produced. The silicon has a higher atomic number than the magnesium. It is thus possible to produce larger atoms as well as smaller atoms by nuclear change. What would occur if the largest atom in the periodic table were treated in a similar way? Would we obtain an atom whose kind never existed in Nature? These questions were thought about by the Italian scientist Enrico Fermi almost as soon as the neutron's existence was verified. He attempted to obtain the answer experimentally; by bombarding atom number 92 (uranium), he hoped to obtain atom number 93.

Fermi's attempt was successful. He found the isotope of ^{238}U captures a neutron to become ^{239}U, an unstable iostope which in turn changes to neptunium (Z = 93) and plutonium (Z = 94). Both of these are new elements that have never been found in Nature but have been synthesized artificially.

In 1938, other scientists, repeating this experiment, discovered that another isotope of uranium, ^{235}U, breaks up into two or more fragments, such as the nuclei of krypton and barium, when struck by a neutron. Such a nuclear change is an example of *atomic fission*. Furthermore, during the break-up of the nucleus of ^{235}U, more neutrons are released as well as great amounts of energy. The approximate equation is:

$$_{92}^{235}U + _{0}^{1}n \rightarrow _{56}^{141}Ba + _{36}^{92}Kr + 3\,_{0}^{1}n$$

Here, neutrons produced a fission which liberated neutrons that could, in turn, produce more fissions, and so on. Thus a "chain reaction" (Fig. 35.5) could be started which would be self-sustaining and which would make possible the release of atomic energy. This became the basis of the atomic bomb. An atomic explosion results when just the right amount of fissionable material is brought together to be split by neutrons in chain reaction. This amount is called the *critical mass* of the atomic bomb.

35:14   The Atomic Bomb

The instantaneous release of vast energy produces temperatures of many millions of degrees. The heat accounts for the flash burns which could be fatal to victims who are as far as a kilometre away from the explosion. The heat also produces a violent expansion of air, with a resulting blast that flattens most buildings within an area of several square kilometres from the centre of the explosion. Along with the heat and blast comes the gamma radiation that is liberated. This travels with the speed of light from the centre of the blast and can be fatal at distances up to a kilometre or more. At shorter distances it is always fatal unless one is shielded by several metres of concrete or earth.

An atomic explosion also contributes danger of another sort. The fission products may themselves be radioactive, and they may cause particles in the atmosphere to become radioactive as well. Such matter is termed *fall-out*. If the explosion occurs high in the air, there is a certain amount of fall-out; but an explosion at ground level or under water would cause far more fall-out. Although its blast

and heat effects would be less widespread, it would render adjacent materials radioactive and would hurl into the air great quantities of radioactive dust or water. Thus a widespread and long-lasting secondary hazard would exist.

35:15   Nuclear Fusion

The source of energy in the nuclear reactor and in the atomic bomb is the fission of ^{235}U or ^{239}Pu nuclei. Even larger amounts of energy per unit mass of nuclear fuel are liberated by the union of nuclei of light elements to form heavier ones, a type of reaction termed *nuclear fusion*. It is by such reactions that the energy emitted by the sun and the stars is produced.

Substances that might be used as fuels for fusion reactions include some of the isotopes of hydrogen, lithium, and boron. A reaction that is particularly efficient, in terms of energy released per gram of fuel, is that in which tritium and deuterium react to give helium, as shown by the equation:

$$_{1}^{3}H + _{1}^{2}D \rightarrow _{2}^{4}He + _{0}^{1}n$$

The chief problem to be overcome in the application of nuclear fusion, especially for industrial purposes, lies in the fact that such reactions take place only at temperatures higher than 1 000 000°C, such as prevail on the sun, but which are very difficult to attain on Earth.

35:16   The Nuclear Reactor

The explosion of an atomic bomb is an instantaneous and uncontrolled chain reaction. In a nuclear reactor, similar fissioning occurs but is con-

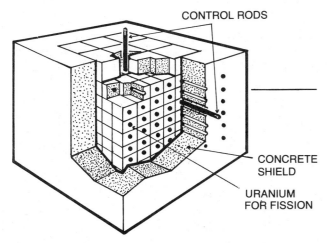

CONTROL RODS

CONCRETE
SHIELD

URANIUM
FOR FISSION

Fig. 35.6:
The nuclear reactor

trolled in such a manner that *one* fission produces
only one *new* fission. The reaction can be made
barely to sustain itself while giving off large
amounts of heat.

One form of nuclear reactor consists of a pile of
graphite blocks through which are dispersed a
number of uranium rods encased in aluminum.
Slots are provided through which boron steel or
cadmium control rods can be inserted. Boron and
cadmium absorb neutrons. The reactor is started by
pulling out the control rods so that neutrons produce more fissions, and it is stopped by pushing
the control rods in until so many neutrons are
absorbed that the reaction cannot maintain itself.
These graphite blocks *moderate* or slow down the
neutrons so that they are readily captured by other
^{235}U nuclei. Trays are provided by means of which
substances to be irradiated can be introduced to the
high neutron flux. The entire mass is enclosed in a
wall of concrete several metres thick to prevent
escape of dangerous gamma rays and neutron
radiation. Provision is also made for circulating
cooling water or some other heat transfer medium
through the reactor.

35:17   Nuclear Energy for Power

The practical application of nuclear energy lies in
the heat developed within the nuclear reactor. A
heat transfer liquid is circulated through the reactor, where it becomes heated. The liquid is then
pumped to a heat interchanger where it converts
ordinary water to steam. From this point the power
is conventional. For example, the steam can be
used to power a ships's propellers or an electrical
generator. In order to control the reaction for such
purposes, a moderator is used to absorb the excess
neutrons which would cause the reaction to proceed at an even faster rate. Even greater power
would be released if science could learn how to
control a fusion reaction of hydrogen to helium.

Nuclear energy is already producing electricity
in Canada and in other countries. The Canadian
model of nuclear reactor, called the Candu, has
been acclaimed by nuclear experts as highly efficient.

However, while it holds the promise of supplying electricity, nuclear energy is criticized for the
possible environmental damage by the nuclear
wastes and thermal pollution resulting from the
operation of the reactor. Nuclear wastes in the form
of unspent fuel will have to be monitored for
thousands of years because of their high level of
radioactivity. Critics of nuclear energy say that
there is no completely satisfactory way of dispos-
ing of these wastes.

35:18   Radioisotopes and their Uses

Many elements or materials may be inserted into
the reactor for irradiation with neutrons, thus
converting them to radioactive forms. This is the
source of the wide range of radioactive materials
now being used by medicine for research and
treatment and by industry for many purposes.

Tracer Research

Radioactive isotopes have the same chemical properties as do normal atoms. They and their compounds undergo the same chemical reactions as their normal counterparts, as a rule. If, for example, a plant uses carbon dioxide for its nourishment, it does not differentiate between the normal carbon dioxide and the radioactive type whose molecules contain a radioactive atom of carbon. By allowing such radioactive carbon dioxide to be inhaled by the plant, an experimenter may then follow the path of carbon dioxide through the plant. Thus he learns what chemical reactions take place involving carbon dioxide. Such information would be extremely difficult to obtain in any other way.

Since, in this method, a compound is followed through the intricate chemical reactions which go on in living organisms, the method is called *tracer research*. One scientist has said that tracer research is as effective in studying the chemistry of living organisms as the microscope and the X ray combined.

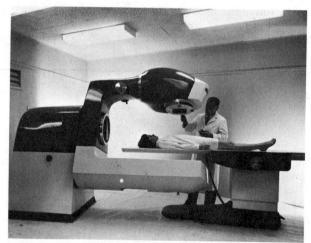

Courtesy Atomic Energy of Canada Limited

Here, radiations from cobalt-60 are being used to treat cancer.

Industrial Applications

In industry, radioactivity is used in several ways. In the oil industry it is sometimes necessary to transport different types of oil in succession through a pipe line. In order to identify a new type of oil that has been introduced into the pipe, some radioactive matter is added to the new batch. Its radiations may be detected by an instrument at the receiving station. Thus, it is easy to tell when the new batch has arrived.

In the paper industry, it is necessary to produce a sheet of uniform thickness. To ensure this, a thickness gauge based on the penetrating power of the rays from isotopes is used. The sheet of paper is passed between the source of radiation and the radiation detector. Such a gauge might be connected to the main power drive to regulate the speed at which the paper is formed, thus regulating the thickness. Similar gauges are used to control the thickness of aluminum, copper, rubber, and glass sheets.

Medical Applications

Radioactive cobalt, ^{60}Co, has taken over much of the medical work formerly done by radium. In one installation, ^{60}Co, in wafers the size of 25-cent pieces, is enclosed in a lead-lined case. Cancerous tissue is exposed by briefly opening a window in the case. The radiation is said to be 25 times as powerful as the strongest radium units, and the cost is less than one thousandth that of an equivalent amount of radium. Thus many small hospitals can now afford an effective radiation source for purposes of treatment.

Radioactivity is being used increasingly in medical diagnosis. A dye tagged with ^{131}I has been proposed for the diagnosis and location of brain tumors. The dye concentrates in the tumor, permitting its location and study by a Geiger counter.

Carbon Dating

One radioisotope of carbon ^{14}C has a half-life of about 5600 years. This isotope has been helpful to

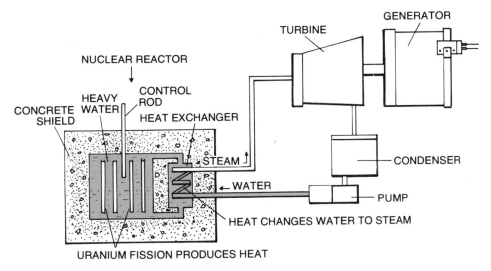

Fig. 35.7:
Power from a nuclear reactor
Uranium fission in the reactor produces heat. The heavy water surrounding the uranium rods serves both as a moderator to absorb extra neutrons emitted by the uranium and as a conductor to absorb heat. In the heat exchanger, the heat from the heavy water converts ordinary water to steam, which drives the turbine which in turn drives the generator.

anthropologists in establishing the dates of articles and events of the distant past.

Radioactive carbon (^{14}C) forms when cosmic rays, upon reaching the Earth, release neutrons in the upper atmosphere which in turn cause nitrogen atoms to change to this radioactive isotope of carbon.

$$^{1}_{0}n + {}^{14}_{7}N \rightarrow {}^{14}_{6}C + {}^{1}_{1}H$$

Such carbon atoms mix with normal ^{12}C atoms in the carbon dioxide of the air. This results in a certain ratio of ^{14}C to ^{12}C in atmospheric carbon dioxide at all times. This ratio carries over to the carbon content of organic substances in plants and animals, notably wood, formed by the carbon dioxide. When an article made of such wood becomes buried, the ^{14}C continues to disintegrate according to its half-life and, as a result, the ratio of ^{14}C to ^{12}C will be different in this article from the normal value.

Scientists can determine this difference and from it calculate the age of the article. This technique is called *carbon dating*.

This book ends as it began, on the theme of problems and their solution by the scientific method. It seems that the process will go on forever because humanity is always faced by new and often bewildering difficulties.

QUESTIONS

1. How is nuclear change different from a physical or chemical change?

2. Describe how nuclear changes are classified.

3. Describe briefly how radioactivity was discovered.

4. What are the main characteristics of the three types of rays given off by radioactive materials?

5. Describe the operation of a cloud chamber.

6. How does a Geiger counter work and for what is it used?

7. List four characteristics of radioactivity.

8. Outline Rutherford's Theory of Radioactivity.

9. Write an equation to demonstrate transmutations. Give the meaning of each number and symbol used.

10. Define *half-life*. What is the purpose of this term?

11. Explain clearly why the mass of an atomic nucleus is generally less than the sum of the masses of the particles that comprise it.

12. Define the term *binding energy*.

13. Describe with the aid of an equation the first successful artificial transmutation.

14. (i)   Explain the operation of the cyclotron.
    (ii) What rays may be produced directly by a cyclotron?
    (iii) How are these rays of greater use than natural radiations?

15. (i) How was a stream of neutrons first produced artificially?
    (ii) Why are neutrons so valuable for producing transmutations?

16. Describe how neptunium and plutonium were first synthesized.

17. (i) Explain how ^{235}U may produce a "chain-reaction."
    (ii) How does such a reaction produce energy?

18. (i) What is meant by "fall-out"?
    (ii) Write a paragraph to explain the dangers encountered in an atomic fission explosion.

19. (i)   What is *nuclear fusion?*
    (ii) Write an equation to demonstrate how deuterium may be used for nuclear fusion.
    (iii) How is nuclear fusion in the H-bomb triggered?
    (iv) Why is controlled nuclear fusion difficult?

20. (i) What are "moderators" as used in a nuclear reactor?
    (ii) Describe how moderators function.

21. What are *radioisotopes?*

22. Write a paragraph to demonstrate some of the uses of tracer research.

23. Explain how ^{14}C is used in carbon dating.

24. How is the energy of nuclear fission changed into usable power at the present time?

25. What are the arguments for and against the adoption of nuclear energy as the most important source of energy for Canada?

Appendix 1

Measurements in science

Measurements in scientific work report three important kinds of information:

1. The *magnitude* of the quantity being measured, reported as a number.
2. The *units* in which the quantity is scaled, indicated by such terms as grams and centimetres.
3. The *limit of accuracy* in the method of measurement, indicated by the *significant figures*.

Thus, for example, a sample is reported as weighing 1.052 ± 0.001 g. Such notation tells us how large the mass is, that the unit of the reported numbers is the gram, and that there is doubt in the last thousandth of a gram.

The numerical part of a quantity is best reported in the exponential notation (Appendix 2). The units of a quantity are indicated, calculated, or checked by reference to the measurement, or to the mathematical formula in which the quantity is calculated. Significant figures must be judged by an appreciation of the apparatus used.

Units

The units of a numerical measurement indicate its nature and the scale upon which it was measured. Only quantities with the same units may be added to or subtracted from each other. If they do not have the same units, they may be interconverted, provided the quantities are of the same dimension. Thus, to add 50 cm to 1 m we must reduce both to centimetres or metres. When quantities of similar units are added, the answer has the same units as the component parts. When lengths of 50 cm and 100 cm are added, a *length* of 150 cm results.

When quantities are multiplied (or divided), the product is in the same units as the original units. For example, if the length of a rectangle is 100 cm and the width is 50 cm, the area is 5000 cm².

Conversion Factors

Conversion factors are used to change from one set of units to another of the same nature; for example, to change tonnes to milligrams. To work out conversion factors it is helpful to use these rules:

1. Write the required units on the left hand side of the equation.
2. Write the given units on the right hand side.
3. Multiply or divide by the suitable *unit factor* to cancel out unwanted terms and replace them by required ones.
4. Write the numerical value for each unit factor.

Example

How many milligrams are there in one tonne?

Required units = given unit × suitable unit factor

Steps 1, 2, and 3:

$$\text{milligrams} = \text{tonne} \times \frac{\text{kilograms}}{\text{tonne}} \times \frac{\text{grams}}{\text{kilogram}} \times \frac{\text{milligrams}}{\text{gram}}$$

Step 4:

$$\text{milligrams} = 1 \times \frac{1000}{1} \times \frac{1000}{1} \times \frac{1000}{1}$$

$$= 10^9 \text{ mg}$$

Significant Figures

Numbers which express the result of a measurement such that only the last digit is in doubt are called significant figures. Thus there is a difference in meaning between the statements a length of 24 cm and a length of 24.0 cm. The first statement indicates that the measurement is reliable to the nearest centimetre only. The second statement indicates that the measurement is reliable to the nearest tenth of a centimetre.

All figures between 1 and 9 are considered to be significant. Moreover, the zero between or after a number is also significant if a decimal is present in the number. The zero before the decimal point and the zero after the decimal point are not considered to be significant.

Examples: 1.04 contains 3 significant figures
1.040 contains 4 significant figures
0.32 contains 2 significant figures

0.032 contains 2 significant figures

0.0320 contains 3 significant figures

When two or more quantities are combined, the accuracy of the result cannot be better than that of the *least* accurate of all the numbers involved. Thus if a length reported to be 1.125 cm is added to another length of 5.4 cm, the final result must be reported only as 6.5 cm, not 6.525 cm. The latter would imply that we know the precision of this length to *four* decimal places. This would be a misrepresentation since the precision of one part of the sum is limited to only two decimal places.

Similarly, when numbers are multiplied or divided, the answer must be consistent with the least accurately known quantity. In rounding off such answers, we increase the last significant digit, if answers, we increase the last significant digit, if the discarded digit is five or greater. For example, if an answer of 0.7684 is valid to only two significant figures, it should be reported as 0.77.

When numbers are expressed in the exponential notation, the number of significant figures is shown by the "digital multiplier"; for example, in 2.4×10^1 there are 2 significant figures and in 2.40×10^{-5} there are 3 significant figures.

Appendix 2

The Exponential Notation

Large and Small Numbers

Many measurements in science involve very large or very small numbers, which often need to be multiplied or divided. So that this can be done conveniently, such numbers should be expressed as the product of two factors. The first factor, known as the digital factor, is a number between 1 and 10. The other, called the exponential factor, is the correct power of 10. Here are a few examples:

Number	= Digital factor	× exponential factor
185	= 1.85	$\times 10^2$
1 850	= 1.85	$\times 10^3$
18 500	= 1.85	$\times 10^4$
0.185	= 1.85	$\times 10^{-1}$

In these examples, the numbers are of different size, although they have the same digits in the same order. In changing them to the exponential form, we divide or multiply the original number, then multiply or divide to an equal and opposite extent by means of the suitable power of 10.

The reason for converting numbers to exponential form is that the numbers between 1 and 10 are by far the easiest to visualize and to work with. The difficulty due to the largeness or the smallness of the number is removed by the use of exponents.

Example

Multiply $20\ 000 \times 0.04$. While this could be done by means of long multiplication, it must be admitted that there is the chance of misplacing the decimal point, and no one can deny that 20 000 is less familiar than 2, and 0.04 is less familiar than 4.

Using exponents, $20\ 000 = 2 \times 10^4$

and $0.04 = 4 \times 10^{-2}$

$$20\ 000 \times 0.04 = 2 \times 10^4 \times 4 \times 10^{-2}$$
$$= 2 \times 4 \times 10^{4-2}$$
$$= 8 \times 10^2 \text{ or } 800.$$

Rules for Handling Exponential Numbers

RULE 1 When powers of ten are moved from denominator to numerator or vice versa, the signs of the exponents are changed. Example:

$$\frac{6}{3 \times 10^{-4}} = \frac{6 \times 10^4}{3}$$

RULE 2 When we wish to multiply powers of ten, we add the exponents. Examples:

(a) $2 \times 10^4 \times 2 \times 10^3 = 2 \times 2 \times 10^{4+3} = 4 \times 10^7$

(b) $3 \times 10^7 \times 2 \times 10^{-4} = 3 \times 2 \times 10^{7-4} = 6 \times 10^3$

RULE 3 When we wish to divide powers of ten, we subtract the exponents. Examples:

(a) $\dfrac{8 \times 10^5}{2 \times 10^2} = \dfrac{8 \times 10^{5-2}}{2} = 4 \times 10^3$

(b) $\dfrac{6 \times 10^{-5}}{2 \times 10^{-2}} = \dfrac{6 \times 10^{-5+2}}{2} = 3 \times 10^{-3}$

RULE 4 Before adding or subtracting exponential numbers, we must change them to the same powers of ten. Example:

$$(2 \times 10^4) + (2 \times 10^5) = (2 \times 10^4) + (20 \times 10^4) = 22 \times 10^4$$

Approximations

In many cases, calculations involve several numbers, each consisting of several digits, e.g. $1850 \times 760 \times 0.022$. In calculations involving such numbers, the numbers are expressed with the aid of the exponential factors. In addition, the digital factor is expressed as an approximation of the nearest whole number so that an idea of the size of the answer can be quickly obtained. This adds confidence to the search for an exact answer by calculation. The exact answer is then found by multiplication and division or by using a slide rule. However the answer is subject to the rules concerning significant figures.

Example
Multiply $1850 \times 760 \times 0.022$
$1850 = 1.850 \times 10^3 \doteq 2 \times 10^3$*
$760 = 7.60 \ \ \times 10^2 \doteq 8 \times 10^2$
$0.022 = 2.2 \ \ \ \ \times 10^{-2} \doteq 2 \times 10^{-2}$
Approximate answer is $2 \times 8 \times 2 \times 10^{3+2-2}$
  or 32×10^3
  or $32\ 000$
Obtained by multiplication of $1.85 \times 7.6 \times 2.2 \times 10^{3+2-2}$, the exact answer is $30\ 932$.

Uncertainties in Measurements

The following is a list of the uncertainties associated with common laboratory instruments:

Platform balance	± 0.1 g
Centigram balance	± 0.01 g
10-mL graduated cylinder	± 0.1 mL
50-mL graduated cylinder	± 0.2 mL
50-mL buret	± 0.02 mL
$-10°C$ to $110°C$ thermometer	$\pm 0.2°C$

There are three methods of expressing the uncertainty in a single measurement.
1. The measurement is followed by the symbol $\pm$ and then the estimated value of the uncertainty. For example, the mass of a sample measured on a centigram balance might be reported as 1.52 ± 0.01 g.
2. The uncertainty can also be expressed as a percentage of the measured quantity. For example, the percentage uncertainty in the

*The symbol $\doteq$ means "approximately equals."

mass of the sample mentioned above would be:
$\dfrac{0.01}{1.52} \times 100 = 0.7\%$
3. A third method of reporting uncertainty is to report the result in such a way that only the last digit is in doubt. In our example above the mass would be reported as 1.52 g. This method does not convey as much information as the other two methods because it does not show by "how much" the last digit is in doubt, but it is satisfactory in most cases.

Propagation of Uncertainty in a Calculation

1. *Addition and subtraction.* When quantities are added or subtracted, the maximum uncertainty is simply the sum of the uncertainties of the component measurements. For example, if 1.52 ± 0.01 g and 0.61 ± 0.01 g are to be added or subtracted the results would be:

1.52 ± 0.01 g	1.52 ± 0.01 g
$+\ 0.61 \pm 0.01$ g	$-\ 0.61 \pm 0.01$ g
2.13 ± 0.02 g	0.91 ± 0.02 g

2. *Multiplication and division.* When quantities are multiplied or divided, the maximum uncertainty is not simply the sum of the uncertainties in the components. For example, if 157 ± 2 cm and 20.2 ± 0.4 cm are to be multiplied or divided, the results could be obtained as follows:

a) *Using the maximum-minimum method*
Maximum: 159 cm $\times 20.6$ cm $= 3\ 275.4$ cm^2
Minimum: 155 cm $\times 19.8$ cm $= 3\ 069.0$ cm^2
  Average: $\dfrac{3\ 275.4 + 3\ 069.0}{2} = 3\ 172.2$ cm^2

The maximum is $3\ 275.4 - 3\ 172.3 = 103.2$ above the average value.
The minimum is $3\ 172.2 - 3\ 069.0 = 103.2$ below the average value.

Therefore, the result could be expressed as 3 172.2 ± 103.2 cm². But since the uncertainty in 103.2 first appears in the hundreds, the final result must be rounded off to 3 200 ± 100 cm².

b) *Using the percentage uncertainty method*
The sum of the percentage uncertainties in the components determines the uncertainty in the result.
The percentage uncertainty in 157 is

$$\frac{2}{157} \times 100 = 1.27\%$$

The percentage uncertainty in 20.2 is

$$\frac{0.4}{20.2} \times 100 = 1.98\%$$

The result can be obtained by adding the percentages of the uncertainties: (157 ± 1.27%) × (20.2 ± 1.98%) = 3 171.4 ± 3.25% cm².
The value of this uncertainty is 3.25% of 3 171.4 = ± 103.1 cm². Again, the final result must be rounded off to: 3 200 ± 100 cm²

c) *Using the significant numbers method*
The ± information is disregarded, and the result must contain the same number of significant figures as the least precise component. In our example, the result would be shown as:

$$157 \times 20.2 = 3\ 171.4 = 3.17 \times 10^3 \text{ cm}^2$$

Appendix 3

The Metric System

Length
one metre (1 m) = ten decimetres (10 dm) = one hundred centimetres (100 cm) = one thousand millimetres (1000 mm)
one kilometre (1 km) = one thousand metres (1000 m)

Volume
one litre (1 L) = one thousand millilitres (1000 mL) = one thousand cubic centimetres (1000 cm^3)

Mass
one gram (1 g) = mass of one millilitre of water at 4°C
one kilogram (1 kg) = 1000 g
one gram (1 g) = ten decigrams (10 dg) = one hundred centigrams (100 cg) = one thousand milligrams (1000 mg)
one thousand kilograms (1000 kg) = one tonne (1 t).

PREFIXES OF THE METRIC SYSTEM

Symbol	Name		Value
T	tera	10^{12} or	1 000 000 000 000
G	giga	10^{9} or	1 000 000 000
M	mega	10^{6} or	1 000 000
k	kilo	10^{3} or	1 000
da	deca	10^{1} or	10
		10^{0} or	1
d	deci	10^{-1} or	0.1
c	centi	10^{-2} or	0.01
m	milli	10^{-3} or	0.001
μ	micro	10^{-6} or	0.000 001
n	nano	10^{-9} or	0.000 000 001
p	pico	10^{-12} or	0.000 000 000 001
f	femto	10^{-15} or	0.000 000 000 000 001
a	atto	10^{-18} or	0.000 000 000 000 000 001

Appendix 4

VAPOUR PRESSURE OF WATER AT VARIOUS TEMPERATURES

Temperature (°C)	Pressure (kPa)	Temperature (°C)	Pressure (kPa)
0	0.61	23	2.8
1	0.65	24	3.0
2	0.71	25	3.2
3	0.76	26	3.4
4	0.81	27	3.6
5	0.87	28	3.8
6	0.93	29	4.0
7	0.99	30	4.2
8	1.0	35	5.6
9	1.1	40	7.4
10	1.2	45	9.6
11	1.3	50	12.3
12	1.4	55	15.7
13	1.5	60	19.9
14	1.6	65	25.0
15	1.7	70	31.2
16	1.8	75	38.5
17	1.9	80	47.3
18	2.1	85	57.8
19	2.2	90	70.1
20	2.3	95	84.5
21	2.5	100	101.3
22	2.6	105	120.8

Appendix 5

Heats of Formation of Common Compounds (kJ/mol)

CaO	548.9	$Hg(ONC)_2$	−270.3
CO	121.5	HNO_3	174.3
CO_2	406.4	H_2S	20.1
C_2H_2	−226.3	KCl	440.0
$C_{12}H_{22}O_{11}$	2 245.8	$KClO_3$	377.1
CS_2	−79.6	MgO	611.7
FeS	100.6	NH_3	50.3
HgO	90.1	$NaCl$	409.8
HCl	92.2	$NaOH$	431.6
HBr	35.2	P_4O_{10}	3 100.6
HF	156.7	NO	−90.5
HI	−25.6	SO_2	289.1
H_2O	286.6	ZnS	192.7

Answers to Problems

Chapter 2

7. (i)   1200 mL
   (ii)   1 200 000 mg; 1.2 kg
   (iii) (a) 108.0 cm,
          (b) 10.80 dm,
          (c) 1.080 m
9. (i)   2500 kg/m³
   (ii)   11.4 cm³
14. (i) 5×10^{11} (ii) 5×10^5
    (iii) 1.2×10^6 (iv) 2×10^{-6}
15. (i) 6×10^7 (ii) 3.1×10^5
    (iii) 6×10^8 (iv) 8×10^{-2}
16. (i)   0 K; (ii) 233K;
    (iii) 273K; (iv) 323K;
    (v)   546K
17. (i)   227°C; (ii) −173°C;
    (iii) −1°C; (iv) −223°C;
    (v)   27°C

Chapter 3

16. Oxygen, 5 mL
17. (i) Oxygen, 7.5 mL
    (ii) Hydrogen, 2 mL
18. 88.79% oxygen
    11.21% hydrogen

Chapter 4

4. 365 kg
6. (i)   A. 0.269 g; B. 0.134 g
15. (i)   2 u; (ii) 40 u
    (iii) 18 u;
    (iv) 342 u;
    (v)   36.5 u;
    (vi) 16 u; (vii) 44 u;
    (viii) 98 u; (ix) 28 u;
    (x)   17 u

Chapter 10

7. 1.58 L
8. 161 mL

9. 368 mL
10. 3.88 L
11. 405 kPa
12. 50.0 kPa
17. 718 mL
18. 240 mL
19. −24°C
20. 313°C
21. 21.4 L
22. 780 mL
23. 138 mL
24. 147 L
25. 841°C
28. (i)   99.9 kPa
    (ii) 1.95 L
29. 0.84 L
32. 2:1
33. 4 cm from end oxygen introduced
34. 4 h

Chapter 11

6. 600 kPa

Chapter 12

9. 1.88×10^{22} molecules

Chapter 13

2. (ii)   1.5 mol
   (iii) 2.08 g
8. 2.016 g
9. 46.1 g
10. 2.28 g
11. 0.57 g
12. 112 L
13. 2.04 L
14. 32.8 g
15. 0.31 g
16. 0.72 g/L
18. 10 g
19. (i) 2.51×10^{23} atoms
    (ii) 1.88×10^{23} atoms
20. 0.23 mol of carbon atoms,
    0.46 mol of oxygen atoms
21. (i)   11.5 g
    (ii) 161.8 g

22. 21 g

Chapter 14

3. (i)   72:6 or 12:1
   (ii)   92.3% carbon;
          7.7% hydrogen
6. AgF
7. $NaHCO_3$
8. Na_2SO_4
9. (i) $CaSO_4$
   (ii) $K_2Cr_2O_7$
11. $C_6H_{12}O_6$
12. (i) SCl
    (ii) S_2Cl_2
13. CO_2
14. C_6H_6
15. H_2SO_4
16. (i)   98 u; (ii) 98 u;
    (iii) 40 u; (iv) 74 u;
    (v)   78 u; (vi) 310 u;
    (vii) 180 u;
    (viii) 342 u;
    (ix) 48 u;
    (x)   246 u
17. (i)   7; (ii) 8; (iii) 3;
    (iv) 5; (v) 7; (vi) 13;
    (vii) 24; (viii) 45; (ix) 3;
    (x)   27
18. 40% calcium; 12% carbon;
    48% oxygen
19. 32.4% sodium;
    22.5% sulfur;
    45.1% oxygen
20. 10.4%
21. 20.9%
22. 8.6 kg
23. 67.2 L
24. 3 L
25. 44.8 g
26. 64 g
27. 0.54 g
28. 19.6 g
29. 42.3 kg
30. 35.5 g
31. 42 g
32. Molecular mass = 30.0 u
    Formula is NO
33. 2.85 g/L

Chapter 15

11. (ii) 2 mol
    (iii) 2 molecules
12. (ii) 1 mol   (iii) 58.5 g
13. (i)   10 mol of water
    (ii) 112 L   (iii) 320 g
14. 10.4 g
15. 322 g
16. 42 g
17. 24 mol
18. (i) 11.2 L   (ii) 24.6 L
19. 55 mol
20. 13.4 L
21. 237 g
22. 67.2 L; 54 g
23. (i)   250 L   (ii) 222 L

Chapter 18

11. (i)   185.3 kJ evolved
    (ii)   465.3 kJ absorbed

Chapter 20

15. 1.12×10^{23} electrons
19. 12.1 g
20. (i)   2 electrons
    (ii) 1.2×10^{24} electrons
    (iii) 1.9×10^5 C

Chapter 21

19. 22 500 J
23. (i)   453 J/g;   (ii) 205 J/g;
    (iii) 44.4 J/g; (iv) 333 J/g;
24. (i)   150 J/g;   (ii) 289 J/g;
    (iii) 4378 J/g; (iv) 2250 J/g;
25. 203 kJ
26. 3000 J
27. 122 kJ
28. (i)   2.26 kJ;   (ii) 6.14 kJ;
    (iii) 48.5 kJ;   (iv) 50 kJ
29. 64 440 J

Chapter 22

17. 56%
18. 64 kg

Chapter 23

17. 7.5 g
25. 6.3 g
26. (i)   101 g;   (ii) 196 g;
    (iii) 61.25 g; (iv) 34.2 g;
    (v)   189 g
27. (i)   29.3 g;   (ii) 22.4 g;
    (iii) 1.1 g;   (iv) 30.6 g;
    (v)   161 g
30. i, iv, v, vi, viii,
    x, xi
31. ii, iii, v, vi, ix, x
32. 1.2 mol/L
33. 0.2 mol/L
34. 600 mL
35. 2.6 mol/L
36. (i)   0.102   (ii) 0.274
    (iii) 0.134   (iv) 0.250
    (v)   0.091

Chapter 24

14. 1.89×10^{23} electrons
15. (i)   1.1 g hydrogen;
           8.9 oxygen;
    (ii) 12.1 L
16. 15.3 g

Chapter 25

12. (i)   0.27 mol/L   (ii) 2.7 mol/L
13. 0.2 mol/L
14. (i)   3.65 g HCl;
    (ii)   8.1 g HBr;
    (iii) 9.8 g H_2SO_4;
    (iv)   9.8 g H_3PO_4;
    (v)   4.0 g NaOH;
    (vi)   7.4 g $Ca(OH)_2$
15. (i)   0.28 mol/L   (ii) 2.0 mol/L;
    (iii) 1.0 mol/L   (iv) 0.04 mol/L;
16. 2.5 mol/L
17. 2.1 g
18. 0.4 mol/L HCl; 0.15 mol/L H_2SO_4;
    Conc H_3O^+ is 0.7 mol/L
27. 5.7 g
28. 6
29. 5
30. 2%

31. 1
32. 1.0×10^{-6}
33. 11

Chapter 27

18. 37.2 g
19. 3.80 L
24. 30 g
25. $AlCl_3$
26. 5 mL of chlorine, 6 mL of
    hydrogen chloride

Chapter 28

13. 20.5 g
14. $MgSO_3$
15. 74.7 kg
33. 0.14 mol/L
34. 1.37:1
35. 81.6 kg

Chapter 29

23. 9.3 L
24. 233 g
25. 2.14 L
26. C_2H_2

Chapter 30

29. C_4H_8
30. 128 g
31. 2.59 g/L
32. 2.66×10^{-5} g

Chapter 31

30. C_2H_5OH
31. 3.12 L
32. 24.0 g

Chapter 34

16. 43.8 g
17. 2.87 g
18. (i)   5.4 g
    (ii) 2.8 g
    (iii) 12 g

GLOSSARY OF TERMS

Absolute temperature (Kelvin). Celsius temperature plus 273.

Acid. A compound able to yield hydrogen ions or to accept a pair of electrons.

Activation energy. The amount of energy that reactants must obtain to enable them to react chemically.

Anion. A negatively charged ion.

Anode. The electrode of an electrochemical cell at which the loss of electrons occurs.

Atmosphere. The mixture of gases surrounding the Earth. As a unit of pressure it is equivalent to 101.3 kPa.

Atom. The smallest quantity of an element able to undergo chemical reaction.

Atomic fission. The splitting of atoms into smaller fragments.

Atomic mass unit (u). The unit for expressing the mass of atoms, molecules and ions; equal to one-twelfth the mass of the most common isotope of carbon.

Atomic number. The number of protons in the nucleus of an atom of a given element.

Avogadro's Number. 6.02×10^{23}, the number of molecules in a mole or in the molar mass.

Base. A compound able to yield hydroxyl ions or to donate a pair of electrons.

Battery. An electrochemical cell able to provide a continuous flow of electrons.

Boiling point. The temperature at which the vapour pressure of a liquid becomes equal to the pressure of its environment. The normal boiling point is the temperature at which the vapour pressure is equal to 101.3 kPa.

Boyle's Law. At constant temperature, the volume of a gas is inversely proportional to its pressure.

Catalyst. A substance that speeds up a chemical reaction without being altered itself.

Cathode. The electrode of an electrochemical cell at which the gain of electrons occurs.

Cation. A positively charged ion.

Celsius. A temperature scale on which the freezing point and the boiling point of water are 0°C and 100°C respectively.

Charge. The unit of electrical character described as positive or negative. The proton is the unit of positive charge; the electron is the unit of negative charge.

Charles' Law. At constant pressure the volume of a gas is proportional to its absolute temperature.

Chemical bonds. The forces that join atoms into molecules and ions.

Compound. A substance composed of two or more elements and having definite composition and chemical properties.

Covalent bond. The bond between two atoms sharing one or more pairs of electrons.

Dalton's atomic theory. A statement that the elements consist of atoms that combine among themselves in chemical reactions.

Dalton's Law of Partial Pressures. The pressure of a gaseous mixture is the sum of the pressures of the individual gases behaving independently of the others.

Dehydrating agent. A substance that can remove water from a mixture or a hydrate.

Electrolyte. A substance whose solution in water is

able to conduct the electric current. The term is also applied to the solution.

Electron. One of the particles involved in the structure of the atom and has the smallest unit of negative charge.

Electron shell. The space within an atom where electrons are likely to be found.

Electronegativity. The property that describes the ability of an atom to attract electrons in its bonds with other atoms.

Element. One of the 105 chemically different atoms. A substance that cannot be further subdivided into simplier substances by chemical means.

Equation. In chemistry, a statement in formulas and symbols showing the reactants and products of a chemical change.

Equilibrium. A condition in which no net chemical change is observable because the rate that reactants are changed to products is equal to the rate of the reverse reaction.

Exponential number. A number expressed as a power of 10.

Gay Lussac's Law of Combining Volumes. The volumes of gases that react with each other or are produced by chemical change are in simple ratio to one another.

Graham's Law of Diffusion. The rates of diffusion of gases are inversely proportional to the square root of their densities.

Greenhouse effect. The raising of the temperature of the Earth's atmosphere as a result of the presence of gases that tend to impede the radiation of heat leaving the Earth. CO_2 is an example of such a gas.

Halogen. An element of group VII of the periodic table (F, Cl, Br, I, At).

Heat of fusion. The amount of heat needed to melt a unit mass of a substance.

Heat of vaporization. The amount of heat needed to vaporize a unit mass of a substance from its liquid state.

Hydrogen bond. A weak electrostatic bond between two molecules containing OH, NH or HF groups. The H of these groups serves as a bridge between the molecules at the site of these bonds.

Ion. A charged atom or group of atoms.

Ionic bond. The bond between oppositely charged ions, responsible for the formation of salts.

Isomer. Compounds having the same formula might have different structures due to different arrangement of their atoms. An isomer is one of these possible structures.

Isotope. Atoms of the same element may have different numbers of neutrons in their nuclei. Isotopes are atoms differing in this respect only.

Kelvin. A temperature scale whose zero is the lowest possible temperature in the Universe. The kelvin is the degree interval on that scale.

Kilopascal. 1000 pascals, an SI unit of pressure.

Kinetic energy. Energy of a moving body.

Logarithms. A system of expressing numbers as powers of 10.

Mass. A measure of the quantity of matter in a substance.

Melting point. The temperature at which a solid melts.

Metric system. A system of measurement whose units of mass, length and time are the kilogram, metre and second.

Molarity. Concentration expressed in moles of solute per litre of solution.

Molecule. The smallest particle of a covalent substance that can display the properties of that substance.

Neutralization. Chemical reaction between an acid and a base.

Neutron. An uncharged particle occurring in the nucleus of an atom. Only the lightest isotope of hydrogen has a nucleus without neutrons.

Nonmetal. An element that forms ions by gaining electrons.

Oxidant. The substance that gains electrons in oxidation-reduction reactions. An oxidant is thus the cause of oxidation of another substance.

Oxidation. The loss of electrons as caused by an oxidant.

Oxidation number. This describes the extent of oxidation of an atom in terms of the number of electrons needed to convert it to its uncharged state. For example, H^+ has an oxidation number of $1+$; Cl^- has an oxidation number of $1-$.

Oxidation-reduction reaction. These involve changes in oxidation numbers of atoms, indicating that electrons have been gained and lost in the course of the reaction.

Pascal. The SI unit of pressure. (Pa)

Period. A horizontal row of elements in the periodic table.

Periodic table. A classification of the elements according to their atomic numbers and properties.

pH. The negative logarithm of the hydrogen ion concentration.

Photosynthesis. The chemical process by which plants convert carbon dioxide, water, and sunlight to carbohydrates and oxygen.

Polar molecule. One that has positive and negative regions.

Precipitate. An insoluble substance.

Pressure. Force per unit area.

Radioisotope. An unstable isotope that emits radiation and other radioactive fission products while decomposing.

Redox. The words *reduction* and *oxidation* abbreviated to a single word. (See Oxidation-reduction reaction, Ch. 20.)

Reductant. The substance that donates electrons in oxidation-reduction reactions. Having donated negatively charged electrons, its own oxidation number has increased. Thus it was oxidized.

Reversible reaction. A chemical change in which the products reconvert to the reactants.

Shell. Describes the location of electrons in atoms.

Spectroscope. An instrument used to analyze the light emitted by substances for identification purposes.

Sublimation. The change of state from solid directly to gas or from gas directly to solid.

Temperature. A measure of the intensity of heat and an indicator of the direction in which heat will flow—always from higher to lower temperature.

Valence. A whole number that shows the combining capacity of an atom.

Valence shell. The outermost electronic shell of an atom. The shell that is involved in chemical reactions.

Index

PERIODIC TABLE OF THE ELEMENTS

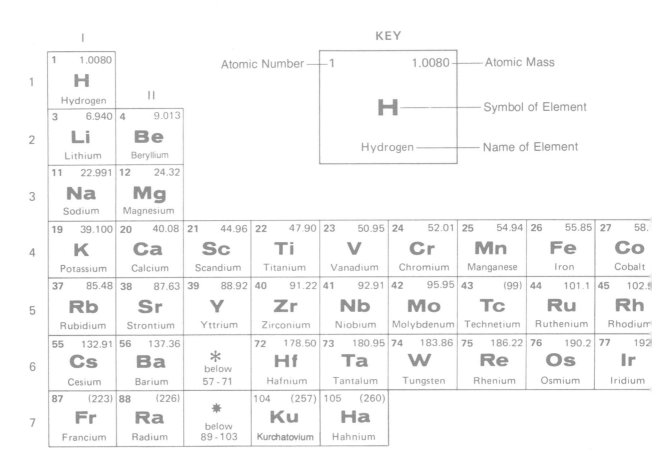

KEY

Atomic Number — 1   1.0080 — Atomic Mass

H — Symbol of Element

Hydrogen — Name of Element

	I	II							
1	1 1.0080 **H** Hydrogen								
2	3 6.940 **Li** Lithium	4 9.013 **Be** Beryllium							
3	11 22.991 **Na** Sodium	12 24.32 **Mg** Magnesium							
4	19 39.100 **K** Potassium	20 40.08 **Ca** Calcium	21 44.96 **Sc** Scandium	22 47.90 **Ti** Titanium	23 50.95 **V** Vanadium	24 52.01 **Cr** Chromium	25 54.94 **Mn** Manganese	26 55.85 **Fe** Iron	27 58. **Co** Cobalt
5	37 85.48 **Rb** Rubidium	38 87.63 **Sr** Strontium	39 88.92 **Y** Yttrium	40 91.22 **Zr** Zirconium	41 92.91 **Nb** Niobium	42 95.95 **Mo** Molybdenum	43 (99) **Tc** Technetium	44 101.1 **Ru** Ruthenium	45 102. **Rh** Rhodium
6	55 132.91 **Cs** Cesium	56 137.36 **Ba** Barium	* below 57 - 71	72 178.50 **Hf** Hafnium	73 180.95 **Ta** Tantalum	74 183.86 **W** Tungsten	75 186.22 **Re** Rhenium	76 190.2 **Os** Osmium	77 192 **Ir** Iridium
7	87 (223) **Fr** Francium	88 (226) **Ra** Radium	✸ below 89 - 103	104 (257) **Ku** Kurchatovium	105 (260) **Ha** Hahnium				

* LANTHANIDE SERIES	57 133.92 **La** Lanthanum	58 140.13 **Ce** Cerium	59 140.92 **Pr** Praseodymium	60 144.27 **Nd** Neodymium	61 (145) **Pm** Promethium	62 150.35 **Sm** Samarium	63 152 **Eu** Europium
✸ ACTINIDE SERIES	89 (227) **Ac** Actinium	90 232.05 **Th** Thorium	91 (231) **Pa** Protactinium	92 238.07 **U** Uranium	93 (237) **Np** Neptunium	94 (242) **Pu** Plutonium	95 (24 **Am** Americium